IV

V.

FUNDAMENTALS OF

INFRARED

TECHNOLOGY

MACMILLAN MONOGRAPHS IN APPLIED OPTICS
Stanley S. Ballard, Consulting Editor

FUNDAMENTALS OF INFRARED TECHNOLOGY
by M. R. Holter, S. Nudelman, G. H. Suits,
W. L. Wolfe, and G. J. Zissis

TABLES OF BLACKBODY RADIATION FUNCTIONS
by M. Pivovonsky, M. Nagel, and the Harvard
Computation Laboratory

FUNDAMENTALS OF
INFRARED
TECHNOLOGY

MARVIN R. HOLTER

SOL NUDELMAN

GWYNN H. SUITS

WILLIAM L. WOLFE

GEORGE J. ZISSIS

THE MACMILLAN COMPANY, NEW YORK
Macmillan New York, London

A DIVISION OF THE CROWELL-COLLIER PUBLISHING COMPANY

First Printing

Library of Congress catalog card number: 61-17160

The Macmillan Company, New York
Macmillan New York, London
Brett-Macmillan Ltd., Galt, Ontario

Printed in the United States of America

INFRA-RED Spectrophotometer

Principle

i.R. Source
(all frequencies)

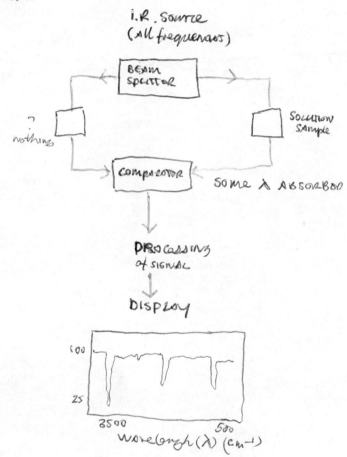

BEAM SPLITTER

? nothing

SOLUTION SAMPLE

COMPARATOR

SOME λ ABSORBED

PROCESSING of SIGNAL

DISPLAY

100

25

3500   500

wavelength (λ) (cm⁻¹)

FOREWORD

The infrared region of the electromagnetic spectrum is proving to be of ever-increasing usefulness in both laboratory and field applications. In the laboratory, infrared spectroscopy is a technique which is familiar to physicists and chemists as a tool with which to explore molecular structure. Since World War II there have been vigorous developments in spectrophotometers, especially the double-beam recording type with which the infrared "finger print" absorption spectra of substances can be run off in seconds or minutes. Thus infrared spectrophotometry can now be regarded as a standard analytical technique, and further startling improvements are not expected in the excellent instruments that are commercially available. Also, the technical literature is fairly complete on this subject, as to both principles of operation of the equipment and the theories involved in their application. Infrared methods have hence proved their worth in academic surroundings and also in broad scale industrial applications, and are considered to be indispensable to the organic chemist and to many others who are interested in the microconstitution of matter.

Field uses of the infrared part of the spectrum have come into prominence more recently, and only since World War II has infrared been accepted as a proven technique. It is, of course, of major interest to the military, for "seeing in the dark" and for the detection and tracking of objects whose surface temperature is so low that they cannot be seen by the human eye. The most recent years have witnessed a rapid growth in the application of infrared techniques to *non*-military operations in the out-of-doors. I do not refer here to infrared photography, which again is an established technique but is sensitive only at wavelengths shorter than about 1.3 microns. The type of infrared discussed in this book deals chiefly with wavelengths considerably longer than 1 micron and hence with radiant energy to which infrared film and photocells are not sensitive.

The September 1959 issue of the *Proceedings of the Institute of Radio Engineers* was notable in that it contained articles describing, for perhaps the first time in the general literature and on such a broad scale, both the physical principles and the applications of infrared technology. The present book covers much of this ground, and includes additional engineering aspects of infrared applications. It represents one of the very few publications which treats this considerable body of knowledge in a unified fashion suitable for classroom use or self-instruction.

The infrared developments since about the time of World War I were surveyed in an article by Arnquist[1] in the journal issue just mentioned. A historical survey of the even earlier developments, starting with the discovery of the infrared spectral region by Herschel in the year 1800, has been given Barr.[2] The reader is referred to these two articles as providing an excellent background in the field of infrared radiation.

Any complete infrared system, be it for laboratory or for field use, consists of five basic and rather separate parts, elements, or subsystems. The first is the source of radiation, called the "target" in military parlance. The target is almost always seen against its radiant background, and this fact must be taken into account when evaluating target radiation. In a field instrument this radiation reaches the infrared equipment only after traversing the atmosphere for a certain distance; this path may be short—just a few inches—or may be many miles in length. So intense is the absorption at certain wavelengths by atmospheric constituents such as carbon dioxide and water vapor that their effect on the transmitted radiation must always be taken into account in extrapolating back from the measured radiation to the true target radiation.

Then the radiation from the target or source, as transmitted by the atmosphere, is intercepted and gathered in by an optical system, which system constitutes one of the most challenging parts of the overall problem to the optical-mechanical design engineer or physicist.

The very heart, or perhaps I should say Achilles heel, of the system is the radiation detector, located at the focal point of the optical system. As a matter of fact, the advanced state in which infrared technology finds itself today is largely due to a break-through that occurred in Germany in the 1930's with the discovery of lead sulfide photoconductivity at near-infrared wavelengths, and the development during the following twenty years of photoconductors sensitive to longer wavelength infrared radiation. Thus the old thermodynamic-type detectors such as bolometers and thermocouples could be replaced by rapid-acting, ultra-sensitive, quantum-type detectors.

The weak signal from the detector must be suitably amplified with the addition of a minimum of electrical noise, and this process is sometimes treated as a separate problem, although at other times the detector-preamplifier is considered as a single unit. Following the preamplifier there are further stages of amplification, and finally there is the display,

[1] Warren N. Arnquist, "A Survey of Early Infrared Developments," *Proc. IRE* 47, 1420–1430 (1959).

[2] E. Scott Barr, "Historical Survey of the Early Development of the Infrared Spectral Region," *Am. J. Phys.* 28, 42–54 (1960).

the read-out, the servo motor, or whatever output is desired from the infrared system.

Thus the five "elements" of the infrared system are the target or source; atmospheric absorption; the optical system; the detector-preamplifier; and finally the read-out or display. All of these items are covered in detail in the present book. In addition, considerable space is given to some other items such as techniques for the measurement of infrared radiation, evaluation and test procedures for detectors, signal processing techniques, and design procedures for specific types of equipments. Also, there are appendixes which deal in more detail with certain specialized subjects. Of special note is Appendix C, "Sources of Information about Infrared Technology," which should be of great practical value to persons doing research and development work in this broad field.

It must be realized that no one person could be expected to have the knowledge and the ability to write a complete book on infrared technology—the subjects involved are too diverse and the amount of detail needed to do an adequate job in each one is overwhelming. Therefore it is not surprising that this book represents the joint efforts of five authors, each of whom is particularly qualified in a special field. (Two additional contributors are authors of Appendixes A and B.) Despite the fact that several persons are involved, there has been a serious effort made to achieve uniformity of style and format.

It is a great pleasure to witness the appearance, at long last, of an extensive, inclusive, satisfying treatment of the vigorous new field of infrared technology.

Stanley S. Ballard

University of Florida
Dept. of Physics
Gainesville

PREFACE

Twice each summer since 1959 we have given a one-week accelerated course in modern infrared technology at The University of Michigan. This book is an outgrowth of the notes used in teaching that course. We hope that it will meet the needs for a text covering the relatively new field of infrared technology as applied to military and civil problems.

The level of the material presented is approximately that of the senior undergraduate year of a typical university curriculum in the physical sciences. It is desirable that the reader's background include experience with elementary and intermediate college physics, mathematics through elementary differential equations, and those elements of communications included in electrical engineering.

The book is made up of four major sections. The first section, Chapters 1 through 4, covers basic radiation concepts: sources and the nature of the radiation processes, radiation measurements, and transmission through various media with particular emphasis on the earth's atmosphere. Chapter 1 also discusses commonly accepted nomenclature for radiation quantities recommended by the Working Group on Infrared Backgrounds; this nomenclature has usually been followed throughout the book. Chapters 5 through 7, which comprise the second part, are devoted to optics, optical materials, and optical instruments. The next section, Chapters 8 through 12, includes that part of solid-state physics appropriate to detectors, physical mechanisms suitable for detection, the interaction of radiation and matter, noise processes in semiconductors, and detector measurements. Finally, Chapters 13 and 14 deal with applications; design procedures are discussed and applied to typical problems. One Appendix describes the major sources of infrared information; another contains atmospheric spectra.

The authors are indebted to the following distinguished scientists for helpful comments on the material of the course and in this book: L. Biberman, M. Krasno, D. Lowe, J. Morgan, L. Mundie, R. Powell, W. Weihe, T. Whitney, and E. Wormser. Each of them presented a guest lecture for the course and made suggestions regarding content. Appendices A and B to this book were contributed by Mr. L. Biberman and Mr. E. Wormser respectively, and are based on lectures given during the course.

We are indebted to the Engineering Summer Conferences of The University of Michigan for support while we prepared several drafts of the notes which were the forerunners of the final manuscript. We also acknowledge with gratitude several government agencies which supported the research programs that provided part of the background for the material in this book. In particular, the Office of Naval Research, Physics Branch; the Army Signal Corps; the Air Force Aeronautical Systems Division; the Air Force Cambridge Research Laboratories; and the Advanced Research Projects Agency have all contributed in this regard.

We gratefully acknowledge the contributions of Professors Stanley S. Ballard and Kathryn A. McCarthy on optical materials; the members of the Working Group on Infrared Backgrounds and Anthony J. LaRocca, who contributed ideas and criticisms on radiometric concepts; and Dr. R. Clark Jones and many members of The University of Michigan Infrared Laboratory staff who have contributed to the discussions on space-filtering techniques. Finally, Professor Ballard's criticisms of the over-all scope and content of the book have been very helpful.

M.R.H.
S.N.
G.H.S.
W.L.W.
G.J.Z.

University of Michigan
Institute of Science and Technology
Ann Arbor

CONTENTS

I.R spectrophotometer   X

CHAPTER 1

THE EMISSION AND ABSORPTION
OF INFRARED RADIATION

1.1 Definitions, Units, and Nomenclature

The adjective *infrared* has been defined as "pertaining to or designating those rays lying just beyond the red end of the visible spectrum... wavelengths... longer than those of visible light and shorter than those of radio waves." Commonly, the infrared region of the electromagnetic spectrum is said to extend from wavelengths of about 0.75 μ to 1000 μ. A brief but interesting history of the development of this spectral region has been written by E. Scott Barr.[1]

The electromagnetic spectrum may also be classified by division into three different types of wavelength distributions. These are continuous, band, and line spectra. If these are observed as dispersed by a low-resolution instrument, the distributions are described as:

(a) A continuum, a continuous variation in radiant power as a function of wavelength.

(b) Bands, a set of wavelength regions ($\Delta\lambda_1 = \lambda_2 - \lambda_1$; $\Delta\lambda_2 = \lambda_3 - \lambda_2$; $\Delta\lambda_3 = \lambda_4 - \lambda_3$; $\Delta\lambda_4 = \lambda_5 - \lambda_4$; ...) with discontinuous changes in power at the edges ($\lambda_1, \lambda_2, \lambda_3, \lambda_4, ...$).

(c) Lines, a set of wavelengths ($\lambda_1, \lambda_2, \lambda_3, ...$) each corresponding to a single value of power.

If high-resolution instrumentation is used, each line is seen to span a region of wavelength values in a continuous variation of radiance, often with more than one maximum. Thus one can observe fine structure, or even hyperfine structure, within what first appeared to be a single line. Similarly, the bands are found to be made up of many lines so that structure is found to exist here also. A true continuum, however, even under high resolution, shows no internal structure.

Table 1-1 lists the symbols, names, units, and descriptions of the radiometric quantities of greatest utility to infrared technology. The symbols are those recommended by the American Standards Association,[2]

1

with units based on the metric system and names as recommended by the Working Group on Infrared Backgrounds*[3,4] (reported by E. Bell[5]). Thus the unit of radiant energy U is the joule, while radiant energy density u is expressed in joule $\cdot$ cm^{-3}. The rate of transfer of radiant energy, or the radiant power P, may be indicated as U_t, where the subscript is used to denote the partial derivative with respect to time. Thus

$$P = \frac{\partial U}{\partial t} = U_t \qquad (1\text{-}1)$$

Radiant emittance, radiant intensity, and radiance are usually considered in reference to a radiating source, and are measures of the proper-

---

*The Working Group on Infrared Backgrounds (WGIRB) was established in 1954, by an *ad hoc* committee representing the three Services, for the purpose of studying significant problems in the field of infrared backgrounds and to make recommendations for their solution. Since that time, the Group has been considering targets, atmospheric transmission, and other related aspects of military infrared technology. The present membership is:

[Niel Beardsley] (deceased)	Raytheon, Santa Barbara
Ely Bell	Ohio State University Research Foundation
Lucien Biberman	University of Chicago Laboratories for Applied Sciences
George Brown	Engineering Research and Development Laboratories
John Hamilton	General Mills, Inc.
R. Clark Jones	Polaroid Corporation
Gilbert Kelton	Emerson Research Laboratories
George Levy	Marquardt Aircraft Company
Donald Lowe	Bendix Systems Division, Bendix Corporation
Max Nagel	SHAPE Air Defense Technical Center, SHAPE, The Hague, Netherlands
Lawrence Nichols	U.S. Naval Ordnance Test Station
Roy Paulson	Syracuse University
John Sanderson	Naval Research Laboratory
Edward Sevadjian	Aerojet-General Corporation
Eric Wormser	Barnes Engineering Company
George Zissis	The University of Michigan

The published reports of the WGIRB,[3,4] as well as extracts of an as-yet-unpublished report by the Group covering infrared target and background measurements, were extremely useful in many of the considerations presented in Chapters 1, 2, and 3.

ties of a source. These properties can be directly determined by measurements made at a distance from the source if the radiation is propagated through a nonattenuating medium.

Table 1-1

Radiometric Quantities[a]

Symbol	Name	Description	Unit
U	Radiant energy		Joule
u	Radiant energy density		Joule-cm^{-3}
P	Radiant power (radiant flux)	Rate of transfer of radiant energy	Watt
W	Radiant emittance	Radiant power per unit area emitted from a surface	Watt-cm^{-2}
H	Irradiance	Radiant power per unit area incident upon a surface	Watt-cm^{-2}
J	Radiant intensity	Radiant power per unit solid angle from a source	Watt-sterad^{-1}
N	Radiance	Radiant power per unit solid angle per unit area from a source	Watt-sterad^{-1}-cm^{-2}
P_λ	Spectral radiant power	Radiant power per unit wavelength interval	Watt-micron^{-1}
W_λ	Spectral radiant emittance	Radiant emittance per unit wavelength interval	Watt-cm^{-2}-μ^{-1}
H_λ	Spectral irradiance	Irradiance per unit wavelength interval	Watt-cm^{-2}-μ^{-1}
J_λ	Spectral radiant intensity	Radiant intensity per unit wavelength interval	Watt-sterad^{-1}-μ^{-1}
N_λ	Spectral radiance	Radiance per unit wavelength interval	Watt-sterad^{-1}-cm^{-2}-μ^{-1}
ε	Radiant emissivity	Ratio of "emitted" radiant power from a source to that from a blackbody at the same temperature	
α	Radiant absorptance	Ratio of "absorbed" radiant power to incident radiant power	
ρ	Radiant reflectance	Ratio of "reflected" radiant power to incident radiant power	
τ	Radiant transmittance	Ratio of "transmitted" radiant power to incident radiant power	
λ	Wavelength		Micron (μ)

[a]Reproduced with the permission of the Institute of Radio Engineers from Reference 5.

The basic quantity involving radiant power is the spectral radiance. This is defined as the limit of the ratio of ΔP to the product $\Delta A \cdot \Delta\Omega \cdot \Delta\lambda$, where ΔP is the increment of radiant power lying between λ and $\lambda + \Delta\lambda$ radiated away from the projection of an element of area ΔA into a solid angle $\Delta\Omega$ in a direction θ from the normal to the area, as all of these elements are reduced in size. Thus

$$N_\lambda = \lim_{\substack{\Delta A \to 0 \\ \Delta\Omega \to 0 \\ \Delta\lambda \to 0}} (\Delta P/\Delta\lambda \cdot \Delta\Omega \cos\theta \cdot \Delta A) = \partial^3 P/\partial\lambda\,\partial\Omega \cos\theta\,\partial A \quad (1\text{-}2)$$

From this radiometric quantity all of the others involving power may be defined by integration. For example, the radiant intensity of a Lambertian source can be found by

$$\int_\lambda \int_A N_\lambda \cos\theta\, dA\, d\lambda = J \qquad (1\text{-}3)$$

If the wavelength region is only a portion of the total spectrum, then $J_{\Delta\lambda}$ is found where

$$J_{\Delta\lambda} = \int_{\lambda_1}^{\lambda_2} \int_A N_\lambda \cos\theta\, dA\, d\lambda \qquad (1\text{-}4)$$

(In the following paragraphs differential definitions of the radiometric quantities are presented; these, however, are equivalent to the integral formulation of the functions defined.)

The limit of the ratio of the increment of radiant power ΔP radiated away from an element of area ΔA, as the area is reduced in size about a point, is defined as the radiant emittance W at that point. Thus

$$\lim_{\Delta A \to 0} \Delta P/\Delta A = W = \partial P/\partial A = P_A \qquad (1\text{-}5)$$

It should be noted that in this definition the radiant power considered is that radiated into the hemisphere (2π steradians) from a point of the source. If we restrict the power considered in the definition to that in an increment of solid angle $\Delta\Omega$ about a particular direction, and reduce this small angle in size, then the limit of the ratio of radiant power to area and solid angle is the radiance of the source at the point and in the particular direction, i.e.,

$$\lim_{\substack{\Delta\Omega \to 0 \\ \Delta A \to 0}} \Delta P/\Delta A\, \Delta\Omega = N = P_{A,\Omega} \qquad (1\text{-}6)$$

The power radiated by an entire source per unit solid angle in a particular direction is the radiant intensity J in that direction and may be defined as

$$\lim_{\Delta\Omega\to 0} \Delta P/\Delta\Omega = J = P_\Omega \qquad (1\text{-}7)$$

Obviously,

$$J = \int_{\substack{\text{Area} \\ \text{of Source}}} N \cdot dA \qquad (1\text{-}8)$$

and

$$W = \int_{\substack{2\pi \\ \text{steradian}}} N \cdot d\Omega. \qquad (1\text{-}9)$$

A determination of radiance from measurements made at a distance from a source, which for simplicity is considered to be *in vacuo*, involves a knowledge of the orientation of the observation direction with respect to the normal at the observed point. This knowledge is often difficult, if not impossible, to obtain. Modification of the definition so that the projected area is used, i.e., so that ΔA is replaced by the projection of the elemental area perpendicular to the direction of observation, offers a simpler and more easily determined quantity. In addition, sources which obey Lambert's cosine law (so that $\partial J/\partial A$ varies as the cosine of the angle θ between the normal to the surface and the direction of the observation) will have a radiance which is independent of the direction of measurement. This modification could be written as:

$$N = \frac{\partial^2 P}{\partial\Omega\,\partial A \cdot \cos\theta} \qquad (1\text{-}10)$$

and this definition of radiance will be used throughout this book.

Finally, the amount of radiant power per unit area received by a surface is given by the irradiance H defined as:

$$H = \partial P/\partial A = \lim_{\Delta A\to 0} \Delta P/\Delta A \qquad (1\text{-}11)$$

The specification of H is not complete, however, without some statement about the directions of the incident radiation. Two cases illustrating this point are the irradiation of a surface by radiation from an extended source such as an overcast sky (so that the radiation comes from the full 2π steradians of the hemisphere), and the irradiance on a surface due to radiation from a point source such as a distant star. Such statements describing the source-receiver geometry are usually sufficient to complete the definition of the particular irradiance measured.

In the definitions presented so far no consideration has been given to wavelength. If ΔP is the increment of radiant power in the interval λ to $\lambda + \Delta\lambda$ in each of the definitions given, then the limits of $\Delta W/\Delta\lambda$, $\Delta N/\Delta\lambda$, $\Delta J/\Delta\lambda$, and $\Delta H/\Delta\lambda$, as $\Delta\lambda$ becomes smaller, will define the spectral quantities

$$W_\lambda = \partial W/\partial\lambda \tag{1-12}$$

$$N_\lambda = \partial N/\partial\lambda \tag{1-13}$$

$$J_\lambda = \partial J/\partial\lambda \tag{1-14}$$

and

$$H_\lambda = \partial H/\partial\lambda \tag{1-15}$$

Similarly,

$$P_\lambda = \lim_{\Delta\lambda \to 0} \Delta P/\Delta\lambda \tag{1-16}$$

The other radiometric quantities listed in Table 1-1 are considered to be defined by the statements listed in the column entitled "Description." However, certain qualifications and cautions should be noted. The absorptance α is a measure of the fraction of incident radiation absorbed by a receiver, and should be distinguished from other concepts, such as the fraction absorbed per unit path or unit concentration. Specification of the reflectance of a single, specularly reflecting surface requires additional statements. The angle of incidence, the curvature of the incident wavefronts, polarization, and other conditions need to be stated. For diffusely reflecting surfaces the situation is more complicated. A common, although by no means universally accepted, concept has been named the partial reflectance. This is the ratio of the radiant power reflected in some angle β to the radiant power incident at some angle γ. The reflectance is then the ratio of the total reflected power, in all directions, to that incident on the surface. Again, for transmittance, several qualifying statements are needed to ensure the complete specification of the particular quantity considered. The definition of emissivity requires a specification of the thermodynamic variable, temperature, of the body. If a single recognizable temperature of the body does not exist, then "emissivity" is a meaningless concept for that body.

All of the quantities α, ρ, τ, and ε may depend upon the spectral distribution of the radiation used in the measurement of these quantities. The wavelength dependencies may be determined by measurements of radiation in very small wavelength regions since

$$\varepsilon(\lambda) = \lim_{\delta\lambda \to 0} \left\{ \frac{\displaystyle\int_{\lambda-\delta\lambda}^{\lambda+\delta\lambda} W_\lambda(\lambda)\, d\lambda}{\displaystyle\int_{\lambda-\delta\lambda}^{\lambda+\delta\lambda} [W_\lambda(\lambda)]_{\text{Blackbody}}\, d\lambda} \right\} \tag{1-17}$$

is the emissivity at λ. Since $\varepsilon(\lambda) \neq \partial\varepsilon/\partial\lambda$, the subscript notation ε_λ is not correct here. Similar considerations apply to the spectral reflectance, transmittance, and absorptance.

1.2 Effects of Attenuating Media

Although the quantities just discussed are generally cited in connection with a source or receiver, it is often useful to be able to specify some radiometric quantities in the radiant field between the source and receiver. This may be easily done by the introduction of a "test" receiver at the point under consideration. Thus, for a point source of intensity J in a nonattenuating medium, a test receiver at a distance s from the source receives an irradiance,

$$H = J/s^2 \tag{1-18}$$

The receiver aperture can next be considered a source with rays limited to those angles that fit the geometry. Now the values of W and N can be stated (in accordance with the previous definitions), and thus the radiometric quantities may be meaningfully applied at any point in the radiant field. This concept is most useful in connection with optical systems, since radiant power, emittance, irradiance, and radiance can be calculated at lenses, mirrors, images, and the like. By the law of conservation of energy the invariance of radiance in a lossless medium can be shown. Even in lossless media with different indexes of refraction, the ratio of the radiance (measured at any point along a ray in an image-forming system) to the square of the relative index of refraction at that point (i.e., N/n^2) is a constant.

These considerations must be modified greatly if the media considered are not lossless. The processes of absorption, scattering, and emission may occur in the medium between source and receiver. The adjective "apparent" is used to modify any quantity describing the source which has been calculated, with no attempt at inclusion of the effects of the intervening medium. For example, if Eq. (1-18) were used to calculate J for a source when actually half the source radiation was lost by absorption in an intervening medium (i.e., $\tau = 1/2$), then the quantity $H \cdot s^2$ would yield the apparent radiant intensity J', while the radiant intensity would be given by

$$J = 2 \cdot J' = 2H \cdot s^2 \tag{1-19}$$

Similarly, one may measure the apparent radiance or emittance of a source. It is of interest to note here that, since an infrared background is defined to include the emission, scattering, and absorption of the atmosphere, measurement of infrared backgrounds can never yield an apparent radiance. The adjective may be applied to the irradiance at a receiver in some instances.   For example, if from Eq. 1-19 the irradiance is given by

$$H = J/2s^2$$

then the apparent irradiance given by

$$H' = J/s^2$$

is the irradiance calculated neglecting the intervening atmospheric attentuation.

1.3 Blackbody Radiation[6-11] and Radiation Laws

As was stated in Section 1.1, electromagnetic radiation may be classified by wavelength distribution as band, line, or continuous radiation spectra, or some combination of these three. Of particular importance in the infrared wavelength region are the continuous spectra which are emitted by all solids. The theoretical treatment of a source with $\rho = 0$, $\tau = 0$, and $\alpha = 1$ (i.e., a blackbody) is the simplest and most informative.

1.3.1 *Kirchhoff's Law*

Kirchhoff's law was first experimentally discovered and expressed by him in 1858 in the form

$$W_{\lambda, \text{Blackbody}}(\lambda, T) = W_\lambda(\lambda, T)/\alpha \qquad (1\text{-}20)$$

that is, the emittance (or emissive power) of a blackbody at a temperature T and at wavelength λ is equal to the emittance at the same wavelength of a nonblackbody source divided by the absorptance of that body if it is at the same temperature T. This relationship is derivable in several ways.

If we assume two infinite bodies in the shapes of facing planes (see Figure 1-1), one of which is a blackbody, then at the condition of equilibrium corresponding to temperature T, the spectral emittances of these sources at wavelength λ is as shown in Figure 1-1. From the second law

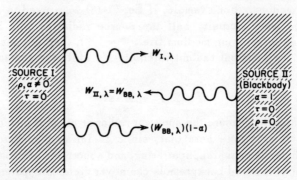

Fig. 1-1. **Radiation balance between an infinite, plane graybody and an infinite, plane blackbody.**

of thermodynamics

$$W_{\lambda,\,\text{Blackbody}} = W_{\lambda,\,I} + W_{\lambda,\,\text{Blackbody}}[1 - \alpha(\lambda)] \qquad (1\text{-}21)$$

and therefore,\

$$W_{\lambda,\,\text{Blackbody}}(\lambda,\,T) = W_{\lambda,\,I}(\lambda,\,T)/\alpha(\lambda) \qquad (1\text{-}22)$$

This derivation may be generalized if we consider two radiation sources that are not blackbodies, as shown in Figure 1-2. Again the equilibrium

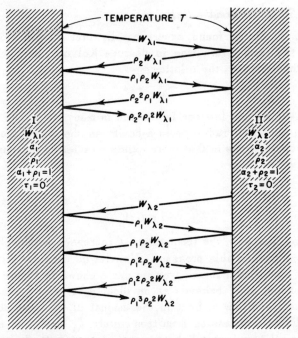

Fig. 1-2. Radiation balance between two infinite, plane graybodies.

condition at temperature T requires that, at a fixed wavelength λ, the spectral irradiance of Source I equals that of Source II. Thus, the amount of radiation coming from Source II to Source I is given by

$$W_{\lambda 2} + \rho_1\rho_2 W_{\lambda 2} + \rho_1^2\rho_2^2 W_{\lambda 2} + \rho_1^3\rho_2^3 W_{\lambda 2} + \cdots + \rho_2 W_{\lambda 1} + \rho_1\rho_2^2 W_{\lambda 1} +$$

$$\rho_1^2\rho_2^3 W_{\lambda 1} + \cdots = W_{\lambda 2} \sum_{n=0}^{\infty} \rho_1^n\rho_2^n + \rho_2 W_{\lambda 1} \sum_{n=0}^{\infty} \rho_1^n\rho_2^n \qquad (1\text{-}23)$$

while the amount coming from I to II is given by

$$W_{\lambda 1} + \rho_1\rho_2 W_{\lambda 1} + \rho_1^2\rho_2^2 W_{\lambda 1} + \cdots + \rho_1 W_{\lambda 2} + \rho_2\rho_1^2 W_{\lambda 2} + \rho_2^2\rho_1^3 W_{\lambda 2}$$

$$+ \cdots = W_{\lambda 1} \sum_{n=0}^{\infty} \rho_1^n\rho_2^n + \rho_2 W_{\lambda 1} \sum_{n=0}^{\infty} \rho_1^n\rho_2^n \qquad (1.24)$$

and these two sums must be equal. Thus

$$W_{\lambda 2} + \rho_2 W_{\lambda 1} = W_{\lambda 1} + \rho_1 W_{\lambda 2} \tag{1-25}$$

Since

$$\rho_2 = 1 - \alpha_2 \quad \text{and} \quad \rho_1 = 1 - \alpha_1 \tag{1-26}$$

$$(W_{\lambda, 1}/\alpha_1)_{\lambda, T} = (W_{\lambda 2}/\alpha_2)_{\lambda, T} \tag{1-27}$$

1.3.2 *The Stefan-Boltzmann Relation*

In 1879, T. Stefan found experimentally that W was proportional to T^4 where the temperature was in degrees Kelvin. In 1884 Boltzmann obtained, theoretically, the relation

$$u = A T^4 \tag{1-28}$$

The Stefan-Boltzmann law can be derived in many ways. We shall derive it by using blackbody radiation in a cavity as shown in Figure 1-3. The radiation acts as a gas in that there exists a radiation pressure

$$p = u/3 \tag{1-29}$$

where

$$u = U/V \tag{1-30}$$

As V approaches zero, the temperature T increases without limit. Thus, work is done against this pressure. Now let us consider the use of this chamber in a particular thermodynamic cycle shown in Figure 1-4, assuming the "photon gas" behaves as an ideal gas. The cycle consists of an isothermal addition of heat in the amount of Q_1 (from point 0 to 1), then an adiabatic expansion from temperature T_1 to T_2, an extraction of Q_2 isothermally, and an adiabatic return to point 0. It will be shown later that the blackbody radiation does not change in character, i.e., the distribution with respect to wavelength remains unchanged during such processes. The first law of thermodynamics is used in the form

$$\delta Q = dU + p \, dV \tag{1-31}$$

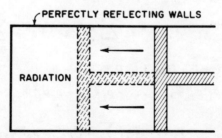

Fig. 1-3. Radiation in a cavity for derivation of the Stefan-Boltzmann relation.

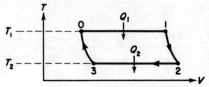

Fig. 1-4. **Thermodynamic cycle used in a derivation of the Stefan-Boltzmann relation.**

Since

$$p = u/3 = U/3V = nRT/V \qquad (1\text{-}32)$$

U is a function of T only. From $U = uV$,

$$dU = u\, dV + V\, du \qquad (1\text{-}33)$$

and thus

$$\delta Q = (u\, dV + V\, du) + (u/3)\, dV \qquad (1\text{-}34)$$

or

$$\delta Q = V\, du + \frac{4}{3}\, u\, dV \qquad (1\text{-}35)$$

In the first step (0 to 1), since T = constant, $du = 0$ and

$$Q_1 = \frac{4}{3}\, u_1\, (V_1 - V_0) \qquad (1\text{-}36)$$

In the second (1 to 2),

$$0 = V\, du + \frac{4}{3}\, u\, dV \qquad (1\text{-}37)$$

$$\frac{du}{u} = -\frac{4}{3}\frac{dV}{V} \qquad (1\text{-}38)$$

and

$$-\frac{3}{4}\left[\ln u\right]_{u_1}^{u_2} = \left[\ln V\right]_{V_1}^{V_2} \qquad (1\text{-}39)$$

or

$$\frac{u_2}{u_1} = \left(\frac{V_2}{V_1}\right)^{-4/3} \qquad (1\text{-}40)$$

Similarly $Q_2 = (4/3)\,(V_3 - V_2)\, u_2$ is used for the third step, and the same relation for (3 to 0) as for (1 to 2). From these it follows that

$$u_1^{3/4}\,(V_1 - V_0) = u_2^{3/4}\,(V_3 - V_2) \qquad (1\text{-}41)$$

and

$$\frac{Q_1}{Q_2} = \frac{T_1}{T_2} = \frac{(V_1 - V_0) u_1}{(V_3 - V_2) u_2} = \frac{u_2^{3/4}}{u_1^{3/4}} \cdot \frac{u_1}{u_2} = \frac{u_1^{1/4}}{u_2^{1/4}} \qquad (1\text{-}42)$$

Thus

$$\frac{u_1}{u_2} = \left(\frac{T_1}{T_2}\right)^4 \qquad (1\text{-}43)$$

It is interesting to note that, for an adiabatic change of blackbody radiation, it can be shown from the above relations that $p\,V^{4/3} = $ constant.

Given the wavelength distribution of blackbody radiation, the Stefan-Boltzmann law may be derived by the relation

$$u = \int_0^\infty u_\nu\, d\nu = \frac{8\pi h}{c}\int_0^\infty \frac{\nu^3}{e^{h\nu/kT} - 1}\, d\nu \qquad (1\text{-}44)$$

where the spectral energy density is defined as

$$\partial u/\partial \nu = u_\nu \qquad (1\text{-}45)$$

rather than as

$$\partial u/\partial \lambda = u_\lambda \qquad (1\text{-}46)$$

and where

$$u_\nu\, d\nu = u_\lambda d\lambda \qquad (1\text{-}47)$$

with

$$\nu = c/\lambda \qquad (1\text{-}48)$$

(c is the speed of light in vacuum).

Equation (1-44) may be written

$$u = K\int_0^\infty \frac{\nu^3}{e^{a\nu} - 1}\, d\nu \qquad (1\text{-}49)$$

Let $x = a\nu$; then $\nu^3 = x^3 a^{-3}$, $d\nu = a^{-1}\, dx$ and $e^{a\nu} = e^x$, where $a = h/kT$. Substitution gives

$$u = Ka^{-4}\int_0^\infty \frac{x^3\, dx}{e^x - 1} \qquad (1\text{-}50)$$

Since

$$x^3(e^x - 1)^{-1} = x^3[e^{-x} + e^{-2x} + e^{-3x} + \ldots + e^{-nx} + \ldots] \qquad (1\text{-}51)$$

and

$$\int_0^\infty x^3 e^{-nx}\, dx = \frac{3!}{n^4} \qquad (1\text{-}52)$$

then

$$u = \frac{8\pi}{c^3 h^3} k^4 T^4 \sum_{n=1}^{\infty} \frac{3!}{n^4} \qquad (1\text{-}53)$$

However,

$$\sum_{n=1}^{\infty} \frac{1}{n^4} = \frac{\pi^4}{90} \qquad (1\text{-}54)$$

so that

$$u = \frac{8\pi^5 k^4}{15 \, c^3 h^3} T^4 = A T^4 \qquad (1\text{-}55)$$

Lastly, one may restate the first law as

$$dS = \frac{\delta Q}{T} = \frac{V}{T} du + \frac{4}{3} \frac{u}{T} dV \qquad (1\text{-}56)$$

where dS is an exact differential. Thus,

$$dS = \left(\frac{V}{T} \frac{du}{dT} \right) dT + \left(\frac{4}{3} \frac{u}{T} \right) dV \qquad (1\text{-}57)$$

or

$$dS = M \, dT + N \, dV \qquad (1\text{-}58)$$

But

$$\frac{\partial M}{\partial V} = \frac{\partial N}{\partial T} \qquad (1\text{-}59)$$

and, therefore,

$$\frac{1}{T} \frac{du}{dT} = \frac{4}{3} \frac{1}{T} \frac{du}{dT} - \frac{4}{3} \frac{u}{T^2} \qquad (1\text{-}60)$$

or

$$\frac{du}{u} = 4 \frac{dT}{T} \qquad (1\text{-}61)$$

and

$$\ln u = 4 \ln T + \text{constant} \qquad (1\text{-}62)$$

Thus, again $u = A T^4$. $\qquad (1\text{-}63)$

1.3.3 The Wavelength Distribution of Blackbody Radiation

The problem of explaining the spectral distribution of radiation from a blackbody was examined and studied by many scientists in the late

1800's. In 1893 Wien presented a development of what became known as Wien's displacement law. To arrive at this relation, he considered black-body radiation in a chamber of the type shown in Figure 1-3. As the "gas" is compressed, work is done and so the radiation gains in energy. At the same time, there exists a doppler shift in the radiation wavelengths due to the motion of the piston. This shift is given by $\Delta\lambda/\lambda = 2v_i/c$, where v is the speed of motion of the piston. The radiation remains blackbody in character during this process, as was shown by Planck.[10]

This deduction of the unchanging distribution of the radiation can be seen by the following reasoning. With blackbody radiation in the cavity, the entropy of the system is S_1. After an adiabatic change, the entropy is still S_1. Let us assume that the character of the radiation changed, departing from the blackbody distribution. By introduction of a small particle with an $\alpha \neq 0$, the radiation is restored to a blackbody distribution. However, by this act we have increased the entropy to S_2. Since an adiabatic change is reversible, we can go back through each point of equilibrium as before and return to the initial $S_1 < S_2$. A decrease in S is not possible, however. Therefore, the radiation did not depart from the blackbody distribution.

From these considerations Wien was able to deduce that the shape of the blackbody curve required a functional form of the following type:

$$u_\nu = \nu^3 f_1(T/\nu) = T^3(\nu^3/T^3)f_1(T/\nu) = T^3 g_1(T/\nu) \qquad (1\text{-}64)$$

$$N_\nu = \nu^3 f_2(T/\nu) \qquad (1\text{-}65)$$

$$u_\lambda = \lambda^{-5} f_3(\lambda T) = T^5 g_3(\lambda T) \qquad (1\text{-}66)$$

$$N_\lambda = \lambda^{-5} f_4(\lambda T) = T^5 g_4(\lambda T) \qquad (1\text{-}67)$$

Now let

$$\frac{dN_\lambda}{d\lambda} = 0 = T^6 g_4'(\lambda T) \qquad (1\text{-}68)$$

Since $T \neq 0$,

$$g_4'(\lambda T) = 0 \quad \text{and} \quad \lambda_{max} \cdot T = \text{constant} \qquad (1\text{-}69)$$

Let us now examine a classical derivation which leads to the information about the radiation distribution stated above. A model is assumed of a cavity in the shape of a box in which there exist standing waves of electromagnetic radiation due to oscillating dipoles. From Maxwell's equations for free space, i.e.,

$$\nabla \times \mathbf{H} = \frac{1}{c}\frac{\partial \mathbf{E}}{\partial t} \qquad (1\text{-}70)$$

$$\nabla \times \mathbf{E} = -\frac{1}{c}\frac{\partial \mathbf{H}}{\partial t} \qquad (1\text{-}71)$$

$$\nabla \cdot \mathbf{E} = 0 \tag{1-72}$$

$$\nabla \cdot \mathbf{H} = 0 \tag{1-73}$$

we may obtain a wave equation

$$\nabla^2 \varphi = \frac{1}{c^2} \frac{\partial^2 \varphi}{\partial t^2} \tag{1-74}$$

whose solution is

$$\varphi = e^{2\pi i \nu t} \psi(x, y, z) \tag{1-75}$$

The function ψ must satisfy the relation

$$\nabla^2 \psi + (4\pi^2 \nu^2/c^2)\, \psi = 0 \tag{1-76}$$

and, to obtain standing waves, $\psi = 0$ at $x = 0$, $y = 0$, $z = 0$ and $x = L$, $y = L$, $z = L$. A specific solution is

$$\psi = A \sin(\beta\pi x/L) \sin(\gamma\pi y/L) \sin(\delta\pi z/L) \tag{1-77}$$

where β, γ, and δ may each take on the integer values 0, 1, 2, 3, ... A general solution is obtainable by a linear combination of solutions of the type shown. If we substitute the solution in the differential equation, we obtain

$$(\beta^2 + \gamma^2 + \delta^2)\,(\pi^2/L^2) = 4\pi^2 \nu_k^2/c^2 \tag{1-78}$$

where ν_k indicates that the kth specific solution was used, and is the frequency of the kth standing wave. Now we may calculate the number of modes per unit volume of the box for ν_k to obtain the energy density as a function of frequency. If we do this, we obtain

$$\text{number of modes/volume} = 4\pi\nu^2/c^3 \tag{1-79}$$

If each mode has associated with it on average energy $\bar{U}$, then

$$u_\nu = (4\pi\nu^2/c^3)\,\bar{U} \tag{1-80}$$

This expression is u_ν for polarized radiation. For unpolarized radiation,

$$u_\nu = (8\pi\nu^2/c^3)\,\bar{U} \tag{1-81}$$

According to classical theory, this average energy is given by $\bar{U} = kT$, which leads to the Rayleigh-Jeans law

$$u_\nu = (8\pi\nu^2/c^3)\,kT \tag{1-82}$$

while the Wien form is given by

$$u_\nu = (8\pi\nu^3/c^3)\,(kT/\nu) \tag{1-83}$$

Neither form followed the distributions found experimentally, so that Wien was led to trying other relations of the type

$$u_\nu = (8\pi\nu^3 k/c^3)\, f(T/\nu) \tag{1-84}$$

The best-known form (arising from the use of Maxwellian distributions for energy in ideal gases) was

$$u_\nu = (8\pi\nu^3 k/c^3)\, e^{-\text{constant}/(T/\nu)} \tag{1-85}$$

Planck's contribution came from a re-examination of the relation $\bar{U} = kT$. The classical treatment of an oscillator by the use of Hamiltonian mechanics leads to an integration in phase space which assumes that phase space may be subdivided into infinitesimal portions. Planck found that, by assuming phase space was not a continuum, the average energy of an oscillator was

$$\bar{U} = h\nu/(e^{h\nu/kT} - 1) \tag{1-86}$$

where h was a small, finite constant with the dimensions of action, i.e., erg-second. Thus, one is led directly to Planck's law, i.e.,

$$u_\nu = \frac{8\pi h\nu^3}{c^3(e^{h\nu/kT} - 1)} \tag{1-87}$$

for unpolarized radiation. Since

$$u_\nu \frac{c}{\lambda^2} d\lambda = u_\lambda\, d\lambda \tag{1-88}$$

$$u_\lambda = \frac{8\pi ch}{\lambda^5(e^{hc/kT\lambda} - 1)} \tag{1-89}$$

The Wien and the Rayleigh-Jeans equations can be deduced from Planck's law by either neglecting the number 1 in relation to $e^{h\nu/kT}$, or by expanding the exponential in a series and neglecting higher-order terms. More rigorous derivations of Planck's law have been made. For example, it can be deduced as a logical consequence of placing a Bose ensemble within an isolated region. Since photons are known to obey Bose-Einstein statistics, this assumption is, simply stated, merely the assumption that blackbody radiation consists of photons in thermal equilibrium with matter and with one another.[12] For a derivation using the Einstein coefficients, see reference 13. The laws derived for blackbody radiation can be applied to greybodies, i.e., those with a constant $\varepsilon \neq 1$, by use of the appropriate value of emissivity.

1.3.4 *Summary of Blackbody Relations*

In summary, the equations developed are, in practical form,

$$u_\lambda = c_1\lambda^{-5}(e^{c_2/\lambda T} - 1)^{-1} \qquad \text{Planck's law} \tag{1-90}$$

$$8 \pi h c = c_1 = (4.9918 \pm 0.0002) \times 10^{-15} \text{ erg} \cdot \text{cm} \qquad \text{(Reference 14)} \qquad \text{(1-91)}$$

$$h c / k = c_2 = (1.43880 \pm 0.00007) \text{ cm} \cdot \text{degree} \qquad \text{(Reference 14)} \qquad \text{(1-92)}$$

$$u_\lambda = c_1 \lambda^{-5} e^{-c_2 / \lambda T} \qquad \text{Wien's law} \qquad \text{(1-93)}$$

$$u_\lambda = c_1 \lambda^{-5} (\lambda T / c_2) \qquad \text{Rayleigh-Jean's law} \qquad \text{(1-94)}$$

$$\lambda_m \cdot T = 2897.9 \ \mu \ ^\circ\text{K} \qquad \text{(Reference 14)} \qquad \text{(1-95)}$$

$$W = \varepsilon \sigma T^4 \qquad \text{Stefan-Boltzmann's law} \qquad \text{(1-96)}$$

$$\sigma = (0.56687 \pm 0.00010) \times 10^{-4} \text{ watt cm}^{-2} \text{ degree}^{-4}$$

$$\text{(Reference 14)} \qquad \text{(1-97)}$$

$$W_{\lambda, \text{Blackbody}} (\lambda, T) = \frac{W(\lambda, T)}{\alpha(\lambda)} \qquad \text{Kirchhoff's law} \qquad \text{(1-98)}$$

For a Lambertian radiator (i.e., one with N the same for all directions), or for any areal source viewed perpendicularly,

$$W_\lambda = \pi N_\lambda \qquad \text{(1-99)}$$

and

$$u_\lambda = \frac{2W_\lambda}{c} \qquad \text{(1-100)}$$

Thus

$$W_\lambda = 3.7403 \lambda^{-5} (e^{c_2 / \lambda T} - 1)^{-1} \qquad \text{(1-101)}$$

1.4 Nonblackbody Radiation

It is perhaps fortunate that the development of high-resolution spectroscopy did not precede the establishment of the theory of atomic spectra by any significant amount of time. The complexities revealed by powerful instruments are not explained by the simpler theories of Bohr, and Bohr-Sommerfeld. Even the explanation of the fine structure of the line spectrum from atomic hydrogen requires the sophistication of relativistic quantum mechanics.

Planck's establishment of the basic premise of quantum theory in 1900, that the energy in an electromagnetic field was in finite amounts or "quanta" $(E = h\nu)$, was recognized by Einstein in his application of this idea directly to light. Einstein's 1905 explanation of the photoelectric effect depended on "needles" or photons of light, characterized by an energy $E = h\nu = hc/\lambda$. Thus the duality of light as a corpuscular, and yet a wave, phenomenon was established. In 1913 Niels Bohr expounded a theory based upon quanta, and processes assumed to be discrete in nature, to explain line spectra.

1.4.1. *Empirical Formulations for Line Spectra*

A brief review of the experimental facts and the attempts to understand the observed regularities in line spectra is in order. An examina-

tion of the wavelengths and frequencies emitted by atomic hydrogen led
to many attempts to express these values in terms of ratios; G. I. Stoney
did so in 1871 and Hartley more elegantly in 1883. J. J. Balmer in 1885
identified a sequence or series of lines which he found to be related by

$$\lambda = C \ \frac{m^2}{m^2 - n^2} \tag{1-102}$$

where $n = 2$, C = constant, and $m = 3$, 4, 5, 6, ... Since, when m increases λ approaches the value C, this constant was called the "limit"
of the series. This series was given the name "Balmer series." In
1906 T. Lyman identified another sequence of lines which could also be
related by a similar equation. Walter Ritz stated the Ritz combination
principle in 1908; it pointed out that the wavenumber of each line could
be considered to be the difference between terms which were given by a
function of an integer n. Any difference between two terms should be
realizable by a spectral line.

Lines identified with the Paschen series were found in 1909, while
other lines in it, as well as several in the Brackett and Pfund series,
came during the period 1922 to 1927. These series could be written as:

$$\tilde{\nu} = R\left(\frac{1}{n^2} - \frac{1}{m^2}\right) \tag{1-103}$$

where R = constant, $\tilde{\nu}$ = wave number, and n and m are as shown in
Table 1-2. In Eq. (1-103), the terms are the set

$$\{T_k\}_{\substack{k=1 \\ \text{to} \\ k=\infty}} = \{R/k^2\}_{\substack{k=1 \\ \text{to} \\ k=\infty}} \tag{1-104}$$

Actually, even in 1887 Rydberg had noted that the terms had to depend
on a "k" which was some integer plus a nonzero fraction smaller than 1.
Ritz used more complex terms as shown:

$$T_{\text{Ritz}} = R/[n + a + (b/n^2)]^2 \tag{1-105}$$

Table 1-2

n and m for Eq. (1-103)

If n is	and m is greater than	then the name of the Series which results is
1	1	Lyman
2	2	Balmer
3	3	Paschen
4	4	Brackett
5	5	Pfund

or

$$T_{\text{Ritz}} = R/(n + a + \alpha T_{\text{Ritz}})^2 \qquad (1\text{-}106)$$

It should be noted that the constant R is traditionally called the Rydberg constant.

The history of the studies of the spectra for lithium, calcium, and, indeed, all elements, is somewhat similar to the foregoing account for hydrogen. However, the terms become more complex. The method of naming these series is somewhat revealing. If one starts with very low energy inputs to a source of atomic lithium radiation, then the first set of lines which appears is the so-called Principal Series. Next some very sharp lines appear, the Sharp Series. Others then appear which seem rather diffuse, the Diffuse Series. Another set develops which seems very similar to the hydrogen lines. This series was therefore thought to be fundamental to the understanding of the lithium spectrum and was called the Fundamental Series. After that the names of the higher energy series are no longer descriptive, and they are called simply the G, H, I, and so on Series.

1.4.2 *Theoretical Considerations for Line Spectra*

For details of these and other historical facts the reader is referred to White.[15]   At the present the terms which are used with the Ritz combination principle to obtain the wavenumbers of spectral lines are considered to represent atomic states which are characterized by different energies. The combinations of terms thus correspond to changes in the energy states of the atom. A very useful form for presentation of these data is in the form of a term diagram or "energy-level" diagram. These are drawn as one-dimensional plots with energy increasing vertically, as shown in Figure 1-5.

Bohr's theory for the hydrogen atom was based on an atomic model in which electrons were in circular orbits, mechanically circling about the positively charged nucleus. For hydrogen a single electron was pictured as shown in Figure 1-6, where the electron and the proton are assumed to be, effectively, point charges. The electron is shown in one orbit of a set of orbits which are stable energetically, that is, contrary to the pictures of classical physics, while in these orbits the electron does not emit radiation. Each orbit is associated with a definite amount of energy, and by changing from one orbit to another, energy may be either absorbed or emitted by the atom. The energy which is associated with any particular orbital configuration of the atom is given by

$$U = \frac{1}{2} m_0 \omega^2 r^2 - \frac{Ze^2}{r} + \text{constant} \qquad (1\text{-}107)$$

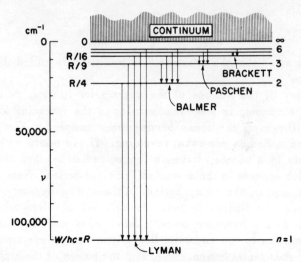

Fig. 1-5. Term diagram for hydrogen atom.

where r = radius of the orbit and ω = angular velocity. However, the stability of the orbit means that

$$\frac{(Ze)e}{r^2} = \frac{m_0 V^2}{r} = m_0 \omega^2 r \qquad (1\text{-}108)$$

When the electron is infinitely far from the nucleus, the energy of the atom is zero. Thus,

$$U = -\frac{1}{2}\frac{Ze^2}{r} \qquad (1\text{-}109)$$

Changes in the energy of the atom must be in discrete nonzero amounts, to agree with the experimental data. Thus the values of U are restricted to a set of discrete values and the difference between two energies can be written so as to give the wavenumber in the following form:

$$\tilde{\nu} = \frac{1}{\lambda} = \frac{U_{\text{initial}} - U_{\text{final}}}{hc} \qquad (1\text{-}110)$$

Finally another condition is needed, namely, that the angular momentum must be quantized, i.e.,

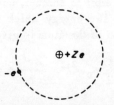

Fig. 1-6. Simplified Bohr model for hydrogen atom.

$$m_0 \omega r^2 = n\hbar = nh/2\pi \tag{1-111}$$

where $n = 0,1,2,3, \ldots$. From these equations, one can obtain:

$$\tilde{\nu} = \frac{2\pi^2 m_0 Z^2 e^4}{ch^3}\left(\frac{1}{n_f^2} - \frac{1}{n_i^2}\right) \tag{1-112}$$

For hydrogen $(Z = 1)$ the constant factor is the Rydberg constant R.

The above treatment represents the formulation of the simple Bohr quantum theory. Refinements may be made by considering the reduced mass μ, where $(1/\mu) = (1/m_0) + (1/m)$, instead of m_0, by allowing elliptic orbits (the Bohr-Sommerfeld model), by considering the relativistic mass m instead of m_0, and so on. Such details are beyond the scope of this book. Similarly, the sophistications of either wave or matrix mechanics are not introduced. The results of treating matter as particles whose distributions are given by probabilities calculable by wavelike equations have been verified many times. Many of the concepts applied by Bohr as axioms come directly from mathematical manipulation of equations based upon far fewer assumptions.

Since the term or energy-level diagram is such an important device for the application of the results of quantum mechanics (regardless of which theories were used to obtain it), an additional consideration of it is useful. In Figure 1-7 the term diagram for hydrogen is shown with indications of the phenomena of ionization, excitation, resonance, and resonance fluoresence, in absorption and emission.

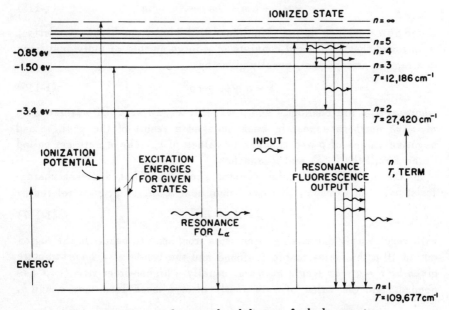

Fig. 1-7. Annotated energy-level diagram for hydrogen atom.

1.4.3 Band Spectra

In the experimental investigation of spectra, emissions which have been named band spectra are often found covering broad wavelength regions. The bands usually have a sharp edge at one end where the intensity goes abruptly to zero as compared to the other end where the intensity gradually drops off. These sharp edges (band heads) are not always found with band spectra. (See Reference 16 for illustrations.)

Attempts were made to obtain relationships between band heads in a Rydberg form. This was found to be possible for some bands in the shorter wavelength regions of the ultraviolet; however, most molecular spectra consist of bands with slowly changing separations. If one selects a visible set of bands (by means of regular intensity changes or some similar characteristic) which belong to one "progression," then usually the separation between bands can be represented by a relationship

$$\tilde{\nu} = \tilde{\nu}_0 - An + Bn^2 \tag{1-113}$$

where $\tilde{\nu}_0$ represents the wave number of the highest wave-number band, A and B are constants, and $n = 0,1,2,3,\ldots$. If one finds several progressions in the near ultraviolet or visible wavelength regions, then intercomparison of the first band in each progression leads to another similar relationship

$$\tilde{\nu}_0 = \tilde{\nu}_{00} + Cm - Dm^2 \tag{1-114}$$

where $\tilde{\nu}_{00}$, C, and D are constants and $m = 0,1,2,3,\ldots$. Thus,

$$\tilde{\nu} = \tilde{\nu}_{00} + Gm - Dm^2 - An + Bn^2 \tag{1-115}$$

If one now examines an individual band with higher and higher resolution, it is found that each band consists of a large number of individual lines in a regular arrangement, usually given by

$$\tilde{\nu} = a + bp + cp^2 \tag{1-116}$$

where a, b, c are constants and $p = 0, \pm1, \pm2, \pm3,\ldots$. Often three sets of wave numbers appear in each band as a result of the positive and negative values of p and changes in values of c. These sets are called "branches," the R, P, and Q branches.

In the infrared, molecular spectra show somewhat different characteristics. For example, HCl has bands near 3.5μ, 1.7μ, etc., related by

$$\tilde{\nu} = An - Bn^2 \tag{1-117}$$

with very sharply decreasing intensities from band to band. In the region out to $10\ \mu$ this relationship is found and the bands also have structure given by $\tilde{\nu} = a + bp + cp^2$; however, usually a higher-order term $(+dp^3)$ is needed, and the value of c is nearly always much less than a and b.

In the far infrared (i.e., $\lambda > 30\ \mu$) the spectra found follow the relationship

$$\tilde{\nu} = fn \tag{1-118}$$

although some spectra require another term $(-gn^3)$ for correct representation.

In the light of the theoretical ideas presented on atomic, or line, spectra, some of the important factors of band or molecular spectra may now be considered briefly. Obviously molecular spectra must, in a sense, "contain" line spectra since the atoms are bound together into molecules. These bonds, or couplings, present other storage places for quanta of energy. In the case of a diatomic molecule, for example H_2, a model may be assumed of two (hydrogen) atoms bound by some elastic bond in a "dumbbell" shape. Transitions between various atomic states are called "electronic" transitions (since electrons are involved). Energy may be stored in vibrations or rotations of the entire molecule leading to rotational and vibrational levels and transitions.

In Figure 1-8, showing a simple diatomic molecule oriented along the Z axis, the energy of vibration is associated with vibrations along the

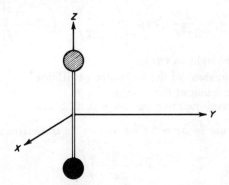

Fig. 1-8. Simplified model for a diatomic molecule.

Z axis while the energy of rotation is primarily in rotations about the X and Y axes.

If the model were first assumed to be a rigid rotator, then the energy of rotation is

$$U = \frac{1}{2}\,I\omega^2 \tag{1-119}$$

where I = moment of inertia about the axis of rotation and ω = the angular velocity of rotation. Obviously, rotation about the Z axis has far less energy associated with it than the energies associated with the X and Y axes. The energy levels associated with a rigid rotator may be shown to be given by

$$E = \frac{\hbar^2 J(J + 1)}{2I}$$
(1-120)

where $J = 0, 1, 2, 3, \ldots$; and $\hbar = h/2\pi$. Transitions give wave numbers as indicated below

$$\tilde{\nu} = \frac{h}{8\pi^2 cI} [J'(J' + 1) - J''(J'' + 1)]$$
(1-121)

If $J' - 1 = J''$ (a selection rule may be derived which shows transitions are nearly impossible except for $\Delta J = \pm 1$), then

$$\tilde{\nu} = \frac{h}{4\pi^2 cI} (J + 1)$$
(1-122)

where $J = 0, 1, 2, 3, \ldots$. Now, if we assume our model to be nonrotational, but capable of vibrations, we can derive transitions between various quantized vibrational states, which, for a simple harmonic oscillator assumption, are given by:

$$\tilde{\nu} = \frac{1}{2\pi^2 c} \sqrt{k/\mu} \left[\left(v' + \frac{1}{2} \right) - \left(v'' + \frac{1}{2} \right) \right]$$
(1-123)

where c = speed of light *in vacuo*
k = force constant of the harmonic oscillator
μ = reduced mass of the system
v = vibrational quantum number = $0, 1, 2, \ldots$.

The selection rule is $\Delta v = \pm 1$ for allowable transitions so that

$$\tilde{\nu} = \frac{1}{2\pi^2 c} \sqrt{\frac{k}{\mu}}$$
(1-124)

Obviously refinements are needed of, and can be made to, a theory which would merely combine these two concepts i.e., the rigid rotator and the harmonic oscillator. These are first, the assumption of an anharmonic oscillator by adding higher terms to the potential energy function of the molecule; second, the assumption of a nonrigid rotator; third, consideration of the energy associated with rotation about the Z axis; fourth, corrections for spin, isotopes, and so on. These are beyond the scope of this of this book, as is the extension of the theory to other than diatomic molecules.[16]

Certainly some mention must be made of the electronic contribution to the total molecular energy, even for the simple models considered. To a very good approximation the molecular energy may be considered a sum of three terms: $U = U_{elec} + U_{vibr} + U_{rot}$ (1-125)

If with these energies we associate terms of T, T_e, G, and F, respectively, then

$$\tilde{\nu} = T' - T''$$
$$= (T'_e - T''_e) + (G' - G'') + (F' - F'')$$
$$= \tilde{\nu}_e + \tilde{\nu}_{vibr} + \tilde{\nu}_{rot}$$ (1-126)

A hypothetical term diagram is shown in Figure 1-9.

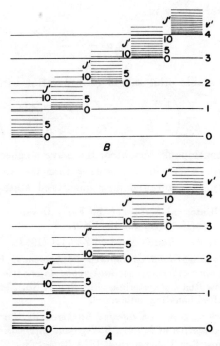

Fig. 1-9. Vibrational and rotational levels of two electronic states, *A* and *B*, of a molecule (*by permission of D. Van Nostrand Co., Inc., from Reference 16*).

1.4.4 *Continuous Emission in Term Diagrams*

The most important feature presented in this section on non-blackbody radiation is the term or energy-level diagram as applied to atoms and molecules. We have briefly considered line and band spectra. Let us now return to continuous spectra and see how, even here, the term diagram has meaning and importance.

In Figure 1-5 there is shown a region marked "continuum." In terms of the Bohr model this represents the energies of orbits (or energy states) which are not quantized. The action of this region has been observed, for example, in the form of a continuous radiation starting at the series limit of the Balmer series for hydrogen. The form of the orbits associated with this continuum is hyperbolic and corresponds to the classical prediction of radiation from acceleration or deceleration of charged particles in fields. The electron (for hydrogen) has a positive energy which is entirely kinetic energy outside of the electrical field of the nucleus:

$$\text{KE} = \frac{1}{2} m_0 v^2 \tag{1-127}$$

In the field, the total energy is

$$U = \frac{1}{2} m_0 v^2 - \frac{e^2 Z}{r} \tag{1-128}$$

Any transition to a stable orbit should give radiation with

$$\tilde{\nu} = \frac{1}{hc} \left(\frac{1}{2} m_0 v^2 - \frac{e^2 Z}{r} + \frac{2\pi^2 m_0 e^4 Z^2}{n^2 h^2} \right) \tag{1-129}$$

Since v and r are continuous variables, the wave number $\tilde{\nu}$ is also a continuously changing number which is greater than the wave number due to transitions between the corresponding quantized states of the system.

1. E. Scott Barr, "Historical Survey of the Early Development of the Infrared Spectral Region," *Am. J. Phys.* **28**, 42 (1960).

2. American Standards Association Standard Z58.1.1 (1953).

3. *Report of the Working Group on Infrared Backgrounds, Part I: Aims, Conclusions, and Recommendations on Background Information.* The University of Michigan, Willow Run Laboratories, IRIA Report No. 2389-7-S (July, 1957). Confidential modified handling authorized.

4. *Report of the Working Group on Infrared Backgrounds, Part II: Concepts and Units for the Presentation of Infrared Background Information.* The University of Michigan, Willow Run Laboratories, IRIA Report No. 2389-3-S (November, 1956).

5. E. Bell, "Radiometric Quantities, Symbols, and Units," *Proc. IRE* **47**, 1432 (1959).

6. A. Sommerfeld, *Thermodynamics and Statistical Mechanics.* New York: Academic Press, 1956.

7. Optical Society Committee on Colorimetry, *The Science of Color.* New York: Crowell, 1953, Chap. 6.

8. F. K. Richtmyer and E. H. Kennard, *Introduction to Modern Physics,* New York and London: McGraw-Hill, 1942.

9. W. E. Forsythe (ed.), *Measurement of Radiant Energy,* New York and London: McGraw-Hill, 1937.

10. M. Planck, *The Theory of Heat Radiation,* 2nd Ed. 1941. Reprinted New York: Dover, 1959.

11. W. Allis and M. Herlin, *Thermodynamics and Statistical Mechanics*, New York and London: McGraw-Hill, 1939, especially pages 199-201 and 208-209.

12. R. H. Fowler and E. A. Guggenheim, *Statistical Thermodynamics*. New York: Macmillan, 1939.

13. Allis and Herlin, *op. cit.*, pages 214-216 and 217-219.

14. E. R. Cohen, K. M. Crowe, and J. W. M. DuMond, *Fundamental Constants of Physics*. New York: Interscience, 1957.

15. H. E. White, *Introduction to Atomic Spectra*. New York: McGraw-Hill, 1934.

16. G. Herzberg, *Spectra of Diatomic Molecules*. New York: D. Van Nostrand, 1950.

CHAPTER 2

SOURCES OF INFRARED RADIATION

2.1 Introduction

The sources of infrared radiation may be natural or man made, but a more useful classification to the worker in infrared technology is that of target and background. A target is an object which is to be detected, located, or identified by means of infrared techniques. A background is any distribution or pattern of radiant flux external to the observing equipment which is capable of interfering with this process. An object may thus at one time be a target and at another be part of the background, depending on the intent of the observer. An electric-power generating plant is part of the background if the target is a ship moving in a nearby river, but is not if the generating plant itself is the target. Likewise, all terrain features are of interest to certain reconnaissance devices and hence are targets. However, information obtained by such equipment is useful background data to others. Summing up, it may be said that "One man's target is another man's background."

There exists one more class—that of calibration sources—which is discussed in Section 2.4.

2.2 Backgrounds

Although published in 1957, the "Report of the Working Group on Infrared Backgrounds, Part I: Aims, Conclusions, and Recommendations,"[1] remains the most complete description of infrared backgrounds. In this chapter, sections of unclassified portions of this report are reproduced in small type.

2.2.1 *Nature of the Sky Background*

The sky constitutes the background for all directions of view above the horizon. It is formed by the atmosphere of the earth, including haze, fog, clouds, and precipitation, and by the moons, planets, and stars, including the sun, beyond the atmosphere. It includes special sources of radiation such as the night airglow of O_2 and N_2 which is about six times as bright as starlight and the infrared emission of OH. It also includes the polar

29

auroras, which are many times brighter than starlight and of unknown infrared intensity. The atmospheric emission bands of water vapor and carbon dioxide and of the ozone layer at 50,000 to 90,000 feet constitute a part of the background.

a. Daylight Sky. The daylight sky background is composed of two main parts:

(1) Sunlight scattered by air molecules, haze, clouds, and other particles comprises the dominant radiance in visible and near infrared wavelengths to approximately three microns. The absorption bands of water and carbon dioxide remove a part of the scattered radiation reaching the surface of the earth but contribute only weak self-radiation because of the low temperature of the atmosphere. Scattered sunlight decreases in intensity on extremely clear days and also decreases with altitude.

(2) Self-radiation by the atmosphere is dominant at the surface of the earth at wavelengths longer than about three microns. The distinction between (1) and (2) is one of relative intensity. If an infrared spectrometer having DC response is aimed at any point of the daylight sky and spectral intensities are recorded wavelength by wavelength, then positive meter deflections result throughout the visible and near infrared regions to about three microns because incoming scattered sunlight is predominant. At about three microns the meter will begin to show negative deflections, indicating that the spectrometer is now radiating more energy per second to space than it receives. Three factors contribute to this effect: (*a*) the solar intensity decreases sharply with wavelength, and (*b*) the scattering of sunlight by air molecules, which makes the sky blue, decreases sharply with wavelength. These two factors reduce the role of the sun. Then, (*c*) beyond three microns the spectral intensity of sources at atmospheric temperatures becomes measurable; the spectrometer, at the higher temperature, loses more energy to the atmosphere and interplanetary space than it gains. The loss is greatest, and the greatest negative meter deflection occurs, in regions where the atmosphere is most transparent and where the spectral intensity of the spectrometer is highest; these regions coincide in the great 8 to 13 micron transmission band. On the short wavelength side of this great transmission band, the self-emission of water vapor in the region five to eight microns represents an incoming background emission to detectors sensitive in that region. On the long wavelength side of the band, the fundamental band of carbon dioxide near 15 microns emits strongly. In each of these bands, a relatively short atmospheric pathlength is sufficient to be opaque; if temperature fluctuations occur in the first several feet or several hundred feet of the atmosphere, the resulting change in emission by these emission bands may create a measurable noise signal in detectors sensitive in these respective wavelengths.

In the middle of the great transmission band, the ozone layer at 50,000 to 90,000 feet absorbs strongly at 9.6 microns, and therefore it emits strongly at this wavelength. Furthermore, temperatures in the ozone band are quite high, not much lower than surface temperature. At the earth's surface the ozone layer produces an appreciable and measurable flux of radiation to detectors pointed toward the sky; at high altitudes the effect must be greater, but it has not been completely investigated.

b. Night Sky. The effects of scattered sunlight are absent in the night sky. The effects of self-radiation remain essentially unaltered. The night sky exhibits one main new feature: the stars appear. Stars produce measurable flux densities of radiation both in the near infrared, below three microns, and in the 8 to 13 micron region; they have been studied in both regions by astronomers and in the near infrared by persons concerned with star seekers.

2.2.2 *Nature of Ground and Sea Backgrounds*

The radiation that arrives at the radiometer from the direction of a given point in the background is a composite of radiation from a variety of sources.

The radiation that leaves the surface of a solid object is partly the thermal emission of the object and is partly reflected radiation. At some wavelengths in the daytime, the reflected radiation may be dominant but at night both the thermal emission as well as reflected sky radiation will contribute to the observed ground radiation.

On its way from the background object to the observer, the radiation proceeding from the object is absorbed and scattered to some degree by the atmosphere, and the atmosphere contributes to the received radiation by thermal emission and by scattering radiation into the given direction.

When viewed from low altitudes, the ground predominates in the background viewed through clear atmospheres. However, even at altitudes as low as 2000 feet, thin clouds may form between the observer and the ground, and thus introduce strong signals.

At near grazing angles of incidence, the reflectivity of a water background changes quite markedly with angle. It is clearly established that a to-and-fro scan in the 7 to 13 micron region gives rise to strong signals because of this effect.

Very little is known about the influence of the following matters on the surface properties of the sea as a reflector of the sky:

1. The effect of wind and waves.
2. The influence of sun angle.
3. The influence of the angle between sun azimuth and wind or wave direction.
4. Influence of the sky condition and meteorological conditions.

2.2.3 *Description of Backgrounds*

A background is completely described by the distribution of spectral radiance associated with it. In functional form this is:

$$N_\lambda(\lambda;\ t;\ x,y,z;\ B_T;\ B_C) \tag{2-1}$$

where λ indicates the dependency upon wavelength, t indicates the dependency upon time, x,y,z indicates the spatial dependency, B_T corresponds to the type of background, and B_C specifies the background conditions.

The problems associated with measurement of backgrounds are primarily those of sufficient resolution, that is, small enough regions of space, time, and wavelength, and those of background conditions. Even if these problems have been handled in a manner satisfactory to the investigator, the problem of data display remains. There are four methods for presentation of background radiance distributions, and background description may call for the use of several of these. They are:

(1) The line scan.
(2) The infrared picture or map.
(3) The one-dimensional Wiener spectrum.
(4) The two-dimensional Wiener spectrum.

In the WGIRB report,[1] there is a discussion of these four methods of describing backgrounds. Each one of these has advantages and disadvantages in application.

One very good way of describing a radiance distribution is to show an infrared picture of the background. It has many advantages, particularly if one has high quality equipment available. The thermal picture shows the high radiance points in the field of view, and a glance suffices to show with what they are associated. One can see the size and shape of the objects of interest. Furthermore, one can put the picture in a simulator and find out how any infrared device will react to the given field of view.

In spite of these many obvious advantages, the infrared picture does have some disadvantages and these limitations are the reasons one must consider other methods. The disadvantages may be considered under four headings: Resolution, Dynamic Range, Linearity, Readability.

In a thermal picture, it is difficult to obtain simultaneously a wide angular field, and high angular resolution, in a useful scanning time. There are many things that contribute to the limited resolution of a thermal picture. Among the many important considerations are the line structure of the scanning pattern and, also, the fact that the finer details often have smaller amplitude, with the result that they tend to get buried in the granularity of the film and the noise of the detector.

With many backgrounds, the limited dynamic range of an infrared picture means that the large radiance variations and the smaller radiance variations cannot be simultaneously represented. Setting of the gain so that the large radiance variations are within the linear range of the film causes smaller radiance variations to become invisible in the film. This is particularly true for the finer details that often have smaller amplitudes.

One can ease the problem of limited dynamic range by the use of electrical compression, but this makes much worse the linearity problem. For use in simulators, it is very desirable to have the image on the film arranged so that the radiance is directly proportional to the reflectance or transmittance of the film. This is difficult at best, and it conflicts with the desire to compress in order to increase the dynamic range.

The infrared picture is particularly suitable for nonrandom spatial backgrounds, particularly ground backgrounds in which landmarks and works of man are prominent.

In order to avoid the difficulties just mentioned, some workers have used line scans. Figure 2-1 shows a chart recording of a line scan. This particular record was obtained by scanning a bolometer-equipped radiometer over a partially cloudy sky at night. The lower record shows a scan made with everything else the same except that the shutters were closed—it thus shows the electrical and microphonic noise of the system.

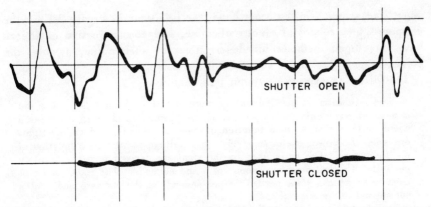

SHUTTER OPEN

SHUTTER CLOSED

Fig. 2-1. Chart recording of a line scan (*by permission of The University of Michigan, from Reference 1*).

This line scan method does succeed in mitigating some of the limitations of the infrared picture. One big advantage is that one can use electrical equalizers. By increasing the gain at the higher frequencies the fine detail shows up better in the record, and by this means one can improve both the effective resolution and the effective dynamic range of the record. A line scan that is recorded on a chart recorder, or perhaps on magnetic tape, gives a record that is very close to being perfectly linear. Finally, a strip chart record is direct reading although as much cannot be said for a magnetic tape record.

Thus, one sees that the line scan method has a number of attractive features even though it must be held in mind that it lacks some of the outstanding advantages of the infrared picture.

Some of the points discussed above should be examined in more detail. If a radiometer is scanned in a pattern which will yield an infrared picture, and its output is properly recorded on magnetic tape, then this output may be reproduced as line-scan traces and as infrared photographs. In this way most of the listed disadvantages may be overcome. Several infrared photographs may be made of one "scene" if necessary to cover different levels of radiance with no loss due to the limited dynamic range of film. The limitation of spatial resolution is not one imposed by the method of data display, and the infrared picture need not have poorer spatial resolution than any other display method. More will be said comparing the methods after a brief discussion of the Wiener spectrum, a display scheme that came into being as an attempt to deal with the severest remaining problem of background description, that of presenting some kind of average for a specified background type. Given a large set of infrared pictures it is not obvious that an "average" picture can be made with any relation to physical reality when all the scenes pictured have random radiance distributions. The same statement may be made about line scans. On the other hand, the line scan in Figure 2-1 may be compared to a record of electrical noise, and communication engineers have developed methods for descriptions of such noise, namely, the presentation of the power spectrum of the noise.

The following exerpts carry out this analogy.[1]

This situation is spelled out in more detail in Figure 2-2. For the moment examine only the upper half of the figure. On the left, one sees a noise voltage plotted as a function of time in seconds, and on the right, one sees the power spectrum of the same voltage plotted as a function of the frequency. The units used on the right are derived from the units on the left. The left-hand plot uses volts and seconds. The right-hand plot uses mean square volts per (cycle per second) in the ordinate and cycles per second in the abscissa.

Now look at the lower half of Figure 2-2. On the lower left, one sees a radiance plotted as a function of the angle in radians. The units of radiance are not indicated but are watts/(steradian-cm^2). Correspondingly, on the lower right is the power spectrum of the radiance. The units in the lower right plot are obtained from those in the lower left in exactly the same way as in the upper half of Figure 2-2—that is to say, the units of the ordinate are radiance squared per (cycle per radian), and the units of the abscissa are cycles per radian.

Here one meets a problem of language. In the upper right plot, the spectrum is properly called a power spectrum because in a one ohm resistance the power is equal to the voltage squared. In the lower right we would need a corresponding name for the radiance squared. There is no existing name for the radiance squared. Instead of introducing a new name

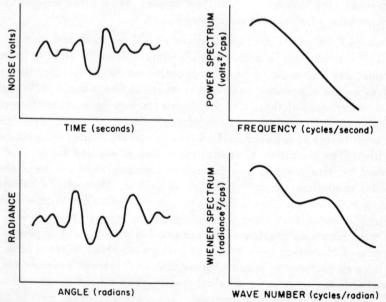

Fig. 2-2. Plots used to illustrate the concepts of power spectrum and Wiener spectrum (*by permission of The University of Michigan, from Reference 1*).

for the square of the radiance, it seems more profitable to introduce a generic term to cover the spectrum of the square of any given quantity. The suggested term is Wiener spectrum.* Accordingly, the function that is plotted in the lower right of Figure 2-2—the function that is measured in radiance^2/cpr—is here called the Wiener spectrum of the radiance (or Wiener transform if one prefers). Similarly, the power spectrum plotted in the upper right may also be called the Wiener spectrum of the voltage. This suggested language of Wiener spectrum and Wiener transform runs parallel to the well-accepted terms Fourier spectrum and Fourier transform.

The lower part of Figure 2-2 supposes that the radiance is given as a function of angle. It might equally well be given as a function of distance in meters. In this case the Wiener spectrum would be in radiance units squared per (cycle per meter), and the wavenumber would be in cycles per meter.

Figure 2-3 shows the Wiener spectrum of the radiance distribution in the sky. The ordinate is the Wiener spectrum in (microwatts/steradian-cm^2)^2

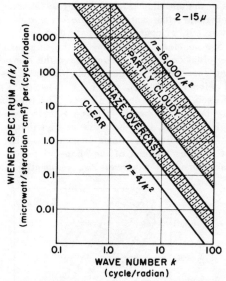

Fig. 2-3. One-dimensional Wiener spectrum $n(k)$ of the winter night sky (*by permission of The University of Michigan, from Reference 1*).

per (cycle/radian). The abscissa is the wave number in cycles per radian. The results were obtained at night in winter with a radiometer that responded equally well in the wavelength band from two to 15 microns. Figure 2-3 summarizes results that were obtained on about 20 different nights. The wide band shows the results that were obtained with partly cloudy skies. The somewhat more narrow band underneath shows the results obtained with hazy or overcast skies; the lower line shows the upper limit of the spectrum when the sky was clear. Small amounts of cloudiness cannot be observed at night; thus the line shown may represent a slight cloud-

---

*This suggestion was first made by R. Clark Jones of Polaroid Corporation.

iness that could not be observed by eye. One notes that the spectrum drops off very rapidly as the wave number increases—it drops off inversely as the square of the wave number. This means simply that the fine detail in the sky has much smaller amplitude than the larger features.

The method of representing backgrounds by the Wiener spectrum will now be examined from the point of view of the four considerations used earlier: resolution, dynamic range, linearity, and readability. So far as presentation is concerned, there is no problem about resolution—the abscissa of Figure 2-3 is the resolution. As to dynamic range, this plot shows a ten million to one range of Wiener spectrum, which corresponds to a 3000 to one range of radiance. Linearity is irrelevant to this method of description, and the presentation being a graphical one, one can read the curve to any desired precision. There is a large amount of information that is summarized in Figure 2-3. The one plot contains most of the statistical information that was originally in the form of 600 feet of chart record. The Wiener spectrum is thus a very compact and efficient method of representing radiance distributions. As indicated in the caption Figure 2-3 is a plot of the one-dimensional Wiener spectrum.

Thus the Wiener spectrum method completely avoids the limitations of the infrared picture but, of course, it has its own limitations. The Wiener spectrum gives one no idea of the shape of the original object. A battleship and a power plant conceivably could have the same Wiener spectrum.

The fourth and last method of describing radiance distributions is the two-dimensional Wiener spectrum, which is shown in Figure 2-4 for the same conditions used in the preceding figure. The two-dimensional Wiener spectrum will not be defined here. It takes completely into account, just as the infrared picture does, that the radiance distribution is actually two-dimensional. It suffers from the same limitation as the one-dimensional spectrum in that it gives no idea of the shape of the objects that are involved in the background. Furthermore, an assumption about the isotropy

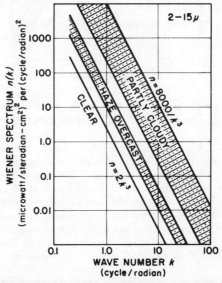

Fig. 2-4. Two-dimensional Wiener spectrum $n(k)$ of the winter night sky (*by permission of The University of Michigan, from Reference 1*).

of the background is involved in Figure 2-4; a nonisotropic background has a two-dimensional Wiener spectrum that is a function of *two* wave numbers. With this two-dimensional spectrum, one can compute the power of the electrical noise one will obtain if a radiometer scans over the background with any given speed and with any given shape or size of scanning aperture. It is thus the key to the computation of the signal-to-noise ratio one will obtain with a given target on a given background. [A discussion and description of the two-dimensional Wiener spectrum has been published in *J. Opt. Soc. Am.* **45**, 799 (1955).]

The applicability of the Wiener spectrum to backgrounds is still a topic of considerable controversy. There remains questions as to validity of the use of this statistical method without knowledge of the nature of the distribution involved. In particular, the question remains whether infrared sky backgrounds are simply Gaussian in their distribution. Some investigators believe that a combination of two or more Gaussian functions may be needed to represent the statistics involved. On the other hand, in some cases the RMS signal-to-background noise can be computed by use of the Wiener spectrum to the accuracy needed for initial system designs.

A little more insight into the data processing needed for Wiener spectra may be gained by consideration of one limited example. Consider two radiometers carried by an aircraft so that a stationary layer of clouds below the aircraft is scanned by the two fields of view shown in Figure 2-5. Radiometer A has one detector (one preamplifier, amplifier, and recorder) while Radiometer B has ten detectors (ten preamplifiers, amplifiers, and recorders). Assuming that the recorded voltage outputs of both radiometers are made directly proportional to radiance by proper calibration and design, then an infrared photograph can be made with the output of Radiometer B by modulation of the brightness of an oscilloscope spot which is swept across a film in the correct pattern. (This can be done, in practice, in many different ways.) On the other hand, the outputs of the ten detectors could be summed to obtain an output exactly equivalent to that from Radiometer A.

Let us consider the electrical output of Radiometer A corresponding to coverage (in a time Δt) of some area which is large enough to be considered representative of the background to be measured. If we send this signal through a system which sequentially

(1) Squares the signal;
(2) Passes the signal through a filter tuned to a frequency f with a suitable narrow bandpass Δf;
(3) Integrates the output over the entire time Δt;
(4) Divides the result by Δf,

then we have obtained one point of the one-dimensional Wiener spectrum corresponding to frequency f. If we reprocess the detector output n times through the filter (which is retuned each time to a different frequency in

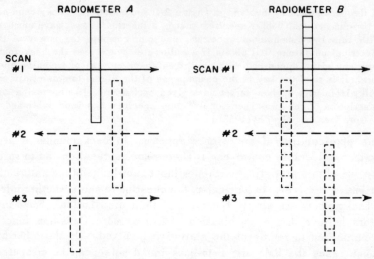

Fig. 2-5. Scan patterns of two radiometers.

the set f_o through f_n), then we have the one-dimensional Wiener spectrum corresponding to the background scanned.

Although the infrared map shows the size, shape, radiance, and relative location of each component in the background, the averaging of these data seems to require some sort of statistical treatment. The Wiener spectrum can show an "average background" incorporating a vast amount of data. Whether or not it represents the optimum method for background description remains to be shown by future studies.

2.3 Targets

The infrared description of a target is a specification of the radiation from it and the changes as various parameters alter. The physical quantity most closely identified with an infrared target is the radiant intensity for targets described as sources with no known variations within the boundaries of the target area, and the radiance for targets described so as to reveal variations or a pattern within the target boundaries. For most targets, the decision as to which description is most meaningful is obvious from the point of view of the user of this information. Most persons who want infrared descriptions of aircraft and/or missiles want information obtained by measurements with the target entirely within the field of view. In other cases, the radiance, and its variations from point to point within the target area, are desired. Finally, the user may need both sets of information, and although ideally one could obtain by integration the radiant intensity from the radiance description of the target, in practice it is nearly always necessary to obtain separate measurements.

2.3.1 Nature of Targets

Very often a target has both solid and gaseous components. Thus, a jet aircraft has a metal body which may be warmer than the ambient air temperature, and a plume of hot gases. This is also true for a factory with smokestacks or a car with exhaust fumes. The solid portions usually possess a well-defined temperature and emissivity. In fact, the radiation from these portions should be a combination of emitted power (dependent upon the temperature and emissivity) and reflected radiation (the amount of which depends upon the incident radiation and the reflectivity). The radiation from gases is more complex. Gases are often transparent in several wavelength regions and opaque in others.

Flames may emit bands, lines, and continua in a variety of mixtures. For example, the exhaust of a liquid-propellant rocket engine utilizing pure hydrogen and oxygen should be expected to emit radiation given by these elements and their compounds. On the other hand, the use of hydrocarbons introduces carbon not only as another atom available for combination, but also brings in the possibility of liquid droplets, particles of carbon, carbonates, and the like. These act as sources for continuous radiation. Flame spectroscopy is a complex research field which is undergoing an intensive and vigorous study at the present time.

2.3.2 Description of Targets

The point has been made before that although targets are described by the radiant intensity and/or the radiance, the quantities *measured* by an investigator are irradiance or irradiance differences at some distance from the target. The problems this introduces are discussed in detail in Chapter 3. However, the data presentation is also complicated since we have the necessity for target description by derived data, i.e., J_λ and N_λ, together with the need to present measured primary data of H_λ, $\tau(\lambda)$, and the like.

In the case of radiometric target measurements, the primary data to be reported are: the values of irradiance at the measuring instrument due to the target if the target does not fill the field of view; or, the values of the *apparent* radiance distributions for the target which more than fills the field of view. Radiometric measurements of infrared backgrounds, as we have seen, provide radiance distributions as primary data. The investigator should report in every case the primary data, any auxiliary data used in analysis, and the derived data, e.g., the radiant intensity in the case of targets which are wholly within the field of view, and the radiance for targets which more than fill the field of view.

The derived data which describe a target are [see Eq. (2-1) for comparison to backgrounds]:

$$N_\lambda(\lambda; \ t; \ x, \ y, \ z; \ \theta, \ \varphi; \ T_T; \ T_c) \qquad (2\text{-}2)$$

where λ indicates the dependency upon wavelength

t indicates the dependency upon time

$x, \ y, \ z$ indicate the spatial dependency both internal to the target boundaries and in terms of reference to the observer

θ indicates the viewing or aspect-angle dependency

φ indicates the dependency on the incident angle for any external
source

T_T indicates the dependency on type of target (i.e., solid-propellant
missile, single-engine jet aircraft, truck, cargo-carrying ship,
etc.)

T_c indicates the dependency on target conditions

and

$$J_\lambda(\lambda; \ t; \ x, \ y, \ z; \ \theta, \ \varphi; \ T_T; \ T_c) \qquad (2\text{-}3)$$

where the variables are the same, except for x, y, z, which represent
coordinates relative to the observer, or some suitable frame of reference.
The problem of data presentation for functions with such a multitude of
variables is practically insoluble if the continuous functional dependency is to be shown. The use of functional values for a selected set of
variable values does offer one way of attack and often the problem is reduced to one involving a display of about three parameters. Even then,
there remains a need for many ingenious data-presentation methods.

It is instructive to examine the various data presentations which have
been considered useful for target descriptions. (It should be remembered
that the discussion presented in connection with backgrounds applies
equally well to "extended" targets as means for displaying the radiance
distributions. Obviously, those methods based on a random distribution
of radiance values do not apply.) A commonly used data-presentation
method for targets completely within the field of view consists of plots
of H_T, the primary data, together with values of the range, R, and other
important auxiliary data, as functions of time. A variation of this method
differs only in that $J' = H_T R^2$ is plotted as a function of time instead of
H_T being so plotted. By presenting all data as functions of time, the
task of deriving a particular form is made relatively easy. Most often for
targets in this class J is a function of aspect as well as of the operating
conditions of the target. The display of J as a function of aspect for a
given set of altitudes or other operational characteristics is an example
of a useful data presentation method which has been discussed by the
WGIRB and, in particular, by Dr. M. Nagel.*

*Private communication. The following treatment of the aspect dependency
of target radiant intensity follows information furnished by Dr. M. Nagel, Scientific
Research Advisor in the SHAPE Air Defense Technical Center.

Although such target-radiation patterns are usually three dimensional, in many cases the patterns are sufficiently rotationally symmetric to permit their presentation in conventional two-dimensional polar diagrams. Data valid for one aspect can then also be reduced easily to describe the radiation from other aspects. This procedure is not satisfactory if symmetry exists only with respect to a plane rather than with respect to an axis. This is, for example, always true for multiple-engine airborne targets where obscuration or reflections from wings, fuselage, and other structural parts affect the pattern. In such cases the pattern is often presented in the form of a *set* of polar diagrams, each for a different rotational angle with respect to the direction of flight of the target. Presentation of the complete "global," or "4π," pattern around the target then requires plotting of a multiplicity of polar diagrams and/or presentation on several graph sheets.

While this method provides detailed information concerning the radiation proper, it may tend to confuse the reader because the graphs do not permit easy reference to the geometrical relationship due to the frequently intersecting lines within the graphs. Hardly more than three graphs can be conveniently placed on one sheet. This kind of presentation is, therefore, often unsatisfactory, especially for vulnerability and detectability studies. In such studies, the connection between radiation values and the geometry of the target must be made obvious, while highly detailed information on the radiation values proper is of comparatively less importance. Therefore, three-dimensional presentation may be indicated for such purposes.

A "projective" method presenting one-half of full three-dimensional radiation patterns may be sufficient for describing the full pattern if one plane of symmetry exists. Where no plane of symmetry exists, two semi-global patterns can be placed side by side. In the projective method of presentation the target is imagined to be placed in the center of an imaginary hollow sphere and to irradiate the inside surface of its shell. The irradiance at a given location of the shell is then proportional to the intensity of the target as measured from the direction determined by that location. The coordinates of the location on the imaginary sphere determine the azimuth and elevation angles of the direction in which the target has the measured intensity. The measured intensity can be plotted for all directions (e.g., locations on the sphere), and lines of equal intensities can be constructed. Such lines of equal irradiance on the shell denote measuring directions, seen from which the target has equal intensities, or J, respectively. Obscuration, shadowing, or reflection effects can, therefore, be recorded by plotting such lines of equal intensity. Projecting the three-dimensional lines of equal intensity in the manner used in the geographical sciences permits two-dimensional presentation of the lines for the semiglobal pattern and, in the manner of maps, for portions of it.

Figure 2-6 shows, as an example, the semiglobal radiation pattern of an imaginary multiengine jet target aircraft. Here the wings are assumed to produce an upward obscuration because the openings of the tailpipes were assumed to be below the wing. Reflections from the skin of the fuselage and the underside of the wing would produce a flat relative intensity maximum that could be observed from a sidewise forward aspect. The break of the lines of equal intensity along the center axis of the graph represents the obscuration of the engines on the

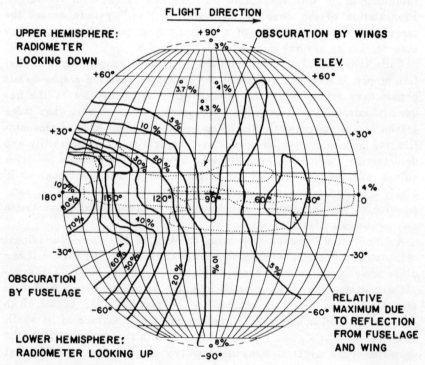

Fig. 2-6. Semiglobal target radiation pattern of an imaginary aircraft (equal-area projection).

right side of the aircraft. These engines can supposedly be seen only if one looks upward toward the target. The uncluttered presentation without intersecting lines should be noted.

It is often particularly advantageous to use Mollweide's Homolographic Projection. This projection is an equal-area method which permits integration of radiation values by measurement of areas on the graph sheet. It shows one-half of the globe as a circle.

Orientation of the target with respect to the globe should be carefully and completely indicated. For this example, the target was assumed to be facing toward the right; thus 0° azimuth and 0° elevation apply to the nose aspect of the target.* Azimuth coordinates will increase in the clockwise direction.† Positive elevation angles will correspond to upward direction of the radiation (aiming direction of the radiometer is downward). Negative elevation angles will correspond to downward direction of the radiation. Tail aspect* will correspond to azimuth coordinates at 180° and elevation angle 0°. If the intensities toward the left side of the target are to be shown, the flight direction of the target might best be assumed toward the left. In this case the azimuth angles shown would run clockwise about the vertical axis from 180° to 360°.

Unfortunately, little more can be said about target data; much of such information is classified.

2.4 Calibration Sources

Calibration methods are discussed in Chapter 3. However, a brief presentation of the purposes of calibration is necessary to any consideration of calibration sources. The basic purpose of calibration is to make the result of a measurement independent of the measuring instrument. In practice, calibration is done in a series of steps. For example, the "primary" standard (such as the krypton 86 lamp for wavelength) may be used in a laboratory to calibrate either a field spectrometer or a secondary source. The secondary source may then be used several times in the field to check calibration of the spectrometer during a field measurement program. After some suitable interval of time the primary calibration may be repeated. It may be desirable to use field sources, not only to check calibration of instruments but also to monitor atmospheric attenuation. Thus a need exists for field-calibration sources whose characteristics can be considered adequately known if the values are within ±10 per cent, as well as for laboratory-calibration sources whose characteristics can never be known well enough.

In the case of sources of blackbody radiation in the infrared spectral regions, sources with $\varepsilon(\lambda)$ and T determined to the degree of precision needed for laboratory work are not easily obtained. Usually they must be handmade, and the spectral purity is assumed to exist on the basis of conformity of design to theory as well as on the basis of measurements of factors such as temperature uniformity.

For instruments requiring a wavelength calibration, it is customary to use the blackbody curve with wavelength "markers" furnished by ab-

---

*The terms "nose aspect" and "tail aspect" determine the direction from which the target is observed. For example, nose aspect means that the radiometer is located in front of the target and measures the radiation emitted into the forward direction.

†This provision corresponds to the commonly accepted denotation of compass directions.

sorption bands due to atmospheric constituents such as CO_2 and H_2O. This can be and most often is supplemented by the use of absorption spectra such as are furnished by ammonia gas or sheets of polyethylene and the like. Hydrogen and helium lamps are used as line sources in the shorter wavelength regions. For precise wavelength calibration, the spectrum of argon as determined interferometrically by Humphrey of the Naval Ordnance Laboratory of Corona, California, is very useful. The subject of wavelength calibration is covered so thoroughly in the literature that no further study will be presented here (see especially Reference 2).

The sections in Forsythe[3] discussing Nernst glowers, globars, and gas mantle lamps are recommended. In the laboratory, each source has its advantages and disadvantages. Some construction details are present in Strong's *Procedures in Experimental Physics*.[4] Many studies have been made of various shapes and materials for sources of blackbody radiation. These have varied from simple wedges of blackened tungsten to large spheres immersed in molten sulfur, with a single small opening. The theoretical treatment by Gouffé[5] was somewhat misleading in that a cylindrical shape was shown to be superior to a conical shape on the basis of several simplifying assumptions. DeVos[6] took into account both possible temperature gradients and combinations of diffuse and specular reflectivities.

It should be emphasized, in the area of realizable calibration sources, that the experimentalist is forced to select his design on theoretical grounds since there does not exist a physically realizable blackbody. Thus, calculations of a type similar to those of DeVos[6] are essential in attacking these problems. In general, the best shape which is relatively easy to make is conical. Experience has led to a design substantially as shown in cross section in Figure 2-7. By varying the spacing of electric windings, it is possible to minimize temperature gradients within the source.

If the source is to have a high temperature, then usually the angle α is kept small, as is the diameter of the opening. The materials used are usually steel, or occasionally graphite or ceramics, depending upon the ultimate maximum temperature. The cone angle and aperture diameter are related to the emissivity in the manner discussed by Edwards.[7]

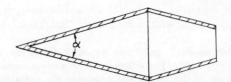

Fig. 2-7. Cross section of a suggested shape for a calibration source.

Large-aperture (areas of about 1 square foot), low-temperature field sources are available if high temperatures (i.e., above 250° C) are not required. For conical shapes α is usually allowed to increase, with acceptance of the poorer value of emissivity. Such sources (limited to temperatures less than 100° C) were designed by LaRocca and Zissis.[8] Other workers have used cylindrical or flat-plate sources. One interesting modification, a "Fresnel" blackbody, is described by M. M. Benarie.[9] Such low-temperature, large-aperture sources are most often placed alongside targets with graybody radiation of comparable temperatures so as to make possible an accurate but simple accounting of the effects of the intervening atmosphere. For this purpose, very high emissivities are not essential.

Several commercial small-aperture sources were described in a paper by workers at NOL Corona.[10] This paper presents the results of experimental intercomparisons between sources. Commercial sources with temperatures as high as 1000° to 1500° C are available with apertures of about 1 inch diameter. Emissivities very close to 1.0 are expected on the basis of theoretical calculations following the methods of DeVos and Gouffé. The importance of proper baffling is discussed in this reference.[10] This subject is one which should be carefully considered by each investigator in designing his calibration procedures. It should be noted that the 5 per cent variations found by the NOL Corona investigators probably represents an outside value. A carefully designed and used laboratory source should be capable of coming closer to unit emissivity than 1 per cent. A high-temperature (2700° K) cylindrical source has been designed for calibration purposes by the National Bureau of Standards.[11]

1. *Report of the Working Group on Infrared Backgrounds, Part I: Aims, Conclusions, and Recommendations on Background Information.* The University of Michigan, Willow Run Laboratories, IRIA Report No. 2389-7-S (July, 1957). Confidential modified handling authorized.
2. E. K. Plyler, A. Danti, L. R. Blaine, and E. D. Tidwell, "Vibration-Rotation Structure in Absorption Bands for the Calibration of Spectrometers from 2 to 16 Microns," *J. Research Natl. Bur. Standards (U.S.)* 64A, 1 (1960). Also available as *NBS Monograph* 16, June, 1960.
3. W. E. Forsythe, *Measurement of Radiant Energy.* New York: McGraw-Hill, 1937.
4. J. Strong, *Procedures in Experimental Physics.* Englewood Cliffs, N.J.: Prentice-Hall, 1938.
5. A. Gouffée, "Corrections d'ouverture des corps noirs artificiels compte tenu des diffusions multiples internes," *Rev. opt.* 24, 1 (1945).
6. J. C. DeVos, "Evaluation of the Quality of a Blackbody," *Physica* 20, 669 (1954).
7. D. F. Edwards, *The Emissivity of a Conical Blackbody.* The University of Michigan, Engineering Research Institute Report No. 2144-105-T (1956).

8. A. LaRocca and G. J. Zissis, "Field Sources of Blackbody Radiation," *Rev. Sci. Instr.* **30**, 200 (1959).

9. M. M. Benarie, "Optical Pyrometry below Red Heat," *J. Opt. Soc. Am.* **47**, 1005 (1957).

10. W. L. Eisenman and A. J. Cussen, "A Comparative Study of Several Black Bodies," *Proc. IRIS* **1**, No. 1, 39 (1956).

11. G. T. Lolas, R. J. Corruccini, and H. P. Broida, "Design and Construction of a Blackbody, and Its Use in the Calibration of a Grating Spectroradiometer," *Rev. Sci. Instr.* **29**, 505 (1958).

CHAPTER 3

THE MEASUREMENT OF INFRARED RADIATION

3.1 Introduction

The measurement of infrared radiation is necessary to obtain the descriptions of sources discussed in Chapter 2. Many times experiments designed to obtain source data have failed because of insufficient consideration of one of the basic six steps in the design of the experiment. As applied to this type of experiment, these are:

(1) Define as exactly as is possible what is to be measured and what result is expected.
(2) Design the instruments needed.
(3) Calibrate (at least before and after the experiment).
(4) Measure.
(5) Reduce the data.
(6) Interpret the data in terms of the results of step 1.

In this chapter, steps 2 through 5 are discussed in considerable detail.

3.2 Instrumentation

Perhaps the most fundamental concept to infrared radiation measurements is rooted in the basic difference between what the instruments *will* measure and what data one would *like* to obtain. For example, one may wish to know how the value of J_λ varies with λ for a jet aircraft at certain operational conditions (altitude, power setting, and the like) through a succession of closely spaced times. What can be measured is that portion of radiant power at the detector to which the detector responds. From this, and a knowledge of the instrumental parameters, one can deduce the irradiance at the instrumental aperture or the radiance at the detector. Given other auxiliary data, calculation of the desired radiometric property of the source may be possible.

Although decisions as to what is to be measured and how the measurements are to be made necessarily precede the choice of instrumentation, these decisions are also influenced by the instrumentation available. Thus, if what is to be obtained is $J_\lambda(t)$, the available systems may force one to compromise in the degree of accuracy obtained either in time or wavelength determination. Broadly speaking, radiation measurements are made to establish the relationship between the radiometric quantity and one or more independent variables so that predictions can be made of the radiometric quantity. Thus, one may study the radiance of an army vehicle as a function of the operational conditions of the vehicle, as a function of wavelength, time, viewing angle, and so on.

The independent variables for the radiometric quantities describing infrared targets and backgrounds are delineated in Chapter 2. The variables of major importance are those associated with wavelength, space, and time. Consequently the four basic instrumental parameters to be considered are:

(1) Spectral resolution
(2) Spatial resolution
(3) Temporal resolution
(4) Instrument sensitivity

These quantities are not entirely independent as, for example, one cannot reduce $\Delta\lambda$ and Δt to zero and thus simultaneously measure these two quantities of time and radiant wavelength. Although this limitation follows from Heisenberg's uncertainty principle, the experimenter is stopped *far* short of this limit by lack of sufficient signal at some limiting combination of $\Delta\lambda$ and Δt.

Even though any infrared "radiation measuring meter" is an infrared "radiometer," within this class there exist several categories of instruments. One categorization is based on the relative size of $\Delta\lambda$. Thus, if the radiometer has substantially equal response to wavelengths in the infrared region, it is called a "total radiation" radiometer. At the opposite extreme are radiometers designed to measure the infrared radiation in as small a $\Delta\lambda$ as is possible. These "spectro-radiometers" usually use a dispersing element such as a grating or a prism.

Regardless of the radiometer's classification, it will always have, even if only in a rudimentary form, the following components:

(1) A detector element which transduces radiant power into an electrical signal.
(2) An optical system which selects the spatial distribution of the measured radiant power.
(3) Optical components filtering the radiation so that they, together with the detector spectral response, determine the spectral response of the radiometer.

(4) An output indicator and amplifying system which, together with the detector, determine the response of the radiometer to the temporal variations of the radiation.

These features are shown schematically in Figure 3-1. Here a lens is shown as the optical component with a detector (D), an amplifier (A), and an output meter (M). Although the radiation is shown traveling from left to right, if the detector were at a higher temperature than the source under observation, the direction should be reversed since the detector would be radiating more power than it receives. The optics might be reflective or even folded reflective systems (Figure 3-2).

In addition, since the source is rarely at infinity, the detector (or field stop, as the case may be) is rarely at the focal point of the optical system. A useful concept, following from the reversibility of light, is the creation of an image of the detector. If it should be at the system field stop, then the detector image, changed as it is by the system aberrations, represents the instantaneous optical field of view. If the variations of

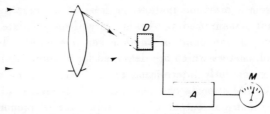

Fig. 3-1. Basic elements of a radiometer.

detector sensitivity across the detector surface are also taken into account as further distortions of the detector image, then the actual instantaneous field of view is obtained. Space scanning can then be described by the motion of this image across the scene in the object plane.

Reference Radiation Level. Each of the four instrumental parameters is considered at length under calibration (Section 3.3). One important and basic feature of radiometers which is pertinent to the discussion here is connected with the concept of reference radiation level. Any radiometer which gives an absolute measure of the radiant power incident upon the detector has an output proportional to a difference between two radiation levels. For a black thermocouple with radiation falling on one junction, the output depends upon the difference in temperature between this junction and the other, the reference junction, so that zero electrical output does not mean zero incident power. Thus, the radiation level which gives zero electrical output is the reference radiation level, and in this particular example, this level may be represented by the temperature of a blackbody which fills the radiometer field of view and gives zero output.

Fig. 3-2. Some optical schemes for radiometers.

Radiometers can be constructed to measure the difference in the amount of radiation received from two neighboring spatial positions. Since only relative levels are obtained, no reference level or temperature exists. A different approach is used in the design of an instrument which compares any element of a large area to the average radiation level associated with the entire area. If this average is defined and measured absolutely, it can be used as the reference level. Similarly, in the time domain the power level due to radiation at one instant may be compared to that from a previous instant, or from an average associated with all of the past measurements. Again, only if an absolute measurement has been made at one point or another can a reference level be assigned.

Most radiometers which are designed for absolute measurements have a system for regularly interrupting the radiation falling upon the detector; that is, the radiation is chopped. In such cases, ac circuits are used so that the electrical output of the radiometer is proportional to the difference in radiation falling upon the detector from the source within the field of view and from the (black) chopper blade. In other designs a chopping mirror is used so that radiation from a controlled and/or monitored reference blackbody alternates with the radiation from the source being measured. As a result of possible losses in reflection, or other optical effects, an external check of the reference radiation level and its relation to the internal reference source is always advisable. This is particularly so for nonblack or selective detectors.

For radiometers viewing sources with high levels of radiation, the reference radiation level often may be negligible, but such instances should be checked if the incident radiant power is to be determined by a measurement.

3.3 Calibration

One of the most important recommendations which can be made to anyone undertaking a measurement of infrared radiation is the statement "know your instrument." This is meant to include familiarity with all parts and all characteristics of the radiometer so as to ensure success during an experiment, as well as the knowledge of the precise capabilities of the device. The familiarity and knowledge can best be gained by thorough, frequent, and careful calibrations.

The calibration of radiometric instruments consists of the specification of the equipment characteristics to the extent and precision necessary, in the ideal case, for reduction of data to values independent of the instrument used. These specifications consist of: (a) the response to known amounts of radiation, (b) the field of view, (c) the frequency response, (d) the spectral response, and (e) the noise level.

3.3.1 *Response to Known Amounts of Radiation* (*Sensitivity*)

The methods of calibration of radiometer sensitivity may be classified in two ways. One system divides these into two classes, one in which the detector is uniformly irradiated, and another in which the radiation used for calibration covers only a small portion of the detector. The first class includes the "extended source"* and "Jones"[1] methods, and the second consists of the "distant small source" method.

Another classification system places in one group those methods in which the instrumental optics are used to produce an image of the source in the detector plane, and in the second group those methods in which the image plane and the detector surface do not coincide. The "distant small source" and "extended source" methods would make up the first group, whereas the "Jones" method and the use of an extended source very close to the radiometer aperture would fall into the second class.

Ideally, all these methods should give the same results. However, extreme care must be exercised if discrepancies are to be avoided. The following precautions are presented as the more important reminders to the investigator. First, the value ε_c, the emissivity of the calibration source, should be as close to 1 as possible. Calibrations with graybodies are always in doubt to an extent related to $1 - \varepsilon_c$ due to the reflection of some undesirable and usually unknown radiation into the system. Second, only the temperature of the calibration source should be allowed to change. The temperature of any other sources as may be within the field of view must be kept constant within the accuracy limits of the calibration. Third, radiation scattered into the radiometer aperture should be kept not only constant but also at a low level. In practice these last two precautions are realized by having no sources in the field of view which might compete with the calibration, keeping the air temperature relatively constant, and shielding the operation so as to avoid sunlight scattered by the intervening atmosphere into the instrument. Chopping or frequent shuttering of the source is a common and useful technique here. Finally, the accuracy of calibrations with appreciable paths be-

---

*An extended source is one whose aperture is significantly greater than the radiometer aperture or the image of the field stop, as may be appropriate.

tween the source and the radiometer is always limited by the necessity for correction for the intervening atmosphere.

For measurements in which the image of the target is always smaller than the detector, the calibration values derived from the distant small source method are more appropriate. The method of calibration employed should be selected on the basis of the type of measurement to be made. In addition, whenever possible the temperatures of the calibration source should bracket the expected temperature of the target (whenever the concept of target temperature is valid).

3.3.1.1 *Theory.* (a) *Distant Small Source Method.* The radiant intensity of a graybody calibration source* is given by:

$$J_c = (A_c \varepsilon_c / \pi) \int_0^\infty W_{\lambda, \text{Blackbody}} (\lambda, T) \, d\lambda \qquad (3\text{-}1)$$

where J_c is the radiant intensity of the calibration source in watt · steradian^{-1}

A_c is the calibration source aperture area in cm^2

$W_{\lambda, \text{Blackbody}}(\lambda, T)$ is the spectral radiant emittance of a blackbody in watt · cm^{-2}-μ^{-1}

λ is the wavelength in microns (μ)

T is the temperature in degrees Kelvin.

In the absence of an intervening attenuating medium, the irradiance at the radiometer aperture, or at the surface of the collecting mirror, due to the source is:

$$H_c = J_c / s_c^2 \qquad (3\text{-}2)$$

where s_c is the distance from the calibration source to the collector in centimeters. Assuming that the air temperature is kept relatively constant, only the attenuating properties of the intervening medium are of importance as T changes an amount $\Delta T \ll T$. Thus, the irradiance can be written as:

$$H_c = (A_c \varepsilon_c / \pi s_c^2) \int_0^\infty W_{\lambda, \text{Blackbody}} (\lambda, T) \tau_c(\lambda) \, d\lambda \qquad (3\text{-}3)$$

where $\tau_c(\lambda)$ is the spectral transmittance of the intervening medium acting on the source radiation. The quantity J'_c, defined by

$$J'_c = (A_c \varepsilon_c / \pi) \int_0^\infty W_{\lambda, \text{Blackbody}}(\lambda, T) \tau_c(\lambda) \, d\lambda \qquad (3\text{-}4)$$

is the "apparent radiant intensity" of the calibration source. This quantity is dependent upon the intervening atmosphere and, therefore, upon s_c.

---

*For distant graybodies, the assumption of a Lambertian radiator should be entirely satisfactory.

The radiant power at the instrument aperture is $H_c A_R$, where A_R is the area of the radiometer aperture (the area of the radiometer collector mirror corrected for obscuration). Since the voltage output signal of the instrument V_c* is proportional to the power absorbed by the detector, then

$$V_c = RA_R(A_c \varepsilon_c/s_c^2) \int_0^\infty N_{\lambda,\text{Blackbody}}(\lambda, T) \tau_c(\lambda)\Gamma(\lambda)\,d\lambda \qquad (3\text{-}5)$$

where R, the constant of proportionality, is the responsivity constant of the detector in volt·watt^{-1}; and $\Gamma(\lambda)$ is a quantity, normalized[†] so that its maximum value is 1, which accounts for the spectral response of the detector, the transmission of optical components such as filters and windows, and the spectral reflectivity of the mirrors. $R\Gamma(\lambda)$ is the power responsivity of the radiometer. $R_H = RA_R$ is the responsivity of the radiometer in units of volt·watt^{-1}·cm^2 at the instrumental aperture, and $R_N = RA_R\omega_c$ (where $\omega_c = A_c/s_c^2$) is the radiometer responsivity in units of volt·watt^{-1}·cm^2·steradian^1. The equations which follow may be written in different forms depending upon which calibration constant is used.

Equation (3-5) may also be written as

$$V_c = RA_c \omega_R N'_d \qquad (3\text{-}6)$$

where $\omega_R = A_R/s_c^2$ is the solid angle of the radiometer collecting mirror, and

$$N'_d = \varepsilon_c \int_0^\infty N_{\lambda,\text{Blackbody}}(\lambda, T) \tau_c(\lambda)\Gamma(\lambda)\,d\lambda \qquad (3\text{-}7)$$

is that portion of the apparent radiance from the calibration source to which the detector responds.

(b) *Distant Extended Source Method.* Here the source is distant and fills the field of view of the radiometer. The effective area of the calibration source is the area of the source subtended by the radiometer field of view ω; that is,

$$A_c = \omega s_c^2 \qquad (3\text{-}8)$$

where

$$\omega = A_d/F^2 \qquad (3\text{-}9)$$

(A_d is the area of the field stop or, in many cases, the detector, and F is the focal length of the optics.) Thus,

$$V_c = RA_c \omega N'_d = R_N N'_d \qquad (3\text{-}10)$$

---

*The symbol V_c used here and later represents a generalized radiometer output, a "voltage" which is proportional to the incident radiant power.

†Normalization procedures are discussed under Data Reduction, Section 3.5.

Sensitivity calibrations directly in R_N have the advantage that the assumption of a geometrically perfect field of view (i.e. $\omega = A_d/F^2$) is not required. If the quantity to be measured is either N or N', calibration by use of radiance is recommended.

(c) *Near Extended Source Method.* In a variation of the previous method, a source larger than the radiometer aperture is placed within a few inches of the aperture so that $\tau_c(\lambda)$ in Eq. (3-7) is nearly equal to 1. Except for this, the equations remain as in (b) above.

(d) *Jones Method.* A small-area source (small in comparison to the radiometer aperture area) placed close to the aperture and under proper alignment conditions will uniformly irradiate the detector. Under these conditions, an equation similar to Eqs. (3-6) and (3-10) can be derived, that is,

$$V_c = RA_c \omega N'_d = R_N \cdot (A_c/A_R) \cdot N'_d \qquad (3\text{-}11)$$

Again $\tau_c(\lambda)$ is nearly unity, so that calculation of R is considerably simplified.

An important aspect of this method is that the radiant power on the detector is independent of A_R and the source location *if* the detector is uniformly irradiated. This restriction places limits on the source size and location, as can be seen in the following discussion which locates the positions for uniform irradiation of the detector, or the field stop, for a few particular optical systems.

For a point source S placed at a distance P from the optical principal plane (see Figure 3-3), the diameter of the uniformly irradiated disc D_f in the focal plane is given by

$$D_f = (F/P), D_{P1} \qquad (3\text{-}12)$$

where F is the focal length of the radiometer optics and D_{P1} is the diameter of the entrance pupil.

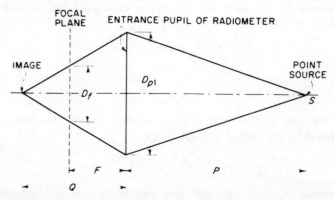

Fig. 3-3. Schematic for uniform illumination of detector by point source for simple radiometer.

If the radiometer's optical system is of the Cassegrain type, an obscured area will result, and the uniformly irradiated area will then be an annular ring of width X and mean diameter D_m. (This case is not shown in the figures.) The width of the angular ring is given by

$$X = \frac{1}{2} \frac{F}{P} (D_{P1} - D_{P2}) \qquad (3\text{-}13)$$

(where D_{P2} is the diameter of the obscured disc produced by the secondary mirror), and the mean diameter is

$$D_m = \frac{1}{2} \frac{F}{P} (D_{P1} + D_{P2}) \qquad (3\text{-}14)$$

If (as is always the case) the source has a finite diameter M_s (see Figure 3-4), the edges of the disc, or ring in the case of a Cassegrain system, will be vignetted by an amount $(F/P) M_s$ divided equally on either side of the unblurred edge. The remaining uniformly irradiated disc diameter is given by

$$D_x = (F/P)(D_{P1} - M_s) \qquad (3\text{-}15)$$

while the width of the uniformly irradiated ring produced with a Cassegrain system is

$$X = \frac{F}{P} \left[\frac{1}{2} (D_{P1} - D_{P2}) - M_s \right] \qquad (3\text{-}16)$$

The mean diameter of the ring remains the same as given in Eq. (3-14).

In the Jones method of calibrating the response of a radiometer to known amounts of radiation, a convenient source aperture and distance are first chosen. Then the size of the uniformly irradiated area must be checked to see whether it covers the detector. For example, if a Cassegrain system is used, the detector must fit in the ring of width X and mean diameter D_m as computed from Eqs. (3-16) and (3-14) respectively. The

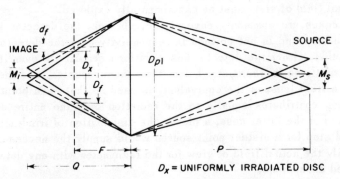

Fig. 3-4. Schematic for uniform illumination of detector by area source for simple radiometer.

source must be placed off-axis such that the annular ring of width X falls on the detector. Care must be taken to avoid shadows and shading by elements such as mirror supports.

3.3.1.2 *Experimental Procedures.* The particular calibration method or methods to be used will be selected on the basis of several considerations besides the advantages and disadvantages mentioned above. The characteristics of available sources must be. considered carefully. In general, the emissivities and highest-attainable temperatures of practical graybody sources decrease as the usable area increases. Extended sources for temperatures above $250°$ C are not available. Thus, if the target approximates a high-temperature graybody, the investigator is restricted to either the Jones method.or the distant small source method. For background measurements, usually either the extended source method or the Jones method is applicable.

It may be more convenient to use the distant extended source method with several sources than to use the near extended source method, if the time required for the source to change temperature is considered inconvenient. On the other hand, if considerable atmospheric attenuation is encountered, greater accuracy may be obtained by calibration with sources very close to the radiometer.

In calibrations using the distant small source, variations in sensitivity across the detector surface may create difficulties. Measurements of the instrumental field of view (Section 3.3.2) are of especial importance in this connection. Such surface variations may be encountered in photo-conductive detectors.

3.3.2 *Actual Instantaneous Field of View*

Using the principle of reversibility of light, calculations on the basis of geometrical optics may be made, to obtain the angular field of view (in milliradians) corresponding to the assumptions of no image distortion and uniform sensitivity across the field stop. However, the optics of a real instrument are never completely free from some distortion. Thus, the actual field of view must be experimentally explored.

Two cases are commonly encountered. In one, the detector acts as the field stop and is not uniform in responsivity over the detector area. In the other, either the detector has a uniform sensitivity over its area (as is usually so for thermistor bolometers, thermocouples, and the like); or else a field lens, or the equivalent, is used so that each point in the field stop contributes equally to the radiation over the entire detector surface. For the latter case, a plot of the distribution of irradiance over the field stop for a distant point source would supply the necessary data to specify the actual field of view for the radiometer with any detector of specified dimensions.

A plot of equal response contours obtained with a very small or approximately point detector may satisfactorily represent the distribution of irradiance in the image of a point source. In many cases, a sufficiently accurate plot may be obtained using available sources and detectors. The source, or the radiometer, is moved so as to obtain response values when the optic axis is increasingly inclined to the line connecting source and receiver. The resulting contour plot can be used to calculate the field of view for any detector which is much larger than the one used to produce the plot, if the criterion of uniformity in response over the field stop is met.

If the radiometer to be calibrated falls into the first class so that optical distortions and variations of response across the detector surface affect the actual field of view, then the experimental procedure should be followed for each detector used and for each variation in the optical components (i.e., for changes in focus or insertion of filters). This experimental determination of the actual instantaneous field of view is particularly important for radiometers employing either detector arrays or reticles. Obviously there exist many ways to realize the distant point source. The use of a collimator is one which requires especial care in precise optical alignment to avoid vignetting.

One last cautionary remark should be made here. If the radiometer scans a region of space, or has some dynamic mode of operation, then the experimental determination of the field of view should be done during typical operations. The factors which define and limit the field of view for such radiometers may involve the characteristics of the electronics to a greater degree than they involve the optics or detector uniformity.

3.3.3 *Frequency Response*

The rapidity with which a radiometer can respond to a change in the level of irradiance at the aperture corresponds to a statement about the temporal resolution achievable with the instrument. This may be determined, as a function of the amount of radiation, by experiments with different values of power which are introduced into the radiometer as step-functions. Such a calibration can specify the response characteristics of the radiometer to single abrupt changes in radiation.

Specification of the radiometer response to fluctuating incident radiant power can be made if the response to a sufficiently complete set of frequencies of sinusoidally varying power is known. What is desired is the amplitude and phase of the radiometer output as a function of frequency of the power variation. If the response spectrum is found to have the form

$$D = [1 + (2\pi f \tau)^2]^{-1/2} \qquad (3\text{-}17)$$

where f = frequency

τ = time constant

D = ratio of output amplitude to input amplitude

then the frequency response is characterized by a single time constant. In this case, the determination of this time constant specifies the frequency response if, as is usual, the phase spectrum is not of importance.

Some radiometers are designed to respond only to fluctuations of radiant power and have a zero response at zero frequency (i.e., zero response to a steady input power level). In particular, radiometers of this type have been made to measure the rate of change in irradiance at the aperture. If they have an experimentally verified linear response to this rate of change, then specification of the upper frequency fall-off characteristic is all that is needed to calibrate the radiometer frequency response.

As a part of the investigation of the radiometer frequency response, it is desirable to determine which element of the system is the limiting factor. This is especially important for modern radiometers which allow rapid and easy change of detectors, preamplifiers, amplifiers, and even recorders.

3.3.4 *Spectral Response*

In Section 3.3.1.1, $R(\lambda) = R \cdot \Gamma(\lambda)$ represents the radiometer spectral responsivity. This includes the wavelength dependency of the reflective and refractive optics, filters, and the detector response. Ideally, the radiometer should be calibrated with a known amount of monochromatic radiation. In practice, relative spectral curves for each component are usually used to arrive at the function $\Gamma(\lambda)$. Other approximations are often made. If the optics are entirely reflective and have fresh coatings, a constant reflectivity can be assumed. The transmission of filters and the spectral response of the detector are often approximated by curves representing typical filters and detectors of the appropriate type. In many cases large errors are introduced by this assumption and curves should be obtained for the equipment actually used for the measurements. For instance, the use of filter-transmission curves for coated filters in a collimated beam as the curves for such filters in highly converging beams, may lead to quite large errors.

The best procedure for spectral response determination is the use of blackbody and a monochromator or a filter-wheel as the source in either the Jones method, the distant point source method (if the power available is sufficient), or the method using a collimator. The relative spectral response, with an absolute determination at one or a few wavelengths, obtained in this manner gives the most complete specification of the spectral response.

In the calibration of spectrometers, or radiometers with quite narrow spectral bandwidths, sources which approach monochromaticity must be used.

3.3.5 *Noise Level*

During measurements of infrared radiation, the most desirable situation is the one in which the signal from the source being measured far exceeds any competing signals. Thus any output variations obtained represent variations in the observed source. This is not always an attainable condition. Whenever signal-to-noise is sufficiently low that the radiometer output contains significant contributions from the noise, then the noise level should be stated. In target measurements the noise may be that associated with the background, which then must be independently measured. Often, however, the limiting noise level is set by the radiometer itself. In that event the complete calibration of the instrument must include a determination of the radiometer noise level.

This is usually done by filling the aperture with a steady source of uniform radiant emittance and observing the radiometer output. Often, however, the noise level is a function of the value of the irradiance at the aperture; therefore, this quantity should be checked at levels of radiation approximating those encountered during the measurements. In addition, it is necessary to verify the linearity of the system (or to measure departures from linearity) under the conditions of measurements. Nonlinearities may appear in the electronics at high power levels, but this does not easily escape detection as do the effects of detector saturation by radiation. This is particularly important for measurements of intense sources, which are small as compared to the field of view, and for radiometers whose actual instantaneous field of view contains small regions of high sensitivity. Certain types of detectors can saturate more easily than others, as is usual for surface as compared to bulk photoconductive detectors.

3.4 Measurement

Much of the discussion presented under Calibration (Section 3.3) applies directly here and also to Data Reduction, Section 3.5. Measurement and calibration are, in a sense, mirror images of one another. This is most strikingly displayed by a brief consideration of the three types of measurements. These are: targets entirely within the field of view; extended targets; and backgrounds. The objects of the measurements are: J_λ; N_λ; and N_λ. The calibration methods which are most directly analogous to the measurement are: distant small source; distant extended source; and near (at the instrument aperture) extended source methods. If the targets and backgrounds are graybodies, and if the calibration sources are viewed at temperatures bracketing the temperatures of the unknown sources, then the radiometer acts as an interpolation device. This comparison has more than academic value. The use of known sources located as near as possible to the target is, whenever it is possible to accomplish, one of the most fruitful arrangements for radiation measurement since it allows a direct evaluation of the effects of the intervening atmosphere.

3.4.1 *Targets Entirely within the Field of View*

Although the quantity desired from most measurements of targets which are entirely within the field of view is the spectral radiant intensity J_λ in watt·steradian$^{-1} \cdot \mu^{-1}$, the only true "observable" is a deflection corresponding to an electric signal which is caused by the radiant power incident upon, and responded to, by the detector. This power can be calculated for a well-calibrated radiometer by use of the radiometer characteristics and a knowledge of the spectral characteristics of the source. The quantity so obtained is the irradiance H in watt·cm^{-2} in a given spectral region at the radiometer aperture from the radiation within the solid angle of the field of view. Since it is independent of the radiometer, H (or H_λ for a spectrometer) is the primary quantity to report. From it can be derived various amounts of information about the source, depending on what is known or assumed about certain factors.

3.4.2 *Extended Targets*

The measurement of infrared radiation from extended targets is designed to obtain the spectral radiance, or else the radiance in some wavelength region, as a function of the variables delineated in Chapter 2. In particular, the spatial distribution of N over extended sources is most often desired. With a radiometer properly calibrated in terms of radiance from calibration sources, the quantity measured is the apparent radiance. This must be used with auxiliary data to calculate the radiance distribution of the source. If known extended sources with the same spectral distribution as the target are placed as described in Section 3.4, then the radiometer can yield the radiance distribution of the target directly.

3.4.3 *Backgrounds*

Since backgrounds, by definition, include all of the sources in the volume viewed by the radiometer, a radiometer calibrated in terms of radiance directly measures the background radiance.

3.5 Data Reduction

As can be seen from the preceding discussion, the conversion of the results obtained by measurement into data usually involves a correction for the effects of the intervening atmosphere. Again it will be useful to consider the three types of measurements separately. First, however, there is one aspect of data reduction which is common to all radiometric measurements. The radiometer responds differently to different wavelength radiation if one considers radiation in the entire electromagnetic spectrum. Even after calibration has been carried out so that the spectral response is completely defined, there remains the problem of the use of this information so that the reported data reflect the spectral characteristics of the instrument. The accepted practice is to reduce the data by a process of normalization. More than one method exists, and it is important to examine these so as to allow selection of the most appropriate method for each measurement.

3.5.1 *Normalization to the Peak*

For illustration of this normalization method we consider a spectral response as shown in Figure 3-5, which shows $R(\lambda)$ plotted as a function of λ. The output of a radiometer with this spectral responsivity to a spectral irradiance H_λ is:

$$V = \int R(\lambda) H_\lambda(\lambda)\, d\lambda \qquad (3\text{-}18)$$

Obviously the wavelength dependency of H_λ is not calculable from the instrument output. However, the measurement does yield an irradiance H which depends upon $R(\lambda)$. The value of H which is said to be "normalized to the peak" of the spectral responsivity curve is given by

$$H = V/R_{max} \qquad (3\text{-}19)$$

where R_{max} is the maximum value of $R(\lambda)$, the value at λ_{max} (see Figure 3-5).

This value of the irradiance has significance only if it is accompanied by a statement of the responsivity versus wavelength curve. Provided that the responsivity function has a relatively narrow bandwidth (the acceptable width being determined by the aims of the experiment), then it is possible also to infer some information about the value of the spectral irradiance at the wavelength λ_{max}. In particular, since the bandwidth of

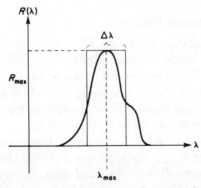

Fig. 3-5. Relative responsivity as a function of wavelength.

the radiometer is defined by

$$\Delta\lambda = R_{max}^{-1} \int R(\lambda)\,d\lambda \tag{3-20}$$

the peak-normalized value of the spectral irradiance H_λ is

$$H_\lambda(\lambda_{max}) = V/R_{max} \cdot \Delta\lambda \tag{3-21}$$

and as indicated this value is assigned to the wavelength λ_{max} at which the responsivity $R(\lambda)$ has its maximum value.

For example, suppose that a given radiometer has the responsivity (volts per irradiance unit) of 3000 volts per (watt $\cdot$ cm^{-2}) at the wavelength $\lambda_{max} = 3.5\,\mu$, where the spectral responsivity shown in Figure 3-6 has its maximum value. A response of 45 volts would then indicate a (normalized to the peak) irradiance of 0.015 watt $\cdot$ cm^{-2}. Suppose further that the bandwidth $\Delta\lambda$ of the responsivity curve as defined by Eq. (3-20) above is $0.2\,\mu$. Then the (normalized to the peak) spectral irradiance H_λ is

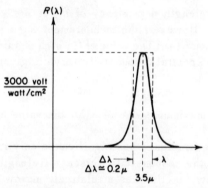

Fig. 3-6. Example of responsivity values as a function of wavelength.

0.075 watt $\cdot$ cm$^{-2} \cdot \mu$, and this value of H_λ is assigned to the wavelength $3.5\,\mu$.

3.5.2 Other Normalization Methods

Although "normalization to the peak" is the usual method of normalization, there are a number of special situations where this method may not be the best. The responsivity versus wavelength curve may be shaped so as to reveal clearly and unambiguously a bandwidth $\Delta\lambda$ without an equally unique maximum. This situation is frequently encountered with responsivity curves as shown as Figure 3-7.

In Figure 3-7(a), $R_{Av} = R_{max}$; however, there exists no λ_{max}. In Figure 3-7(b), $R_{Av} \neq R_{max}$. In both cases $\Delta\lambda$ is clearly defined. One may then prefer to normalize to the bandwidth, in which case the value R_{Av} is determined by this selection of $\Delta\lambda$. For example, in a reflective

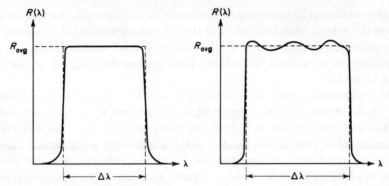

Fig. 3-7. (a) and (b). Responsivity curves illustrating normalization to the spectral bandwidth or to the average responsivity.

system with a constant reflectivity of 0.95, with a coated germanium filter and a thermistor detector, $\Gamma(\lambda)$ could be satisfactorily approximated by the following, where $R(\lambda) = R_{A_v} \cdot \Gamma(\lambda)$:

$$\Gamma(\lambda) = 0 \qquad (\lambda < 1.8 \ \mu)$$

$$\Gamma(\lambda) = 0.43 \qquad (\lambda \geq 1.8 \ \mu)$$

If $\Delta\lambda$ is sufficiently small, then $H_\lambda = V/R_{A_v} \cdot \Delta\lambda$ \hfill (3-22)

Finally, another case may be encountered; this is illustrated in Figure 3-8. If it is known that very little radiation is at wavelengths shorter than λ_1, one may either normalize to the $\Delta\lambda = \lambda_2 - \lambda_1$, or to some arbitrarily selected R at a λ within $\Delta\lambda$. The choice should be clearly stated, however.

3.5.3 Calculation of Radiant Intensity for Sources Smaller than the Field of View

In calculating the radiant intensity of a distant source, the degradation of the signal due to losses in the intervening atmosphere and in the radiometer must be taken into account, as must other factors introduced

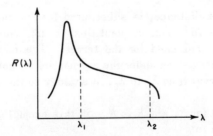

Fig. 3-8. Example of arbitrary selection of spectral bandwidth.

by the measurement procedure. Difficulties are encountered due to the generally complicated (and often little known) wavelength dependence of the atmospheric losses and of the energy of the source itself. In all calculations of radiant intensity, some approximations, of necessity, must be made.

As an example, consider a problem in which values of H are obtained for observations of the target with contributions from the surrounding background, and values of H from the background alone. The difference between these two values is ΔH, the "incremental irradiance." Since ΔH is the irradiance at the collector due to the radiation from the target (i.e., H_T) diminished by that due to the background radiation obscured by the target (i.e., $H_{B'}$), it is necessary to determine $H_{B'}$ in order to obtain H_T. In some measurements this correction may be negligible, so that $\Delta H = H_T$; otherwise

$$\Delta H = H_T + H_B - (H_B + H_{B'}) = H_T - H_{B'} \tag{3-23}$$

Multiplication of H_T by the target distance (D) squared yields the apparent radiant intensity,

$$(J'_T)_{\Delta\lambda} = (H_T)_{\Delta\lambda}D^2 = \int_{\lambda 1}^{\lambda 2} J_{\lambda, T}(\lambda)\tau_T(\lambda)\,d\lambda \tag{3-24}$$

Equation (3-5) may be rewritten for a distant target T which forms an image smaller than the detector, or field stop, by substitution of the subscript T and c. Thus,

$$V_T = R_{Av}A_R\Gamma A_T D^{-2} \int_{\lambda 1}^{\lambda 2} N_{\lambda, T}(\lambda)\tau_T(\lambda)\,d\lambda \tag{3-25}$$

or

$$\frac{V_T D^2}{R_{Av}A_R\Gamma} = \int_{\lambda 1}^{\lambda 2} J_{\lambda, T}(\lambda)\tau_T(\lambda)\,d\lambda \tag{3-26}$$

where D, the target distance, is substituted for s_c, and the temperature dependence of the radiometric quantities is not shown to avoid confusion with the symbol used for the target. The function Γ is shown removed from the integration under the assumption of normalization to the average in the interval from λ_1 to λ_2, in analogy to the example shown in Section 3.5.2.

Solving Eq. (3-5) for R, which is R_{Av} in this example, and substituting in Eq. (3-26), leads to:

$$(H_T)_{\Delta\lambda}D^2 = \frac{V_T D^2}{V_c s_c^2} A_c \varepsilon_c \int_{\lambda 1}^{\lambda 2} N_{\lambda,\,\text{Blackbody}}(\lambda)\tau_c(\lambda)\,d\lambda =$$

$$\int_{\lambda 1}^{\lambda 2} J_{\lambda,\,T}(\lambda)\tau_T(\lambda)\,d\lambda \quad (3\text{-}27)$$

It should be noted that, if the assumption of a constant Γ in the wavelength interval of interest holds with sufficient accuracy, then, when the calibration constants are used in reduction of measured data, the magnitude of Γ drops from the expression of final results, as does R. Thus, the validity of the assumed shape of $\Gamma(\lambda)$ may be more important than the accuracy of the magnitude of Γ used in calculations.

If $H_{B'}$ is not negligible, then V_T and H_T in Eq. (3-27) are replaced by ΔV and ΔH [Eq. (3-23)], and correction must be made for $H_{B'}$. This requires a measurement of the background radiance N_B which may then be used as follows.

The background radiation in a solid angle equal in size to that subtended by the target leads to an irradiance at the radiometer aperture given by

$$(H_{B''})_{\Delta\lambda} = (A_T/A_\omega)\,\omega(N_B)_{\Delta\lambda} \quad (3\text{-}28)$$

where $(N_B)_{\Delta\lambda}$ is the background radiance, A_T is the target area, and A_ω is the area subtended by the radiometer field of view ω. This value $(H_{B''})_{\Delta\lambda}$, it must be remembered, represents the radiation in all of the solid angle subtending $A_{T'}$ whereas the desired value $(H_{B'})_{\Delta\lambda}$ is only that obscured by the target. However, if necessary, a refinement can be introduced to evaluate the difference between $(H_{B'})_{\Delta\lambda}$ and $(H_{B''})_{\Delta\lambda}$.

A far more difficult problem lies in the removal of the attenuating effects of the intervening atmosphere. Because of the complexity of this problem as well as the large amount of background information required for its treatment, the detailed discussion has been placed in Chapter 4, *Atmospheric Phenomena*. For the purposes of this example, let us assume the following simplifying conditions.

(a) The target is a graybody so that the target emission has a wavelength distribution given by the Planck distribution function, e.g.,

$$f(\lambda) = c_1 \lambda^{-5} (e^{c_2/\lambda T} - 1)^{-1} \quad (3\text{-}29)$$

(b) The target temperature is such that in the interval λ_1 to λ_2 the spectral radiant intensity changes slowly with wavelength.

(c) A reasonably applicable spectral transmission is known.

In this case it is relatively simple to compute

$$\overline{\tau_T} = \frac{\displaystyle\int_{\lambda 1}^{\lambda 2} f(\lambda)\tau_T(\lambda)\,d\lambda}{\displaystyle\int_{\lambda 1}^{\lambda 2} f(\lambda)\,d\lambda} \tag{3-30}$$

and

$$(H_T)_{\Delta\lambda}D^2/\overline{\tau_T} = (J)_{\Delta\lambda} = \int_{\lambda 1}^{\lambda 2} J_\lambda(\lambda)\,d\lambda \tag{3-31}$$

Combining Eqs. (3-23), (3-27), and (3-28) with (3-30) and (3-31),

$$(J)_{\Delta\lambda} = \left\{ \left[\frac{V_T A_c \varepsilon_c}{V_c S_c^2} \int_{\lambda 1}^{\lambda 2} N_{\lambda,\,\text{Blackbody}}(\lambda)\tau_c(\lambda)\,d\lambda \right] + \right.$$

$$\left. + \frac{A_T}{A_\omega}\omega(N_B)_{\Delta\lambda} \right\} D^2 \frac{\displaystyle\int_{\lambda 1}^{\lambda 2} f(\lambda)\,d\lambda}{\displaystyle\int_{\lambda 1}^{\lambda 2} f(\lambda)\tau_T(\lambda)\,d\lambda} \tag{3-32}$$

3.5.4 *Sources Larger Than the Field of View*

In measurements of sources larger than the field of view, many of the considerations apply that have already been presented. In particular, Eq. (3-24) may be written as

$$V_T = RA_R\omega\int_0^\infty N_{\lambda,\,T}(\lambda)\tau_T(\lambda)\Gamma(\lambda)\,d\lambda = R_N\int_0^\infty N_{\lambda,\,T}(\lambda)\tau_T(\lambda)\times$$

$$\Gamma(\lambda)\,d\lambda \tag{3-33}$$

where R is the power responsivity constant, $\omega = A_d/F^2$ is the angular field of view, and R_N is the radiance responsivity constant. Thus

$$V_T = RA_R\omega N'_d = R_N N'_d \tag{3-34}$$

where N'_d is that portion of the target apparent radiance to which the detector responds. Under the assumptions used in Section 3.5.3,

$$V_T = R\Gamma A_R(H_T)_{\Delta\lambda} = R_N\Gamma(N'_T)_{\Delta\lambda}. \tag{3-35}$$

The radiance of the target is defined as

$$(N_T)_{\Delta\lambda} = \int_{\lambda 1}^{\lambda 2} N_{\lambda,\,T}(\lambda)\,d\lambda \qquad (3\text{-}36)$$

so that

$$(N_T)_{\Delta\lambda} \doteq (H_T)_{\Delta\lambda}/\omega\overline{\tau}_T = (N'_T)_{\Delta\lambda}/\overline{\tau}_T \qquad (3\text{-}37)$$

while

$$N_d = (N_T)_{\Delta\lambda}\cdot\Gamma \qquad (3\text{-}38)$$

These equations show that there remains the very difficult problem, encountered before, of calculating $\overline{\tau}_T$.

3.5.5 *Backgrounds*

For the reduction of data on backgrounds,

$$V_B = RA_R\omega \int_0^\infty N_{\lambda,\,B}(\lambda)\tau_B(\lambda)\Gamma(\lambda)\,d\lambda = R_N \int_0^\infty N_{\lambda,B}(\lambda)\tau_B(\lambda)\,\times$$

$$\Gamma(\lambda)\,d\lambda \quad (3\text{-}39)$$

However,

$$N_B = \int_0^\infty N_{\lambda,\,B}(\lambda)\tau_B(\lambda)\,d\lambda \qquad (3\text{-}40)$$

so that, in accordance with the previously stated definition, the background *includes* the atmosphere and its effect, and no atmospheric effects reduction is needed.

3.6 Summary

It should be remembered that the preceding discussions of calibration, measurement, and data-reduction methods have been presented for simple optical systems to illustrate the fundamental concepts involved. The application of these techniques to any particular optical device, whether it is a rapid-scan spectroradiometer or a multiple-detector filtered radiometer, requires a thorough study of each optical element and its action on the radiation. (For examples see References 2, 3, and 4.) Experiments involving sources whose spectral distributions are unknown are especially difficult to execute. The procedures of calibration and data reduction are far more rigorous when, for example, the wavelength variations within the response curve of the instrument are slight. If the source is believed to be an emitter of band spectra, then a spectral determination made with a resolution such that rotational structure is resolved is obviously the most desirable measurement. If, as is often true, resolutions of this order are not compatible with other requirements of the experiment, then great care must be observed in reduction and reporting of the data obtained so that misstatements may be avoided.

1. R. Clark Jones, Polaroid Corporation Memo No. 614, September 19, 1955.
2. N. Ginsburg, W. R. Fredrickson, and R. Paulson, "Measurements with a Spectral Radiometer," *J. Opt. Soc. Am.* **50**, 1176 (1960).
3. A. Oetjen, E. E. Bell, J. Young, and L. Eisner, "Spectral Radiance of Sky and Terrain at Wavelengths between 1 and 20 Microns; I, Instrumentation," *J. Opt. Soc. Am.* **50**, 1308 (1960).
4. E. E. Bell, P. B. Burnside, and F. P. Dickey, "Spectral Radiance of Some Flames and Their Temperature Determination," *J. Opt. Soc. Am.* **50**, 1286 (1960).

CHAPTER 4

ATMOSPHERIC PHENOMENA

4.1 Introduction

The effects of the earth's atmosphere must be seriously considered in the design and use of infrared sensing equipments. The infrared radiation incident on an infrared receiver is nearly always extensively changed by the atmosphere intervening between it and the target. This intervening medium is an inhomogeneous and continuously changing mixture of gases, liquid droplets, and particulate solid matter. The gases of primary interest to students of infrared technology are water vapor (H_2O), carbon dioxide (CO_2), nitrous oxide (N_2O), and ozone (O_3). These gases will absorb and emit radiation as a function, among other things, of the number of molecules present, the wavelength involved, and the energy states of the molecules. The prediction of scattering effects is made difficult by the fact that the applicable Mie scattering theories require knowledge of particle numbers, densities, shapes, sizes, and electrical characteristics which depend on the materials that make up the particles. These parameters are not easily determined, and the theory cannot take all of the factors into account unless many simplifying assumptions are made. The transmitted radiation is also subject to refraction by the medium traversed. Absorption, emission, scattering, and refraction all vary with time and space throughout the path of transmission. The constant motion of the atmosphere, on both micro- and macroscopic scales, create these variations in as unpredictable a pattern as the variations in other meteorological parameters. Only on a statistical basis is any prediction possible.

In spite of the complexity of the problem, a useful insight might be obtained by an understanding of the fundamental physical processes involved. The absorption and emission spectra of the more important gases are describable in the regions of interest. Meteorologists and climatologists may tell us much about the composition of the atmosphere and what is known about its variations. Theories of scattering and refraction have been developed and employed with some success, particularly in the

69

often-encountered cases in which these are secondary effects. Finally, there exist several measurements of the transmittance, at wavelengths from 0.7 μ to beyond 15 μ, of real and synthetic atmospheres. These works constitute the heart of the attack on the problem of atmospheric effects in the infrared region.

In this chapter an attempt is made to indicate what data exist and what methods using these data have been most generally accepted. Occasionally, some use is made of portions of the results obtained from theory. In essence, then, this chapter is a brief guided tour through the lore of literature on atmospheric phenomena in the infrared region, with a chronological sequence of presentation and a discussion of some of the more useful methods for transmission corrections.

4.2 The Atmosphere—Constituents and Their Distribution*

Let us first examine what is known about the atmosphere. From the first survey of the atmosphere in 1860 and the second in 1912, the constituents began to be known in quantitative terms. By 1917–18, Benedict at Carnegie Institute of Technology had made measurements on the amounts of oxygen and carbon dioxide present. The addition of data from measurements made at Boston, at Pike's Peak, and on several ocean voyages led to a value of 20.946% (by volume) of the atmosphere for oxygen (O_2), and 78.084% for nitrogen (N_2). These were found to be a constant to within $\pm 0.004\%$. The amount of CO_2 has been found to vary from 335 to 295 ppm, or 0.033% by volume. From measurements made in 1938–40, Calander found a systematic increase in CO_2 totaling about 30 ppm for the period, an observation which is still controversial today. Other permanent gases have been determined with varying degrees of success. Helium, although it is continually escaping from the earth's atmosphere, has been found to nearly always be about 5.239 ppm. In addition to nitrogen (difficult to fix chemically and thus difficult to measure), there exist several gases with no sink-source system, or with balanced inputs and outputs. These include argon at 0.934%, neon, krypton, nitrous oxide (0.5 ppm at the earth's surface), methane, and hydrogen. Sulfur dioxide is formed at the earth's surface by combustion, and nitrous oxide is highly soluble in water. The presence of ammonia is still somewhat doubtful. Ozone is formed at altitudes of about 50 km, and must then be moved by convection to levels below 40 km to escape disassociation. At the surface, of course, this active gas combines with organic materials. Thus, at 30 to 35 km there is a peak amount of less than 10 ppm.

---

*F. Elder and D. Portman of the Meteorology Group of The University of Michigan's Institute of Science and Technology gathered most of the information presented in Section 4.2. For pertinent references on the composition of the atmosphere see References 1–8, and for those on the occurrence of water vapor in the atmosphere see References 9–14.

We may also examine the distributions of suspended particles. These consist of dust particles (with no growth due to condensation of water) of about 10^{-5} to 10^{-3} cm diameters, and condensation nuclei of 10^{-7} to 10^{-4} cm diameters. Condensation nuclei have been found present in amounts as shown below:

In cities	150,000 particles/cc
In small towns	50,000 particles/cc
In the country	10,000 particles/cc
In mountains and forests	1,000 particles/cc

The most important single constituent of the atmosphere is water, which is found in all three of its phases. Considerable study has been made of the variations in amount of water vapor. Unfortunately, the meteorologist has used about ten different quantities and units for these data. These are, briefly,

1. Vapor pressure (partial pressure) e_w in millibars, mm Hg, inches of water, etc.
2. Density or absolute humidity ρ_w in gm/m^3.
3. Relative humidity R.H. in per cent. [R.H. = 100 (e_w/e_s) where e_s is the saturation vapor pressure, a function of temperature only.]
4. Mixing ratio w dimensionless, (w = mass of water vapor/mass of dry air).
5. Specific humidity q dimensionless (q = mass of water vapor/mass of moist air).
6. Dew point, the lowest temperature to which moist air at constant pressure can be cooled before condensation can occur. At this temperature, $e_w = e_s$.
7. Wet-bulb depression, the wet-bulb temperature subtracted from the dry-bulb temperature.
8. Vertical water content by mass m where $m = \int_0^z \rho_w \, dz$.
9. Vertical water content in cm precipitable water.

We have learned that the water vapor variation in time, for example at a spot a few meters over an open grassy area, is a combination of short periods (from 1 to 5 seconds long), diurnal variations, one- to seven- or eight-day changes, and seasonal variations. As to spatial variations, it is interesting to note that, contrary to older ideas, most of the water vapor in the atmosphere originates during passage of air masses over large bodies of water such as the Gulf of Mexico and the Pacific Ocean.

4.3. General Absorption Features

An examination of the transmittance of the atmosphere shows features characteristic of the three types of energy transitions associated with molecular absorption. These are changes purely in rotational energy states, simultaneous rotational and vibrational energy changes, and changes simultaneously in rotational, vibrational, and electronic energies. Electronic transitions produce systems of rotational-vibrational bands in the ultraviolet and visible spectral region as a result of the energies involved, while rotational lines in the wavelength region from 10 μ to 10 cm arise from purely rotational transitions.   The in-between region, 1 to 20 μ, contains rotation-vibration bands. In particular, from 0.03 to 0.13 μ the electronic bands and dissociation continua of N_2 and O_2 are found, while in the 0.13–0.22 μ region, oxygen alone exhibits nearly complete absorption.   Ozone acts to create an opaque region from 0.22 to 0.3 μ. The region from 1 to 24 μ contains two electronic bands of O_2 (at 1.06 and 1.27 μ), many rotation-vibration bands of H_2O, CO_2, and other gases, and, in the semi-transparent window between 15 and 24 μ, rotational lines of H_2O.   The rotational water vapor lines virtually close the atmosphere from 24 to 1000 μ.   In the millimeter region O_2 lines at 2.5 and 5.0 mm exist due to changes in the spin vector in the ground electronic state.   At 1.35 cm the rotational H_2O line is found.   This subject is discussed in considerably greater detail in Reference 15.

4.4. Early Work

It is fortunate that there exists one paper which presents the state of the art for atmospheric absorption as of 1942. This paper, by W. Elsasser,[16] is now considered by many to be a classic in this field.   It contains an excellent bibliography, presenting almost all of the important prior papers to which the reader is referred, as well as a theoretical treatment which is today the starting point for all theoretical works in this area.   Accordingly, we shall present a few of the assumptions and results of Elsasser after a short digression into the basic equations of absorption.

Smith, Jones, and Chasmar[17] present the following development of of what is called Lamberts' law, but what may more properly be called Bouguer's law:[18] If we have given a parallel beam of monochromatic radiation passing through a homogeneous medium, then at a distance x we have $P_\lambda(x)$, where $P_\lambda(0)$ is the initial spectral radiant power. Under the assumption of equal absorption per unit length of material, we have, for the amount absorbed by a layer of thickness dx,

$$dP_\lambda = -a(\lambda) P_\lambda(x) dx \qquad (4\text{-}1)$$

where $a(\lambda)$, the proportionality factor, is the absorption coefficient in cm^{-1} which may be a function of λ and x. Thus

$$P_\lambda(x) = P_\lambda(0) e^{-a(\lambda)x} \qquad (4\text{-}2)$$

while if $a = a(\lambda, x)$ then

$$P_\lambda(x) = P_\lambda(0) e^{-\int_0^x a(x', \lambda) dx'} \qquad (4\text{-}3)$$

If we now have a band of wavelengths $d\lambda$, then

$$P_\lambda(x,\lambda)\,d\lambda = P_\lambda(0,\lambda)\,e^{-a(\lambda)x}\,d\lambda \tag{4-4}$$

and

$$[P(x)]_{\Delta\lambda} = \int_{\lambda_1}^{\lambda_2} P_\lambda(0,\lambda)\,e^{-a(\lambda)x}\,d\lambda \tag{4-5}$$

Also

$$\frac{[P(x)]_{\Delta\lambda}}{P(0)} = \frac{\displaystyle\int_{\lambda_1}^{\lambda_2} P_\lambda(\lambda,0)\,e^{-a(\lambda)x}\,d\lambda}{\displaystyle\int_{\lambda_1}^{\lambda_2} P_\lambda(\lambda,0)\,d\lambda} \tag{4-6}$$

If $a(\lambda)$ = constant in $\Delta\lambda$, then

$$[P(x)]_{\Delta\lambda} = [P(0)\,e^{-ax}]_{\Delta\lambda} \tag{4-7}$$

Elsasser's interests were such that he began with a more general relation than Bouguer's law, that is, he began with Schwarzchild's equation for radiative transfer. This is:

$$dW_\lambda = -k\,(H_{\lambda,0} - W_{\lambda,\text{Blackbody}})\,\rho\,dx \tag{4-8}$$

where $H_{\lambda,0}$ is the incident irradiance corresponding to $P_\lambda(0)$ before, ρ is the density of the layer with thickness dx, k is the absorption coefficient defined by this equation, and $W_{\lambda,\text{Blackbody}}$ is the emittance of the layer acting as a blackbody. One obtains Bouguer's law by assuming a nonemitting layer.

Several cases of interest to the problems of heat transfer are treated by Elsasser through use of the Schwarzchild equation. In addition, a chart is introduced which makes possible the evaluation of heat transfer for several interesting cases. Elsasser then considers absorption in spectral lines. Assuming that collision broadening predominates so that the Doppler width is sufficiently less than the broadening due to collisions, the spectral variation of $a(\nu)$ is found. That is, the Lorentz shape is assumed for the line, and thus:

$$a(\nu) = \frac{S\,a(\nu_0)\,\Delta\nu_0^2}{\pi[(\nu - \nu_0)^2 + \Delta\nu_0^2]} \tag{4-9}$$

where ν_0 is the center wave number ($\nu = 1/\lambda$) of the line, as shown in Figure 4-1, S is the line strength with

$$S = \int_{-\infty}^{+\infty} a(\nu)\,d\nu \tag{4-10}$$

and $\Delta\nu_0$ is the half-intensity breadth of the line.

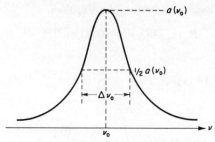

Fig. 4-1. Absorption as a function of frequency for a spectral line with Lorentz shape.

Calculation shown by Elsasser (as made by Landenberg and Reiche[19]) of the absorbed fraction of radiation leads to a Bessel-function relation. An evaluation of this relation is made for two extremes: very thin and very thick layers. For thin layers, the amount absorbed is found to be directly proportional to the product of the line intensity and the layer thickness. For thick layers, the dependency is upon the square root of this product. One can expect such a law, physically, since for thick layers the center of the line represents complete absorption, and additional absorption must take place in the wings of the line.

The next step by Elsasser is the assumption of equally spaced Lorentz lines with half-widths substantially less than the space between the lines, as the model for bands. This so-called "Elsasser model" leads to an expression for the absorption due to a band which is an error function (or probability integral) dependency[16,20,21] where the error function of x is

$$\operatorname{erf}(x) = \frac{2}{\sqrt{\pi}} \int_0^x e^{-t^2}\, dt \qquad (4\text{-}11)$$

Experimentally it has been found that the CO_2 absorption bands are sufficiently regular to be treated by this model, but the H_2O bands are not.[20,21] Here, the Goody model[22] has greater success.

It is interesting to note that, at about the time of Elsasser's paper, H. Gaertner in Berlin had written a paper discussing infrared transmission through cloudy atmospheres. This paper was translated and issued as Navord Report 429[23] in 1947. It represents an important contribution to the general area of atmospheric effects, dealing, however, primarily with scattering. Rayleigh theory is briefly touched upon, with the λ^{-4} dependency developed and used for particles small compared to λ. Experimental values from Fowle, and also Adel (see Reference 23 for these papers), are used together with some values for particle distributions. Next, Mie scattering is applied to particles with diameters on the same order as the wavelength. Finally, the results of a series of measurements are compared with theory. The lack of good data for particle sizes in fogs and clouds stopped Gaertner from definitive answers although the principles are well outlined. This discussion of scattering represents the state-of-the-art as of the end of the war as compared with recent work summarized in References 24 and 25.

4.5 Work Since World War II

After World War II, many papers were written on the subject of infrared transmission through the atmosphere. We shall briefly examine and comment upon some of the more important works.

In 1949, C. Hilsum[26] published an ARL (Admiralty Research Laboratory) report which presented 1230 references in an exhaustive bibliography on the subject. It was at about this time that a laboratory study was begun at OSU (Ohio State University),[27, 28] to investigate the absorption by water vapor and carbon dioxide bands. This marked the beginning of a long and highly successful program by workers at OSU in atmospheric absorption infrared spectroscopy, which later included the use of controlled, or "synthetic," atmospheres. The work, begun in 1949, was reported in 1949 and 1950,[28, 29] and in 1952 Howard and Chapman published the results in the *Journal of the Optical Society of America.*[30]

Besides the studies of CO_2 and H_2O gases, work was carried on by others to examine the N_2O absorptions and distributions[31, 32] and, on a fairly large scale, to obtain solar spectra.[33, 34] Of somewhat greater practical importance was the work carried out by Gebbie, Harding, Hilsum, Pryce, and Roberts in England[35, 36] in which the experimentally measured atmospheric transmission as a function of wavelength was obtained from 1 to 14 μ.* These data, first reported in 1949, were and remain an invaluable contribution.

In 1951, using the Ohio State University data together with those gathered by Gebbie *et al.*, Yates[41] calculated transmissions through various atmospheres of the radiation from blackbodies with different temperatures. The semiempirical approach may be contrasted to one calculation using the Elsasser and Goody models, which was carried out for CO_2 transmission in England in 1952.[42]

A very important paper by Elder and Strong[43] presented in 1953 the results of an ONR (Office of Naval Research) sponsored research program. Elder and Strong reviewed nearly all of the reported experimental work and, having divided the spectrum into eight windows, found for each of these a relation of the form

$$\overline{\tau}_{window} = -K \log w + T_0 \qquad (4\text{-}12)$$

---

*The spectral transmission per cent per sea mile obtained by Gebbie *et al.*,[35,36] is shown in Appendix D together with reproductions of several of the curves obtained by Yates and Taylor.[37-40]

where K and T_0 are empirical constants and w is the water vapor concentration in the path.

Mention should be made of several solar spectra obtained by British scientists from aircraft at about this time. The first work[44] was extended in 1954[45, 46] to altitudes of 40,000 ft. The results were reported in the open literature in 1956.[47]

In 1953 the AFCRC (Air Force Cambridge Research Center) sponsored a more extended study by Ohio State University scientists which led to reports published in 1954 and 1955,[48, 49] as well as a series of papers in the open literature.[21] This work used a large multiple-traversal cell capable of total paths of more than 2000 meters. The cell could be evacuated and then filled with precise amounts of absorber together with varying amounts of nitrogen to attain different pressures. Measurements were made of the "total absorption $\int A_\nu \, d\nu$ for entire infrared absorption bands of atmospheric gases."[21] This quantity, called A_ν by Howard, Burch, and Williams, is, in the notation used in this book,

$$S = \int_{-\infty}^{+\infty} a(\nu) \, d\nu \equiv A = \int A_\nu \, d\nu \qquad (4\text{-}13)$$

The theoretical treatment by Landenberg and Reiche[19] was applied to CO_2 to furnish a guide to the attempts to find an empirical relation which would cover the pressure dependency of A. In the equations previously discussed, the value of $a(\nu)$, under an assumption of the Lorentz line shape (for a complete discussion of line shapes see references 50 a and b), was related to $\Delta\nu_0$, the half-width of the line. This quantity is, in turn, changed as a result of collisions between the molecules of the gas. From kinetic theory one finds the number of collisions per unit is directly proportional to the pressure and inversely proportional to the square root of the absolute temperature. For a single strong line, neglecting the temperature effect, this leads to

$$\int A_\nu \, d\nu \sim (wP)^{1/2} \qquad (4\text{-}14)$$

which is also true for a band of widely separated lines of this type. However, experiments have shown a failure of the $P^{1/2}$ relation. Thus, for CO_2 and small values of A, the relation

$$\int A_\nu \, d\nu = cw^{1/2}(P + p)^k \qquad (4\text{-}15)$$

was successfully tried, where w is a measure of the number of absorbers in units of atmosphere cm,[21] P is the total pressure, p the partial pressure of CO_2, and k and c are constants. For large values of A, when overlapping occurs and portions of the bands are opaque, a relation experimentally found was used, namely

$$\int A_\nu \, d\nu = C + D \log w + K \log(P + p) \qquad (4\text{-}16)$$

Values of c, k, C, D, and K are given in Tables 4-1 and 4-2. Exactly the same relations prevail for water vapor, with different values for the constants and with w in units of centimeters of precipitable water. In the fourth paper of this series[21] an evaluation was made of the extent of the agreement between calculations from the Elsasser and Goody models for CO_2 and H_2O, respectively, and the experimentally found results. Thus, an error function was calculated for the $15\,\mu$ CO_2 band to give a value of 173 cm^{-1} for A, while the empirical equation gave 177 cm^{-1}. Similarly, the random model due to Goody was compared, with equal success, to the empirical H_2O relations. An additional factor of interest is that, in cases such as for the $2.7\,\mu$ region, where there are CO_2 and H_2O bands, one may use the relation

$$\tau_{CO_2 + H_2O}(\nu) = \tau_{CO_2}(\nu) \cdot \tau_{H_2O}(\nu) \tag{4-17}$$

and get correct results.

Among the reported data[48] are curves of A_ν as a function of wave number, with resolution on the order of $0.1\,\mu$. These curves, which are

Table 4-1

Summary of Empirical Relations for CO_2[a,b]

I. "Weak Band" Fit: $\int A_\nu d\nu = cw^{\frac{1}{2}} (P + p)^k$

CO_2 Band (μ)	Band Limits (cm^{-1})	c	k	Transition $\int A_\nu d\nu$ (cm^{-1})
15	550–800	3.16	0.44	50
5.2	1870–1980[c]	0.024	0.40	30
4.8	1980–2160[c]	0.12	0.37	60
4.3	2160–2500	—	—	50
2.7	3480–3800	3.15	0.43	50
2.0	4750–5200	0.492	0.39	80
1.6	6000–6550	0.063	0.38	80
1.4	6650–7250	0.058	0.41	80

II. "Strong Band" Fit: $\int A_\nu d\nu = C + D \log w + K \log (P + p)$

CO_2 Band (μ)	C	D	K
15	−68	55	47
4.3	27.5	34	31.5
2.7	−137	77	68
2.0	−536	138	114

[a]Reproduced with the permission of the Optical Society of America from Reference 21.

[b]w in centimeters of atmospheric water vapor; P, p in millimeters of Hg; logarithms are to base 10. Band limits apply also to "Strong" Fit. "Weak" Fit applies for $\int A_\nu d\nu$ less than "Transition $\int A_\nu d\nu$"; "Strong" Fit for higher values.

[c]These band limits were arbitrarily chosen to "separate" overlapping bands.

Table 4-2

Empirical Relations for H_2O Bands[a,b]

I. "Weak Band" Fit: $\int A_\nu d\nu = c w^{1/2} (P + p)^k$

H_2O Band (μ)	Band Limits (cm^{-1})	c	k	Transition $\int A_\nu d\nu$ (cm^{-1})
6.3	1150-2050	356	0.30	160
3.2	2800-3340[c]	40.2	0.30	500
2.7	3340-4400	316	0.32	200
1.87	4800-5900	152	0.30	275
1.38	6500-8000	163	0.30	350
1.1	8300-9300	31	0.26	200
0.94	10100-11500	38	0.27	200
3.7 (HDO)	2670-2770	0.325	0.37	

II. "Strong Band" Fit: $\int A_\nu d\nu = C + D \log w + K \log (P + p)$

H_2O Band (μ)	C	D	K
6.3	302	218	157
2.7	337	246	150
1.87	127	232	144
1.38	202	460	198

[a]Reproduced with the permission of the Optical Society of America from Reference 21.

[b]w in centimeters of precipitable water; P, p *in* millimeters of Hg; logarithms to base 10. Band limits apply also to "Strong" Fit. "Weak" Fit applies for $\int A_\nu d\nu$ less than transition value; "Strong" Fit for larger values.

[c]This band limit was arbitrarily chosen to "separate" overlapping bands.

arranged in sets for various amounts of absorber, can be used by interpolation and extrapolation for calculations of transmission through different wavelength intervals which do not necessarily correspond to an entire band as is the case in Tables 4-1 and 4-2. (This point is discussed more in detail in Section 4.6).

In addition to this important work, carried out from 1953 on, an excellent review of the earth's atmosphere and its absorption spectrum appeared in 1954,[15] as did more information on solar spectra.[51, 52]

In 1956, Naval Research Laboratory Report 4759[37] was issued to present measurements by Taylor and Yates of the spectral atmospheric transmission from 0.8 to 15 μ over paths of 1000 ft, 3.4 miles, and 10.1 miles over Chesapeake Bay. This excellent paper, of even greater value than the one by Gebbie *et al.*,[35, 36] contains a significant portion of the best experimental field data available today. If these are supplemented by other works by Yates and Taylor,[39, 40] this statement may be changed to say "the largest portion." Certainly calculations of atmospheric transmission over long paths at sea level are best made by interpolation with these data.

In 1956, Larmore,[53] and Passman and Larmore,[54] published the results of calculations using the Gebbie and the OSU data for CO_2 and H_2O to obtain transmission from 1 to 6 μ for different absorber concentrations. In 1957, several other papers were written as practical and fairly detailed procedures for corrections for atmospheric transmission. Altshuler[55,56] originally used the Elsasser model together with the calculations of Larmore[53] in a report, with a later modification involving the use of a "King" model.[55-57] Birch[58] treated the case of CO_2 absorption in a slant path, while Carpenter et al.,[59] gave a treatment which led to a procedure for use of the OSU synthetic atmosphere data as reported in the OSURF (Ohio State University Research Foundation) Scientific Report 1,[48] together with a pressure and temperature correction to standard conditions for long slant paths.

An excellent theoretical treatment of models between the extremes of the Elsasser and Goody structures, with line shapes due to Doppler broadening as well as the Lorentz or collision shapes, was prepared by Plass.[60] In a continuing attempt to provide the experimental data needed to check predicted pressure dependencies, more high-altitude solar spectra were obtained. The works published in 1956 and 1957 by Migeotti et al.,[61] remain, of course, the guiding atlases for comparison with the high-altitude data obtained by United Kingdom scientists[47,62] using aircraft at altitudes above 45,000 ft, and by a program of the Physics Department of the University of Denver[63,64] using balloons to altitudes of 90,000 ft.

Work on scattering in the infrared has been reported by the Chicago Midway Laboratories of the University of Chicago,[65,66] while extensive theoretical studies have been made by Deirmendjian.[67] Absorption at longer wavelengths has been studied more actively in the recent past. At Johns Hopkins University, C. Harvey Palmer, Jr.,[68,69] carried out an interesting study of the 50 μ pure rotation band of water vapor using a 196-meter path for a variety of absorber concentrations and pressures. He thus obtained, experimentally, transmission functions in the region 20 μ to 50 μ which can be used to obtain a generalized absorption coefficient for the region.[70]

The particularly difficult problem of atmospheric absorption of emitted band spectra was treated by Carpenter[71] for CO_2 at 4.3 μ. In connection with such treatments, studies, both theoretical and experimental, of the emissivity of gases are essential. In 1959 Plass[72] reported a calculation for CO_2 in the 1800–2500-cm^{-1} region (4.3 μ band), while Edwards[73] measured the properties of CO_2 at much higher temperatures and pressures than had been reported before.

A procedure for atmospheric transmission correction using extrapolation of the curves by Yates and Taylor[37-40] was reported by Prostak et al.,[74,75] while a method of selection of the optimum band model for representation of experimental absorption data was given by Plass[76] late in 1960.

4.6 Correction of Data for Atmospheric Attenuation

The atmosphere is important to infrared technology in two types of computation. One of these is the reduction to derived data of the primary data obtained by measurement of the radiation from infrared sources, and the other is the design, or the calculation of performance, of some infrared device. In the second case, the infrared designer is concerned with concepts such as the "most probable" performance, and he designs for successful operation against some "worst case or conditions" which occur with sufficient frequency (or importance). In the first case, however, the data analyst wants the effects of a particular atmosphere taken into account. Design and evaluation of equipment, because they involve statistical concepts (i.e., "average atmospheres" and "worst atmospheres") are usually easier to treat and also require less accuracy than the reduction of data on targets. For this reason, in this section we shall emphasize the atmospheric attenuation corrections needed for data reduction.

Now that the literature of this field and a few of the basic concepts have been briefly reviewed, let us examine again the problem posed in Chapter 3, that is, the calculation of either radiant intensity or radiance of source, given either the apparent radiant intensity or apparent radiance. This requires a knowledge of the spectral transmittance of the intervening medium and the spectral characteristics of the source. The relationship

$$J_\lambda(\lambda, t) = H_\lambda(\lambda, t) D^2 / \tau(\lambda, t) \qquad (4\text{-}18)$$

where all of the spectrally dependent quantities are the *instantaneous*, *monochromatic* values, is a rigorous one. Unfortunately, all measurements involve a $\Delta\lambda$ and a Δt, so that Equation (4-18) must always be approximated.

In some cases it is possible to avoid the problem by a direct measurement of J or N, or, failing this, to measure directly the relative spectral distribution of the source and $\tau(\lambda)$. The latter quantity quite often is measurable by use of a known source (a gray- or blackbody) placed immediately next to the target. Whenever such measurements are possible, every effort should be made to carry them out. Finally, lacking the above, the investigator is reduced to a deduction of the source wavelength dependency from theoretical and/or special laboratory or simulatory studies, while $\tau(\lambda)$ must be calculated.

One may ask what values of $\Delta\lambda$ could be used satisfactorily in Eq. (4-18). Since any real measurement integrates over the product $J_\lambda(\lambda) \cdot \tau(\lambda)$, removal of one or the other of the two quantities from within the integration interval is required. When it is stated that removal of one function from within the integration is possible for intervals so small that negligible changes of the function occur, the implication, for band emitters and absorbers, is that the region of integration is small compared to the half width of the band rotational structure. Either this is implied, or else the understanding of the phenomena is sufficiently complete that the results of averaging over several lines is predictable. Such high resolutions, in either case, are not easily attained outside of a few laboratory experiments.

Edwards,[73] in his paper on absorption by CO_2 at elevated temperatures and pressures, discusses this point and classifies approaches to these problems into four groups. The "exact method" is one in which the absorption coefficient is obtained by summing over each line, thus requiring the complete description of the band involved. (An example cited by Edwards is the treatment by Kaplan[77] of absorption by the Q branches of two CO_2 bands near 15 μ.) In the "band-model" method, a model is created to represent the band with specified line shapes, intensities, and distributions, where the specification of these quantities is such as to best fit experimental data with much lower resolution than those used in the "exact method." The "band-energy" approach is the method used by Howard et al.,[21] while a fourth approach involves measurement of total absorptance using blackbody radiation and nonselective radiometers.

The customary and probably most practical procedure is to deduce the target wavelength distribution from a combination of theoretical considerations and a few carefully selected experiments. For example, in the case of flames containing particles and gases, one can first calculate the expected band emission and the continuum from the heated particles. Then measurements can be made, in relatively transparent regions of the atmosphere, of the continuous portions of the radiation. Finally, some verifying measurements can be made in the absorbing regions by removal of the absorber from the intervening path. Assuming this last procedure is difficult and probably costly to achieve, the first two steps tend to reduce to a minimum the effort involved.

If the relative wavelength distribution of the source is obtained in this manner to within the required confidence level, then there remains the problem of prediction of $\tau(\lambda)$. This calculation requires a knowledge of the values of amounts and energy states of the absorbers and scatterers in the intervening path. Thus, for example, for reduction of data from measurements on distant airborne targets the information desired is the number, constitution, sizes and shapes of the scattering particles, and the amount of water vapor, CO_2, O_3, N_2O, and other absorbers, together with the temperature and pressure of these gases in the path from source to receiver. Few of these parameters are directly measured. Instead, the data analyst has some values of pressure, temperature, and relative humidity, together with a few visibility observations. The amount of CO_2 may be treated by him on the basis of the observed constancy of CO_2 in the atmosphere (see Section 4.2), while gases other than CO_2 and H_2O are treated on a statistical distribution basis. If solar spectra are available through the same atmosphere, a powerful tool is given the analyst for determination of the composition, and even the transmission, depending upon the nature of the data available.

With the values of the parameters listed above, assuming for the moment all of them were known, the calculation of $\tau(\lambda)$ is attempted in the following parts:

$$\tau(\lambda) = \tau_\sigma(\lambda) \cdot \tau_{H_2O}(\lambda) \cdot \tau_{CO_2}(\lambda) \cdot \tau_{N_2O}(\lambda) \cdot \tau_{O_3}(\lambda) \cdot \tau_{others}(\lambda) \qquad (4\text{-}19)$$

At some wavelengths it is expected that one of the "partial" transmittances will be the dominating term, but in many regions several will be equally important. For example, Deirmendjian,[67] in his calculation of the expected attenuation due to scattering in the 8–12 μ region, found that an unreasonably high number of scattering particles would be needed to explain the observations of Gebbie et al.[35,36] This, he concludes, substantiates the presence of wing absorption of molecular lines in this region. Rotational lines of the 6.3 μ H_2O and the 15 μ CO_2 bands may be seen in this region in, for example, the curves by Yates and Taylor[40] while the absorption due to the 9.6-μ band of ozone is also observed.

Visibility data may be used in an attempt to calculate $\tau_\sigma(\lambda)$ by fitting curves, obtained from theory and models of the scattering atmosphere, to the transmission values from the visibility observations. This corresponds to the procedure used by Deirmandjian[67] in his comparison to the data of Gebbie et al.[35,36] Another, alternative method is the use of empirically determined relations such as those obtained by Yates and Taylor.[40] There, the relationship

$$\tau = e^{-\sigma x} \qquad (4\text{-}20)$$

was considered where $\sigma(\lambda) \sim \dfrac{(\text{radius})}{\lambda}$. Determinations were made of σ at twelve wavelengths selected to be far from strong absorption bands. Unfortunately, data on particle types, sizes, compositions, and distributions corresponding to these observations have not been reported, so that a theoretical check does not appear to be possible.

The calculation of the transmittance associated with molecular absorption can be similarly attacked. Interpolations and extrapolations can be made with field data on real atmospheres or with laboratory data on synthetic atmospheres. Theory can be used extensively as a guide in these approaches, or avoided except for a few relative dependencies. Thus, for transmission involving entire bands the Ohio State University formulations for $\int A_\nu d\nu$ and the empirically determined constants (see Section 4.5, and Tables 4-1 and 4-2) can be used.

If the spectral regions of interest to the data analyst include part (or parts) of bands, then the correction can be made using the data reported by Howard et al.,[48] in the form of A_ν versus plots using the method of Carpenter et al.,[59] or using Plass'[60] treatment as a guide. It should be noted that the laboratory data are limited to resolutions on the order of 0.1 μ at 3.0 μ.

As was stated in Section 4.4, CO_2 bands have been treated most successfully by the Elsasser model while the statistical (Goody) model has been used for H_2O bands. In the treatment by Plass,[60] a "random Elsasser" model has been made by use of Elsasser bands (equally spaced, identical lines with half-widths small as compared to the spacing) randomly superimposed so as to allow variation from the pure Elsasser to the random or statistical model (randomly spaced lines with random intensities). From a knowledge of the number of lines in the interval considered and their frequency distribution, it is possible to select the most suitable model. The extrapolation of the laboratory data to give the desired $\tau(\lambda)$ for the conditions during the measurement of J' or N' can then be made on the basis of the selected model.

In the procedure given by Carpenter et al.,[59] considerations presented led to the use of the "equivalent sea-level optical path length"

$$u_e = \int_0^x \frac{P(x)}{P_s} \sqrt{\frac{T_s}{T(x)}} \, \rho(x) \, dx \qquad (4\text{-}21)$$

where the optical path length would be defined as

$$u = \int_0^x \rho(x) \, dx \qquad (4\text{-}22)$$

and the units for u_e and u are kg/cm^2. Useful charts and tables are presented for the calculation of u_e for the ARDC model atmosphere with instructions as to corrections for other meteorological conditions if the relative humidity and other parameters are nearly constant in the path. If they are not, and if the deviations from the model atmosphere are deemed significant, then Equation (4-21) may be numerically integrated. The curves of A_ν by OSU[48] are to be changed to curves with u_e as the parameter instead of P.

The question of the applicability of the pressure correction i.e., first power of (P/P_o) as contrasted to some other exponent $(P/P_o)^k$, still remains. The University of Denver[63,64] studies and the United Kingdom efforts[62] have yielded values of $k \neq 1$. Empirically, values from $k = 0.5$ to $k = 1$ have been obtained, so that for many cases use of a value of about 0.8 may be satisfactory.

If one requires better resolution than that of the Howard et al.,[48] data, or if the real atmospheres are regarded as more trustworthy for a particular problem, then the procedures of Larmore,[53] Passman and Larmore,[54] Altshuler,[55,56] and Prostak et al.,[74, 75] may be used.

In each of the above procedures, separability of the wavelength-dependent quantities within the integration interval is assumed. In several cases, where very rapid changes in wavelength are expected, such procedures are not applicable. The methods available for use in these cases are illustrated by the treatment of emission and absorption by the 4.3 μ CO_2 band by Carpenter[71] and of the emissivity of the same band by Plass.[72] If however, the source contains many regions where nonequilibrium conditions prevail, the resulting difficulties remain unsolved.

4.7 Summary

In summarizing this area of infrared technology it is noteworthy that the understanding needed to solve the problem of calculation of atmospheric attenuation (to the degree of accuracy which now seems desirable) appears to be at hand. The actual calculations which need to be made have been made for only a few cases, and the experimental data (such as the OSU work)[44-47] require considerable extension to other gases, and to other pressures, concentrations, and conditions for the gases measured to date, as well as to higher resolutions for all of these absorbers and experimental conditions. As yet, no definitive check of calculation of $\tau(\lambda)$ by extrapolation of laboratory data, as discussed before, has been made. A calculation, designed to produce as accurately as possible the data of Yates and Taylor,[37-40] would be invaluable in this regard. Hopefully, several attempts will be made in the next few years.

1. R. Minzner, K. Champion, and H. Pond, *ARDC 1959 Model Atmosphere, AF Surveys in Geophysics No. 115.* AFCRC-TR-59-267 (August, 1959).
2. E. Glueckauf, "The Composion of Atmospheric Air," *Compendium of Meteorology.* Boston: American Meteorological Society, 1951.
3. F. W. Paul Gotz, "Ozone in the Atmosphere," *Compendium of Meteorology.* Boston: American Meteorological Society, 1951.
4. Hans Neuberger, "Significance of Condensation Nuclei in Atmospheric Pollution," Am. Inst. Mining Met. Engrs. Tech. Publ. No. 2396.
5. Hans Neuberger, *Introduction to Physical Meteorology.* University Park, Pennsylvania: The Pennsylvania State University, 1951.
6. S. K. Mitra, *The Upper Atmosphere.* Calcutta, India: The Asiatic Society, 1952.
7. Homer E. Newell, Jr., "Temperatures in the Upper Atmosphere," *Temperature, Its Measurement and Control in Science and Industry.* New York: American Institute of Physics, Reinhold, 1955, Vol. 2, Chap. 24.
8. American Meteorological Society, *Meteorological Abstract and Bibliography, Bibliography on Carbon Dioxide in the Atmosphere.* New York: American Meteorological Society, 1952, Vol. 3, No. 2.
9. G. S. Benton, R. T. Blackburn, and V. O. Snead, "The Role of the Atmosphere in the Hydrologic Cycle," *Trans. Am. Geophys. Union* 31, 61-73 (1950).

10. G. S. Benton and A. Estoque, "Water-vapor Transfer over the North American Continent," *J. Meteorol.* 11, 462–477 (1954).
11. B. R. Bean and B. A. Cahoon, "A Note on the Climatic Variation of Absolute Humidity," *Bull. Am. Meteorol. Soc.* 38, 395, 395–398 (1957).
12. A. L. Shands, "Mean Precipitable Water in the United States," U. S. Weather Bureau Tech. Paper No. 10, Washington, 1949. Available from the Superintendent of Documents, U. S. Government Printing Office, Washington 25, D.C.
13. G. E. Martin, *Tables of Atmospheric Precipitable Water for Horizontal Paths.* U. S. Naval Avionics Facility, Indianapolis, NAFI-TP-33 (1957).
14. J. R. Garhardt, "Refractive Index and Air Temperature Fluctuations," *Exploring the Atmosphere's First Mile.* New York: 1957, Vol. 1, pp. 220–227.
15. G. P. Kuiper, *The Earth as a Planet.* The University of Chicago Press, 1954, Chap. 9 (by L. Goldberg).
16. W. Elsasser, "Heat Transfer by Infrared Radiation in the Atmosphere," Harvard Meteorological Studies No. 6 (1942).
17. R. A. Smith, F. E. Jones, and R. P. Chasmar, *The Detection and Measurement of Infrared Radiation.* London: Oxford U.P. 1957.
18. Committee on Colorimetry, Optical Society of America, *The Science of Color,* New York: Crowell, 1953, Chap. 6.
19. R. Landenberg and R. Reiche, "Ueber Selektive Absorption," *Ann. d. Physik* 42, 181 (1913).
20. J. N. Howard, D. E. Burch, and Dudley Williams, "Infrared Transmission of Synthetic Atmospheres. IV. Application of Theoretical Band Models," *J. Opt. Soc. Am.* 46, 334 (1956).
21. J. N. Howard, D. E. Burch, and Dudley Williams, "Infrared Transmission of Synthetic Atmospheres," *J. Opt. Soc. Am.* 46, 186 (1956), Article I; 46, 237 (1956), Article II; 46, 242 (1956), Article III; 46, 334 (1956), Article IV; 46, 452 (1956), Article V.
22. R. M. Goody, "A Statistical Model for Water-Vapour Absorption," *Quart. J. Roy. Meteorol. Soc.* 78, 165–169 (1952).
23. H. Gaertner, *The Transmission of Infrared in Cloudy Atmosphere* (June, 1942). A translation was published as Navord Report 429 (June, 1947).
24. G. P. Kuiper, *The Atmospheres of the Earth and Planets.* The University of Chicago Press, 1952, Chapter III (by Van de Hulst).
25. H. C. Van de Hulst, *Light Scattering by Small Particles.* New York: Wiley (1957).
26. C. Hilsum, *Atmospheric Attenuation of IR and Visible Radiation.* Admiralty Research Laboratory, ARL/R, 3/E-600 (December 1948).
27. J. Howard, "Atmospheric Transmission in the 3- to 5-Micron Region," *Proc. IRIS* 2, No. 1, 59 (1957).
28. R. M. Chapman, J. N. Howard, and E. A. Miller, *Atmospheric Transmission of Infrared-Summary Report.* Ohio State University Research Foundation on W44-099-eng-400 (June, 1949).
29. J. N. Howard, *Atmospheric Transmission of Blackbody Radiation—Summary Report.* Contract DA44-009-eng-12, Report No. 1, Ohio State University Research Foundation (March, 1950).
30. J. Howard and R. Chapman, "The Pressure Dependence of the Absorption by Entire Bands of Water Vapor in the Near Infrared," *J. Opt. Soc. Am.* 42, 423 (1952) and 42, 856 (1952).
31. R. McMath and L. Goldberg, "Near Infrared by Entire Bands of Carbon Dioxide," *Proc. Am. Phil. Soc.* 93, 362 (1949).
32. L. Goldberg and E. A. Miller, "The Vertical Distribution of Nitrous Oxide (N_2O) and Methane (CH^4) in the Earth's Atmosphere," *J. Opt. Soc. Am.* 43, 1033 (1953).

33. O. C. Mohler, A. K. Pierce, R. McMath, and L. Goldberg, *Photometric Atlas of the Near Infrared Solar Spectrum* λ *8465 to* λ *25,242.* Ann Arbor: University of Michigan Press, 1950.

34. J. H. Shaw, R. Chapman, J. N. Howard, and M. Oxholm, "A Grating Map of the Solar Spectrum from 3.0 to 5.2 μ," *Astrophy. J.* 113, 268 (1951).

35. H. A. Gebbie, W. Harding, C. Hilsum, A. Pryce, and V. Roberts, "Atmospheric Transmission in the 1–14 μ Region," *Proc. Roy. Soc. (London)* A206, 87 (1951).

36. H. A. Gebbie, W. Harding, C. Hilsum, A. Pryce, and V. Roberts, *Atmospheric Transmission in the 1–14 μ Region.* ARL/R.4/E-600 (December, 1949).

37. J. H. Taylor and H. W. Yates, *Atmospheric Transmission in the Infrared.* NRL Report 4759 (July, 1956).

38. J. H. Taylor and H. W. Yates, "Atmospheric Transmission in the Infrared," *J. Opt. Soc. Am.* 47, 223 (1957).

39. H. W. Yates, *The Absorption Spectrum from 0.5 to 25 μ of a 1000 ft. Atmospheric Path at Sea Level.* NRL Report 5033 (September 1957).

40. H. W. Yates and J. H. Taylor, *Infrared Transmission of the Atmosphere.* NRL Report 5453 (June, 1960).

41. H. Yates, *Total Transmission of the Atmosphere in the Near IR.* NRL Report 3858 (September, 1951).

42. *Infrared Transmission Functions for CO_2.* A report by The English Electrical Co. (November, 1952).

43. T. Elder and J. Strong, "The Infrared Transmission of Atmospheric Windows," *J. Franklin Inst.* 255, 189–208 (1953).

44. D. A. Brown and V. Roberts, "A Simple High-Speed Spectrometer for the Infrared Region," *J. Sci. Instr.* 30, 5 (1953).

45. J. Hampson, Telecommunications Research Establishment, RRE, Malvern, England, Tech. Note 187 (Secret) (1954).

46. J. Hampson, Telecommunications Research Establishment, RRE, Malvern, England, Tech. Memo No. 1068 (Secret) (1954).

47. F. E. Jones and V. Roberts, "Solar Infrared Spectroscopy from High-Altitude Aircraft," *Proc. Roy. Soc. (London)* A236, 171 (1956).

48. J. N. Howard, D. L. Burch, and D. Williams, *Near-Infrared Transmission Through Synthetic Atmospheres.* Ohio State University Research Foundation Report No. 1 on AF 19(604)-516 (December, 1954).

49. D. L. Burch and J. N. Howard, *Near-Infrared Transmission Through Synthetic Atmospheres.* Ohio State University Research Foundation Report No. 2 on AF 19(604)-516 (1955).

50a. R. G. Breene, Jr., *The Shift and Shape of Spectral Lines.* Geophysical Research Paper No. 41, AFCRC-TR-55-214 (September, 1955).

50b. R. G. Breene, Jr., "Line Shape," *Revs. Modern Phys.* 29, 94 (1957).

51. O. C. Mohler, *Table of Solar Spectrum Wavelengths, 1.20–2.55 μ.* Ann Arbor: University of Michigan Press, 1955.

52. L. Goldberg, "Infrared Solar Spectrum," *Am. J. Phys.* 23, 203 (1955).

53. L. Larmore, "Transmission of Infrared Radiation Through the Atmosphere," *Proc. IRIS* 1, No. 1, 14 (1956).

54. S. Passman and L. Larmore, "Correction to Atmospheric Transmission Tables," *Proc. IRIS* 1, No. 2, 15 (1956).

55. T. L. Altshuler, *A Procedure for Calculation of Atmosphere Transmission of Infrared,* General Electric Tech., Rept., TIS R57ELC15, Adv. Electronic Center at Cornell (May, 1957).

56. T. L. Altshuler, *J. Opt. Soc. Am.* 47, 1055 (A) (1956), Abstract of Paper SA 12.

57. J. I. King, "Universal Transmission Function for Far-Infrared Radiation: The Line Cluster Model," *J. Opt. Soc. Am.* **47**, 1054 (A) (1957), Abstract of Paper F64.

58. J. S. Birch, "The Atmospheric CO_2 Transmission of IR in a Slant Path," *Proc. IRIS* **1**, 68 (December 1957).

59. R. O. Carpenter, J. A. Wight, A. Quesada, and R. F. Swing, *Predicting Infrared Molecular Attenuation for Long Slant Paths in the Upper Atmosphere.* Report No. 1 on AF 19(604)-2405 by Baird-Atomic, Inc. (November 1957).

60. G. N. Plass, "Models for Spectral Band Absorption," *J. Opt. Soc. Am.* **48**, 690 (1958).

61. Migeotti, Neven, and Swensson, *The Solar Spectrum from 2.8 to 23.7 μ. Part I. Photometric Atlas. Part II, Measures and Identification.* (Report on AF 61(514)-432, University of Liege, Belgium, No. 1 (1956) and No. 2 (1957).

62. J. T. Houghton and J. S. Seeley, "Spectroscopic Observations of the Water Vapor Content of the Stratosphere," *Quart. Roy. Meteoral. Soc.* **86**, 358 (1960).

63. D. Murcray, J. Brooks, F. Murcray, W. Williams, F. Leslie, and C. Shaw, *High Altitude Studies of the Atmosphere.* Scientific Reports Nos. 1–4 on Contract AF 19(604)-1005 and AF 19(604)-2069 by the University of Denver Physics Dept. (1958–1960).

64. D. Murcray, J. Brooks, F. Murcray, and W. Williams, "Atmospheric Absorptions in the Near Infrared at High Altitudes," *J. Opt. Soc. Am.* **50**, 107 (1960).

65. S. W. Kurnick, R. N. Zitter, and D. B. Williams, "Attenuation of Infrared Radiation by Fogs," *J. Opt. Soc. Am.* **50**, 578 (1960).

66. *Atmospheric Transmission of Infrared Radiation.* University of Chicago, Chicago Midway Laboratory, CML-56-Tech. Note E 103–12 (April, 1956).

67. D. Deirmendjian, "Atmospheric Extinction of Infrared Radiation," *Quart. J. Roy. Meteorol. Soc.* **86**, 371 (1960).

68. C. Harvey Palmer, Jr., "Long Path Water Vapor Spectra with Pressure Broadening, Parts I and II," *J. Opt. Soc. Am.* **47**, 1024 and 1028 (1957).

69. C. Harvey Palmer, Jr., "Ratio-Recording System for the Johns Hopkins 100-Foot Absorption Cell," *J. Opt. Soc. Am.* **47**, 367 (1957).

70. C. Harvey Palmer, Jr., "Experimental Transmission Functions for the Pure Rotation Band of Water Vapor," *J. Opt. Soc. Am.* **50**, 1232 (1960).

71. R. O. Carpenter, *Emission and Absorption in the 4.3-Micron CO_2 Band.* A Baird-Atomic, Inc. Report on work done on Contract AF 19(604)-2405. Also reported in *Proc. IRIS* **4**, 5 (1959) (Secret).

72. G. Plass, "Spectral Emissivity of Carbon Dioxide from 1800–2500 cm^{-1}," *J. Opt. Soc. Am.* **49**, 821 (1959).

73. D. D. Edwards, "Absorption by Infrared Bands of Carbon Dioxide Gas at Elevated Pressures and Temperatures," *J. Opt. Soc. Am.* **50**, 617 (1960).

74. A. Prostak, A. LaRocca, J. Livisay, and R. Nichols, "A Method for Calculating Atmospheric Transmission," *Proc. IRIS* **5**, No. 2, 51 (1960).

75. A. Prostak, A. LaRocca, J. Livisay, R. Nichols, and W. Wolfe, "Atmospheric Transmission Coefficients and Constants," *Proc. IRIS* **5**, No. 3, 235 (1960).

76. G. Plass, "Useful Representations for Measurements of Spectral Band Absorption," *J. Opt. Soc. Am.* **50**, 868 (1960).

77. L. D. Kaplan, "The Absorption Spectrum of Carbon Dioxide from 14 to 16 Microns," *J. Chem. Phys.* **15**, 809 (1947).

CHAPTER 5

REVIEW OF THE PRINCIPLES OF OPTICS

5.1 Introduction

The subject of optics may be reviewed in a number of ways. The one used here is to outline briefly the quantum nature of optics, which in one sense is the most fundamental; then, physical optics as described by electromagnetic theory; and finally, the geometrical approximations which are of such practical importance. Some familiarity is assumed, so that emphasis will be placed on the subjects of special importance to infrared instrumentation, although a few fundamental subjects are treated with reasonable detail.

5.2 Quantum Optics

Although most problems in infrared technology do not require the quantum-mechanical treatment of light, the notable exceptions being the interaction of radiation with optical materials and also photoelectric detection, it is advisable to review some aspects of the theory briefly. It has been seen that one of the very foundations of the quantum theory was the work of Planck. He was able to explain blackbody radiation by assuming that the radiation came in small particles or quanta; then the laws of Wien and of Rayleigh and Jeans were seen to be approximations which are good only under certain conditions. From the Davisson and Germer experiments and the theoretical work of de Broglie, it was determined that the quanta also have certain properties of waves. Therefore, each particle has an associated mass m, a velocity v, a momentum $p (= mv)$, an energy E, a frequency f, and a wavelength $\lambda (= v/f)$. One of the relations among these is the one between radiation frequency and energy given by Planck: the energy of a quantum is associated with the frequency of the radiation by

$$E = hf = \hbar\omega \qquad (5\text{-}1)$$

where h is Planck's constant, $\hbar$ is $h/2\pi$, and ω is the angular frequency $(= 2\pi f)$. The energy-mass relationship is the famous one of Einstein:

$$E = mc^2 \tag{5-2}$$

where c is the velocity of light. Therefore

$$hf = mc^2$$

Classically, the momentum p is mv or dE/dv, where E is $1/2 mv^2$. Then quantum-mechanically.

$$p = mc = hf/c = h/\lambda$$

Finally,

$$\lambda = h/p \tag{5-3}$$

This is the expression of the wavelength of a free particle, often called the de Broglie wavelength. Energy, momentum, and mass are seen to be related to the velocity of light, its wavelength, and Planck's constant.

While it is of great importance to know how to relate these wave and quantum phenomena, it is equally important to know something about when each applies; it is also important to know to what precision optical experiments or optical instruments may be extended. For these purposes the Principle of Complementarity and the Principle of Uncertainty are necessary. The mathematical formulation of the latter, which was first stated by Heisenberg, is

$$\Delta p_y \, \Delta y \gtrsim \hbar = h/2\pi \tag{5-4}$$

The product of the uncertainty of the momentum of a particle moving in the y direction and the uncertainty of the instaneous y position of the particle is greater than or about the same magnitude as Planck's constant divided by 2π. Another way of saying this is that both the position of a particle and its momentum can never be known exactly. This uncertainty is immaterial for problems in classical mechanics, since the quantities involved are so much greater than the uncertainty, but it is of the utmost importance when p_y is small and $\Delta p_y/p_y$ becomes appreciable. The momentum of a quantum is not large! The application of quantum mechanics to optics is further clarified by the Complementarity Principle, usually attributed to Bohr, which states that wave and corpuscular properties can never be determined by a single experiment at a single time. A complete description of optical phenomena can be made only when quantum and classical treatments are applied separately in appropriate ways. For example, when interference phenomena are observed, they should be explained by the interaction of waves; when photoelectric emission is the subject, quanta should be considered the conceptual tool.

The use of a very fast shutter is an excellent example of the application of the Uncertainty Principle. If, in an experiment, one wishes to obtain pulses of a monochromatic plane wave of light to test detector time constant as a function of wavelength, he may use a Kerr cell or a very fast mechanical shutter. It is of interest to determine the effects of uncertainty. Suppose that a pulse of light which is formed by the shutter contains only one photon. Since the portion of the monochromatic incident wave is limited in time by the shutter, the resulting wave packet is no longer monochromatic, and it must be represented as a distribution of frequencies. The distribution can be determined by Fourier analysis. Assume that the incident wave has unit amplitude and angular frequency $\omega_0 = 2\pi f_0$; then the frequency spectrum of the wave packet is

$$F(\omega) = \int_{-T/2}^{T/2} e^{j\omega_0 t} e^{j\omega t} dt$$

$$= \frac{e^{j(\omega_0 + \omega)T/2} - e^{-j(\omega_0 + \omega)T/2}}{j(\omega_0 + \omega)}$$

$$= T\left[\frac{\sin(\omega_0 + \omega)T/2}{(\omega_0 + \omega)T/2}\right]$$

$$|F(\omega)|^2 = T^2\left[\frac{\sin^2(\omega_0 + \omega)T/2}{(\omega_0 + \omega)^2 T^2/4}\right]$$

This is illustrated in Figure 5-1. The first zero of the function occurs for $(\omega + \omega_0)T/2\pi$; the half-width of the central peak is determined by the frequency spread around ω_0.

$$2\pi\Delta f T/2 = \pi$$

$$\Delta f = 1/T = f_0/Tf_0 = f_0/N$$

where $N (= f_0 T)$ is the number of waves in the packet. Now the Uncertainty Principle can be applied:

$$\Delta p_x = \Delta(h/\lambda) = (h/c)\Delta f = hf_0/Nc$$

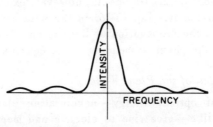

Fig. 5-1. Distribution of intensity of the frequencies in a finite wave train.

Clearly the uncertainty in position is given by the velocity of the wave times the period of the radiation,

$$\Delta x = cT = cN/f_0$$

since $N = f_0 T$. Thus

$$\Delta x \Delta p_x = \frac{h f_0}{Nc} \frac{Nc}{f_0} = h$$

It is interesting to note in this connection that any time-limited wave is not monochromatic; it is of course true that no optical source lasts forever, and therefore *no* wave is monochromatic.

Other examples of the application of quantum mechanics will be found in most optics text books, in particular those of Jenkins and White,[1] and of Strong.[2]

The purpose of this brief review of the fundamental principles of quantum optics has been to remind the reader of certain basic limitations in dealing with optical design. It should be emphasized that the experiments outlined above are *Gedanken* or "thought" experiments—the results will not be changed by improved equipment. Also, the reader should realize that particle or quantum considerations need be used only where they apply; the principal applications in this book are detectors and optical materials.

5.3 Physical Optics

The basis of physical optics is the classical theory of electricity and magnetism; the phenomena studied in this book are those which are either unique to the range of optical frequencies or possibly which are more striking in that region. Maxwell's equations are of course fundamental, and, the wave equation derived from them is the basis of most of what follows. For a derivation of these equations or a more complete treatment of them, reference is made to Stratton,[3] Panofsky and Phillips,[4] Born and Wolf,[5] or any of a number of other texts.

The next section includes derivations of the expressions for the plane wave from electromagnetic theory. The reader may choose to go immediately to section 5.3.2. He should, however, examine Eq. (5-16) and the text accompanying it. Eq. (5-16) is the solution to the wave equation that describes the propagation of light in an absorbing medium, and the text describes the physical meaning of the equation.

5.3.1 *Representation of the Plane Wave*

The sources of optical energy—accelerating electrons, oscillating dipoles, and the like—give rise to electric and magnetic fields which vary with time. These fields interact in such a way that they can transmit energy in the form of a wave. The plane wave is the simplest and probably the most important of these. Thus, one can start with Maxwell's equations (in mks units) for instantaneous field quantities and derive the expression for the plane wave from them. These equations are (vectors indicated by boldface type):

$$\nabla \times \mathbf{E} = - \frac{\partial \mathbf{B}}{\partial t}$$

$$\nabla \times \mathbf{H} = \frac{\partial \mathbf{D}}{\partial t} + \mathbf{J}$$

$$\nabla \cdot \mathbf{E} = \rho$$

$$\nabla \cdot \mathbf{H} = 0$$

(5-5)

The material equations are:

$$\mathbf{D} = \varepsilon \mathbf{E}$$

$$\mathbf{B} = \mu \mathbf{H}$$

$$\mathbf{J} = \sigma \mathbf{E}$$

(5-6)

where ε and μ, the absolute dielectric constant and absolute permeability, may be either constants or tensors reflecting the variation of electric and magnetic properties of the material with orientation, and $\mathbf{E}$, $\mathbf{D}$, $\mathbf{B}$, $\mathbf{H}$, $\mathbf{J}$, ρ, and σ have their usual meanings. Finally, the equation of continuity expresses the conservation of charge:

$$\partial \rho / \partial t + \nabla \cdot \mathbf{J} = 0$$

(5-7)

To obtain the wave equation, the curl of the first Maxwell equation is taken and the others are used appropriately, as follows:

$$\nabla \times (\nabla \times \mathbf{E}) = - \nabla \times (\partial \mathbf{B} / \partial t)$$

$$= - \frac{\partial}{\partial t} (\nabla \times \mathbf{B})$$

$$= - \frac{\partial}{\partial t} \left(\mu \mathbf{J} + \mu \varepsilon \frac{\partial \mathbf{E}}{\partial t} \right)$$

$$= - \mu \sigma \frac{\partial \mathbf{E}}{\partial t} - \mu \varepsilon \frac{\partial^2 \mathbf{E}}{\partial t^2}$$

A useful vector identity is:

$$\nabla \times (\nabla \times \mathbf{E}) = \nabla (\nabla \cdot \mathbf{E}) - \nabla^2 \mathbf{E}$$

Thus,

$$\nabla^2 E - \nabla(\nabla \cdot E) = \frac{\partial}{\partial t}\left(\mu J + \mu\varepsilon \frac{\partial E}{\partial t}\right)$$

$$\nabla^2 E - \mu\sigma \frac{\partial E}{\partial t} - \mu\varepsilon \frac{\partial^2 E}{\partial t^2} = \frac{\nabla\rho}{\varepsilon} \tag{5-8}$$

Eq. (5-8) is the wave equation for instantaneous values of the fields in regions with charge density. It can be assumed for most optical problems that the region is charge-free, so that $\rho = 0$. Also, for optical problems one can assume that the field quantities vary sinusoidally. (No generality is really lost since Fourier techniques can be used for arbitrary time variations.) Thus, the wave equation for sinusoidally varying fields in a charge-free region is obtained by setting $\rho = 0$, $E = Ee^{-i\omega t}$, and $H = He^{-i\omega t}$; the exponential form is used, and the real part of the complex function is always implied. The use of exponentials greatly simplifies the calculation. With these assumptions, the wave equation becomes

$$\nabla^2 E + i\omega\mu\sigma E + \mu\varepsilon\omega^2 E = 0$$

This can be rewritten,

$$\nabla^2 E + \mu\varepsilon\omega^2 [1 - i(\sigma/\omega\varepsilon)]E = 0 \tag{5-9}$$

For uniform plane waves which are of primary interest in optical considerations, $\partial/\partial x = 0$ and $\partial/\partial y = 0$; then Maxwell's equations are:

$$\hat{n} \times (\partial E/\partial \xi) = - \partial B/\partial t$$

$$\hat{n} \times (\partial H/\partial \xi) = \sigma E + \partial D/\partial t$$

$$\hat{n} \cdot (\partial D/\partial \xi) = 0 \tag{5-10}$$

$$\hat{n} \cdot (\partial B/\partial \xi) = 0$$

where ξ represents the coordinate in the direction of propagation and $\hat{n}$ is the unit vector normal to the wave front. From the second of these, it is seen that

$$\hat{n} \cdot [\sigma E + (\partial D/\partial t)] = \hat{n} \cdot \hat{n} \times (\partial H/\partial \xi)$$

But $\hat{n} \times (\partial H/\partial \xi)$ is perpendicular to $\hat{n}$; the dot product of $\hat{n}$ and a vector perpendicular to it is zero. Thus

$$\hat{n} \cdot [\sigma E + (\partial D/\partial t)] = 0$$

This equality is possible if both E and $\partial D/\partial t$ are perpendicular to $\hat{n}$; these are the transverse components of the field. The equality is also possible if

$$\varepsilon(\partial E_i/\partial t) + \sigma E = 0$$

Whence

$$E = E_n \exp(-\sigma t/\varepsilon)$$

where E_n is an arbitrary constant vector in the direction of propagation.

This means that the only longitudinal component of the electric field is electrostatic, and that this component decays exponentially with the conductivity of the medium and with time. Similarly,

$$\hat{n} \cdot (\partial B/\partial t) = -\hat{n}[\hat{n} \times (\partial E/\partial \xi)] = 0$$

Thus, the only longitudinal magnetic component is a stationary, uniform field; any time-varying solution must be transverse.

Each transverse component of the electric (or magnetic) field obeys the one-dimensional, vector, wave equation,

$$\partial^2 E/\partial \xi^2 + \mu\varepsilon\omega^2[1 - i(\sigma/\varepsilon\omega)]E = 0 \tag{5-11}$$

This can be verified by carrying out the scalar operations on Eq. (5-10), which are analogous to the vector operations which were performed on Eq. (5-5).

The solutions for Eq. (5-11) are:

$$E = E_0 \exp(\pm i\{\mu\varepsilon\omega[1 - i(\sigma/\varepsilon\omega)]\}^{1/2} \xi) \tag{5-12}$$

where E_0 is an arbitrary constant vector.

This can be written as

$$E = E_0 \exp(\pm \gamma \xi)$$

where

$$\gamma = \alpha + i\beta = \{\mu\varepsilon\omega[1 - i(\sigma/\varepsilon\omega)]\}^{1/2}$$

$$\beta = \omega\sqrt{(\mu\varepsilon/2)\sqrt{1 + (\sigma^2/\omega^2\varepsilon^2)} - \mu\varepsilon/2}$$

$$\tag{5-13}$$

$$\alpha = \omega\sqrt{(\mu\varepsilon/2)\sqrt{1 + (\sigma^2/\omega^2\varepsilon^2)} + \mu\varepsilon/2}$$

The constant γ is called the propagation constant; α is the (amplitide) attenuation coefficient; β is the phase factor. One can use these expressions to describe the wave and then relate them to the optical constants n and k; this is done in Chapter 6.

To see most easily the physical interpretation of these equations, assume that the medium is perfect ($\sigma = 0$). Then the wave equation is

$$\partial^2 E/\partial \xi^2 + \mu\varepsilon\omega^2 E = 0 \tag{5-14}$$

The solution is

$$E = E_0 e^{\mp i\omega\sqrt{\mu\varepsilon}\,\xi}$$

Then since $E_0 = E_0 e^{-i\omega t}$ was assumed,

$$E = E_0 e^{-i\omega(t \mp \sqrt{\mu\varepsilon}\ \xi)} \tag{5-15}$$

This equation is of the form

$$E = E_0 e^{-i\omega[t \pm (\xi/v)]}$$

so one can identify $(\mu\varepsilon)^{-1/2}$ as the velocity of phase propagation of the wave in a perfect dielectric. Equation (5-12) can also be written

$$E = E_0 e^{-i\omega t} e^{\pm i\beta\xi} e^{\pm\alpha\xi} \tag{5-16}$$

This form of the equation makes it apparent that the wave has a sinusoidal variation in time of frequency $\omega/2\pi$, a velocity of phase propagation β^{-1}, and an exponential amplitude attenuation α. The refractive index is defined as the ratio of the velocity of light in two media, and will be used and more carefully defined in Section 6.2.3. The electric and magnetic fields are transverse and normal to each other in free space. The direction of propagation and the energy in the fields are given by the Poynting vector, $E \times H = P$.

5.3.2 Polarization.

So far, a one-dimensional electromagnetic wave has been discussed. If a two-dimensional vector wave is considered, then the problem of polarization enters. If the wave originates from sources which are incoherent, the E vectors are arbitrarily oriented, the radiation is unpolarized. If the E vector is always in the same direction, the wave is linearly polarized. Figure 5-2 can be considered to show a linearly polarized wave. If E_x and E_y have different phase and magnitude (elliptic polarization), then they can be represented by

$$E_x = E_1 \cos \omega[t - (\xi/v)] \tag{5-17}$$

$$E_y = E_2 \cos \{\omega[t - (\xi/v)] + \psi\} \tag{5-18}$$

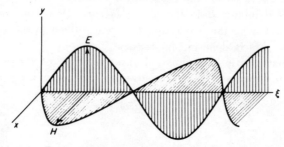

Fig. 5-2. Pictorial representation of a uniform plane wave.

In any plane, e.g., $\xi = 0$, these reduce to

$$E_x = E_1 \cos \omega t$$

$$E_y = E_2 \cos (\omega t + \psi) \tag{5-19}$$

These are the parametric equations for an ellipse. If $E_1 = E_2$ and $\psi = + \pi/2$, the wave is circularly polarized. Since $\alpha = \tan^{-1} (E_y/E_x) = \mp \omega t$, the vector E rotates clockwise (looking in the direction of propagation). Thus if $\psi = -\pi/2$, the polarization is right hand or clockwise polarization, and vice versa. The vector diagram for elliptical polarization is shown in Figure 5-3.

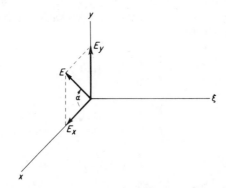

Fig. 5-3.   Vector diagram for elliptic polarization.

The nature of the uniform, plane, electromagnetic wave which is fundamental to so much of optics has been outlined. The reader should be cautioned that there are times when such a wave represents an approximation to a more complicated wave. It is then necessary to reconsider the three-dimensional wave equation in the appropriate coordinate system. Usually, considerably more complicated mathematics will be necessary.

5.3.3 *Reflection and Refraction*

The laws of reflection and refraction can be derived from Maxwell's equations and the appropriate boundary conditions. It is interesting and valuable to carry out such a process. This has been done in books like those by Stratton,[3] and Panofsky and Phillips,[4] and the reader is referred there or to a number of other texts on optics or electromagnetic theory. The results are the familiar ones:

$$n \sin \theta = n' \sin \theta'$$

$$\theta = \theta' \tag{5-20}$$

In words, these laws are:

1. The product of the refractive index of the first medium and the sine of the angle of incidence is equal to the product of the refractive index of the second medium and the sine of the angle of refraction.
2. The angle of reflection is equal to the angle of incidence.

Almost all of geometrical optics—and all within the scope of this book—depends upon these two laws.

5.3.4 *Interference*

The average energy or power flow in a single wave is given by the average of Poynting's vector $\mathbf{P} = \mathbf{E} \times \mathbf{H}$. If sinusoidal variations are assumed, and if T is the period, the energy can be written in terms of the square of the electric field vector:

$$<\mathbf{P}> = \frac{1}{T} \int_0^T \mathbf{E} \times \mathbf{H} \, dt \qquad (5\text{-}21)$$

$$= \frac{1}{T} \int_0^T E^2 \frac{k}{\omega\mu} \, dt$$

$$= \frac{1}{T} \int_0^T \mathbf{k} \frac{E_0^2}{\omega\mu} e^{2j(\omega t - k\xi)} dt \qquad (5\text{-}22)$$

For convenience we write

$$P = a^2 \cos^2 (\omega t - \phi) \, dt$$

rather than writing the exponential, where the a includes all multipliers and ϕ represents the phase of the wave.

If this energy is averaged over one period, then

$$P = \frac{1}{T} \int_0^T a^2 \cos^2 (\omega t - \phi) \, dt \qquad (5\text{-}23)$$

$$P = a^2 / 2$$

If two waves which differ only in phase and amplitude are considered, then

$$E = a_1 \cos (\omega t - \phi_1) + a_2 \cos (\omega t - \phi_2)$$

$$P = \frac{a_1^2}{T} \int_0^T \cos^2 (\omega t - \phi_1) \, dt + \frac{a_2^2}{T} \int_0^T \cos^2 (\omega t - \phi_2) \, dt$$

$$+ \frac{2a_1 a_2}{T} \int_0^T \cos (\omega t - \phi_1) \cos (\omega t - \phi_2) \, dt \qquad (5\text{-}24)$$

When the integrand of the last integral is expanded and evaluated, the integral yields $2a_1 a_2 \cos (\phi_2 - \phi_1)$. Thus,

$$P = \frac{1}{2} [a_1^2 + 2a_1 a_2 \cos (\phi_2 - \phi_1) + a_2^2] \qquad (5\text{-}25)$$

This important result shows that for constructive interference the phase difference between the two waves $\delta = \phi_2 - \phi_1$ must be even multiples of π. For destructive interference the phase difference must be odd multiples of π. For constructive interference,

$$P = \frac{1}{2} (a_1 + a_2)^2$$

For destructive interference,

$$P = \frac{1}{2} (a_1 - a_2)^2$$

If the intensities are equal, the destruction is complete.

The above treatment has been for collinear, coherent waves; that is, the normals to the wavefronts of the two waves are parallel and the phase difference is constant. To deal with incoherent waves one should sum many single waves, each having a slightly different phase. This results essentially in the fact that $\cos (\phi_1 - \phi_2) = 0$; therefore $P = \frac{1}{2} (a_1^2 - a_2^2)$.

To deal with noncollinear waves, one must write the argument of the cosine (exponential) so that the directions are properly given. Substitution of direction cosines will do this.

Many more complicated and special cases of interference are treated in the literature, but the essence of the phenomenon is the addition of intensities of more than one wave with due regard for phase differences in the waves. An illustrative classical experiment is briefly described immediately below, and several applications—the Michelson and Fabry-Perot interferometers, and interference filters—are discussed in Chapter 7.

5.3.5 Young's Double-Slit Experiment.

If a source, two slits, and an observing screen are arranged as shown in Figure 5-4, then the following equations apply.

$$E_1 = a_1 \cos (\omega t - \phi_1)$$
$$E_2 = a_2 \cos (\omega t - \phi_2)$$

The problem is that of interference of two coherent noncollinear light waves. Usually, the two slits are close enough together that the am-

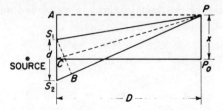

Fig. 5-4. Schematic of Young's double-slit experiment.

plitudes a_1 and a_2 can be assumed constant $(= a)$. Then

$$E_1 + E_2 = a[\cos(\omega t - \phi_1) + \cos(\omega t - \phi_2)].$$

The intensity expression is easily obtained in Eq. (5-25) by setting $a_1 = a_2 = a$. Then

$$P = \frac{1}{2} a^2 [1 + 2 \cos(\phi_2 - \phi_1) + 1]$$

$$P = a^2 [1 + \cos(\phi_2 - \phi_1)]$$

$$P = 2a^2 \cos^2 \left(\frac{\phi_2 - \phi_1}{2}\right)$$

The phase difference δ can be evaluated from the path difference Δ; $\delta = \phi_2 - \phi_2 = (2\pi/\lambda)\Delta$. From the figure, $\Delta = S_2 B$. If $S_1 B$ is drawn so that $S_1 P = BP$, PC is perpendicular to $S_1 B$, and the angles $\angle S_2 S_1 B$ and $\angle PCP_0$ are equal. The sines and tangents can be replaced by the respective angles and

$$\Delta/d = x/D$$

or

$$\delta/2 = (2\pi/2\lambda)(xd/D) = (\pi/\lambda)(xd/D)$$

Thus, the intensity P is a maximum when $\delta = (m\pi/\lambda)(xd/D)$, and minimum when $\delta = \left(m + \frac{1}{2}\right)(\pi xd/\lambda D)$; that is, when

$$x = m\lambda D/d$$

$$x = \left(m + \frac{1}{2}\right)(\lambda D/d) = (2m + 1)(\lambda D/2d)$$

5.3.6 *Diffraction*

Light does not always travel in straight lines. When it passes a straight edge, the edge of a half-plane, a narrow slit, or any object or aperture with dimensions approximately equal to the wavelength, some of the light is bent or diffracted. This is due, of course, to the fact that light is a wave motion.

The diffraction pattern behind single and double slits and an entire series of them, as well as the patterns behind other bodies, is part of diffraction theory. The rigorous treatment of the theory is quite complex and difficult; it calls for the solution of Maxwell's equations with the appropriate boundary conditions. Even these solutions—which often involve Fresnel integrals and Riemann surfaces—are often unsatisfactory because of the complicated integrals or the slowly converging series. Only simplified treatments are given here: those which should be sufficient for rudimentary understanding and experimental applications.

There are two general types of diffraction: Fresnel and Fraunhofer. In Fresnel diffraction, the diffracting aperture is near the source, the observing screen, or both; in Fraunhofer diffraction, both the source and the screen must be at distances from the aperture which are large compared to its linear dimensions.

The basis for the solution of both kinds of diffraction problems is the Fresnel-Kirchhoff form of Huygens Principle expressed mathematically as the Fresnel-Kirchhoff integral. Briefly, the light disturbance at a point is assumed to arise from the superposition of secondary waves which originate at the source of the diffraction. Due consideration must be given to the geometrical aspects of the problem and the fact that these wavelets can interfere with each other destructively and constructively. A spherical wave may be represented by the following expression,

$$E = \frac{E_0}{r} \exp i(\omega t - kr)$$

The expression arises from the solution of the wave equation in spherical coordinates. It is easy to see that the well known inverse square law holds for the intensity of such a wave. If the time variation is dropped temporarily,

$$E = (E_0/r) \exp(-ikr)$$

If r is the distance from the source to a point on the aperture and s is the distance from the point on the aperture to the place at which the field is to be determined, see Fig. 5-5, then it may be shown that[5]

$$E = \frac{-iE_0}{2\lambda} \iint_S \frac{\exp[-ik(r+s)]}{rs} [\cos(n,r) - \cos(n,s)]\, ds \qquad (5\text{-}26)$$

where (n,r) is the angle between the normal to the aperture and r,
   (n,s) is the angle between the normal to the aperture and s,
   ds is an element of aperture area,
   S is the integration surface, the area of the aperture.

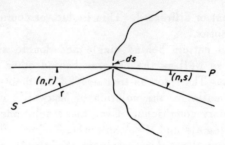

Fig. 5-5. Single-slit geometry.

Eq. (5-26) is the Fresnel-Kirchhoff diffraction integral. If the source and the viewing screen are both very far from the aperture (relative to the aperture's linear dimensions), then Fraunhofer diffraction obtains. The cosine terms and the product rs can be moved outside the integral since throughout the region of integration S both vary slowly compared to $\exp[-ik(r+s)]$. Further, r and s can be written in terms of r' and s' which are vectors from the source point and field point respectively to the center of the aperture and the coordinates ξ, η in the aperture plane; then

$$E = \frac{-i}{\lambda}\left[\cos(n,r) - \cos(n,s)\right]\frac{\exp[-ik(r'+s')]}{r's'}\iint\limits_{S}\exp[-ikf(\xi,\eta)]d\xi\,dy$$

where $f(\xi,\eta)$ is the power series of the geometrical factors r', s', ξ, and η. This expression may now be applied to Fraunhofer diffraction problems. Consider a rectangular slit whose linear dimensions are a and b; the source and screen are assumed to be very far from the diffracting aperture so that the cosine terms are not significantly different from one; higher order terms in the power series can be ignored so that Eq. (5-26) becomes

$$E = \frac{-i}{\lambda}E_0\frac{\exp[-ik(r'+s')]}{r's'}\int_{-a/2}^{a/2}\int_{-b/2}^{b/2}\exp[-ik(p\xi+q\eta)]d\xi\,d\eta$$

where

$$p = \sin\theta, \qquad q = \sin\varphi$$

Note that

$$\int_{-a/2}^{a/2}\exp(-ikp\xi)\,d\xi = \frac{\exp(-ikpa/2) - \exp(ikpa/2)}{-ikp} = \frac{2\sin kpa/2}{kp}$$

Thus

$$E = \left(\frac{-iE_0}{\lambda}\right)\left[\frac{e^{-ik(r'+s')}}{r's'}\right]\left(\frac{ab}{2\cdot2}\right)\left(\frac{\sin kpa/2}{kpa/2}\right)\left(\frac{\sin kqb/2}{kqb/2}\right) \quad (5\text{-}27)$$

The terms in Eq. (5-27) may be interpreted as follows: the factor $\dfrac{-i}{\lambda}$ arises from the diffraction integral and seems to indicate that the secondary waves have a phase delay of $\pi/2$ $(e^{-i\pi/2} = -i)$ and have amplitudes smaller than the primary wave by $1/\lambda$; E_0 is the original amplitude of the incident spherical wave. The factor in the first parenthesis describes the attenuation and phase of the incident wave; the next describes attenuation and phase for the spherical secondary waves; the next factor is the aperture area; and the last two are the diffraction terms describing the redistribution of energy due to the a dimension and the b dimension respectively. It will be shown in Chapter 14 that the last two terms are identical to terms which arise from spatial filtering theory. The intensity pattern is shown in Figure 5-6. The minima appear at $n\pi$, but the maxima are not exactly at $(n + 1/2)\pi$, but are close to these values of the abscissa.

If a slit is sufficiently narrow, $b \longrightarrow 0$ and the usual single slit pattern is obtained, since $\dfrac{\sin 0}{0} = 1$. Of course the intensity in each case is found by multiplying E by its complex conjugate, see Fig. 5-6.

The derivation for the intensity distribution behind a pair of slits follows as for the single slit. The integration must be carried out over both slits and appropriate geometrical factors must be used.

$$I = 4A^2\, \frac{\sin^2\beta}{\beta^2}\cos^2\gamma$$

where A is a constant including the first three terms of Eq. (5-27). It should be noticed that this is simply the single-slit diffraction expression multiplied by an interference expression. The intensity will be zero when either factor is zero. Thus there are minima for $\beta = \pi,\ 2\pi,\ \ldots$, and $\gamma = \pi/2,\ 3\pi/2,\ 5\pi/2,\ \ldots$. The configuration of the pattern can be interpreted in an approximate manner by the following considerations: As the value of b (or d, equal to the slit center-to-center distance) is reduced compared to the slit size a, more interference maxima fall within the central maximum of the diffraction pattern or narrows the interference pattern.

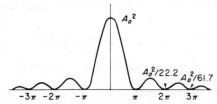

Fig. 5-6. Diffraction pattern of the single slit.

If the two slits are increased to N in number, then analysis along the lines shown above leads to the expression

$$E = \frac{A}{x} \frac{\sin \beta}{\beta} \frac{\sin N\gamma}{\sin \gamma} \exp j(\omega t - kx)$$

This is the appropriate expression for describing the amplitude distribution behind a plane transmission grating.

The intensity is given by

$$A^2 = \frac{\sin^2 \beta}{\beta^2} \frac{\sin^2 N\gamma}{\sin^2 \gamma}$$

where the first term is the diffraction term, and the second is the interference term. The principal maxima occur at $\gamma = 0, \pi, 2\pi \ldots$, the same as for the double slit. Further, the value of $\sin^2 N\gamma/\sin^2\gamma$ is N^2 at these values. To find the entire distribution, one multiplies this by $(\sin^2 \beta)/\beta^2$. As the number of slits N increases, the ratio of the intensity of the primary maxima to the intensity of the secondary maxima increases greatly.

It also can be shown that the minima occur when $N\gamma = m\pi$, for $m = 0$, 1, 2, ... when maxima do not occur. Maxima occur, as indicated above, when $m = 0, N, 2N, \ldots$. The path difference corresponds to $d \sin \theta = m\lambda/N$, where $m = 0, 1, 2, \ldots$ (but excluding values which give maxima).

The principal maxima formed by a grating constitute the spectrum. If light is incident on the grating at an angle i, then the grating equation is

$$d(\sin i + \sin \theta) = m\lambda$$

A further treatment of the grating—overlapping of orders, dispersion, blazes, resolution, etc.—is given in Chapter 7.

5.4 Geometrical Optics

When the apertures and obstacles upon which a light wave is incident are very large compared to the wavelength of the light, it is possible to simplify many calculations. Rather than using Huygen's Principle to calculate the way the light propagates, it is sufficient to determine the path of the normal to the wavefront; this path is called a ray. The tools which are necessary for these calculations are the laws of solid analytic geometry, Snell's Law, and the law of reflection. The latter two are, respectively,

$$n' \sin \theta' = n \sin \theta$$

$$\theta'' = \theta$$

where θ is the angle of incidence
θ' is the angle of refraction
θ'' is the angle of reflection

n is the refractive index of the first medium

n' is the refractive index of the second medium

5.4.1 *Conventions*

In order to make most useful the results of geometrical optics, certain sign conventions are adopted. The conventions are not always the same, so those which are used in this text are listed below:

1. Slope angles are positive when the ray must be rotated clockwise through an acute angle to be coincident with the axis.
2. Angles of incidence and refraction are positive when the ray must be rotated clockwise through an acute angle to make it coincident with the surface.
3. Light travels from left to right (in all figures).
4. All object distances are positive when measured to the left of a lens, negative to the right.
5. All image distances are positive to the right, negative to the left.
6. Both focal lengths are positive for a converging lens, negative for a diverging lens.
7. Transverse directions are positive upward, negative downward.
8. All convex-to-the-left surfaces have a positive radius of curvature, concave-to-the-left, negative.

5.4.2 *Ray Tracing*

Figure 5-7 presents the geometry associated with a ray incident on a spherical surface. It may be assumed that the point where the ray crosses the optical axis is a point on an object. The distance from that point to the surface is the object distance o. The point at which the ray crosses the optical axis in image space determines the position of the image—at a distance i from the surface. The problem of ray tracing is to find i, and quantities derivable from it, in terms of known quantities: the angle of incidence θ, the inclination angle ϕ, the object distance o, the radius of curvature of the surface, and the refractive indices of the two media.

From the figure

$$\frac{\sin \phi'}{r} = \frac{\sin \theta'}{i - r} \qquad (5\text{-}28)$$

$$i = r + r(\sin \theta'/\sin \varphi') \qquad (5\text{-}29)$$

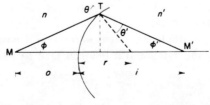

Fig. 5-7. Geometry for obtaining ray-tracing equations.

The problem now is to find $\sin \theta'$ and $\sin \phi'$. Snell's Law applies to ϕ' and ϕ:

$$\sin \phi' = (n/n') \sin \phi \qquad (5\text{-}30)$$

The remaining unknown, $\sin \theta'$, is found by considering triangle MTM'. The angles have the following relationships (θ' is negative because of the sign convention):

$$-\theta' + \theta + \phi' + \pi - \phi = \pi$$
$$\theta' = \phi' + \theta - \phi \qquad (5\text{-}31)$$

This relationship can now be used with Eq. (5-29) to obtain an expression explicitly in terms of r, θ, and ϕ, by trigonometric expansion, but the expression is very unwieldly. Usually one solves for θ' and ϕ' in terms of θ, ϕ, n, and n', and then substitutes values into Eq. (5-29), thereby obtaining i.

The complete ray-tracing operation, the equations for which have just been derived, is straightforward but extremely tedious. A large number of representative rays must be chosen and their paths traced.

There are two ways to avoid these computational tedia. One is to extend the mathematical treatment presented here to methods of matrix algebra and iteration techniques so that much of the work can be done on a computer. The other is to approximate the trigonometric functions with one or more terms of their series expansions. The first of these alternatives is too great a task for present purposes—the techniques used being quite specialized and sophisticated. The second, or approximation technique, is the one more useful for an infrared engineer, who may "scheme" an optical system but leave the design to someone else.

The initial steps of an "optical schemer" are usually estimates based on the first-order theory which will be discussed immediately. Two very good references on the subject are the books by Conrady[6] and by Herzberger.[7]

5.4.3 *First-Order Theory*

The second alternative indicated above consists of writing the series expression for all sine functions: For small angles, $\sin x$ is approximately equal to x; when this approximation is made, the so-called first-order theory obtains.

The equation for a single spherical surface will now be derived on the basis of first-order theory. Snell's law can then be written

$$n\varphi = n'\varphi' \qquad (5\text{-}32)$$

Refer to Figure 5-8

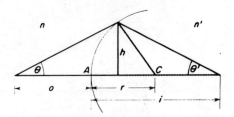

Fig. 5-8. Geometry for deriving spherical-surface formulas.

$$\varphi = \theta + \beta$$
$$\beta = \phi' + \theta'$$
$$n'\beta = n'\theta' = n\theta + n\beta$$
$$n\theta + n'\theta' = (n' - n)\beta \tag{5-33}$$

For small angles,

$$\theta = h/o, \quad \beta = h/r, \quad \theta' = h/i$$

Thus

$$n/o + n'/i = (n' - n)/r \tag{5-34}$$

This expression can also be derived from the ray-tracing equations above; the proper substitutions are left for an exercise.

It is instructive to see the derivation based on the wave theory of light. First, the sagittal formula is needed. See Figure 5-9.

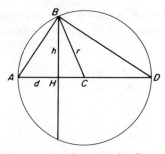

Fig. 5-9. Geometry for deriving the Sagittal formula.

$$AH/BH = BH/DH$$

If $AH = d$, $BH = h$, $DH = r + r - d = 2r - d$, then $d/h = h/(2r - d)$

Thus

$$d = h^2/2r \quad \text{for small } d \tag{5-35}$$

Now consider Figure 5-10. By Malus' theorem, which states that there

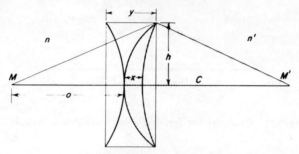

Fig. 5-10. Geometry for deriving spherical-surface formulas.

are equal optical paths between wavefronts (see Reference 1), one has

$$ny' = ny = n'x.$$

For paraxial rays y can actually be the geometrical separation; the equality is exact. If in the above equation a series of small segments which really are sagittas of circles are substituted for y and x, then

$$n\frac{h^2}{2o} + n\frac{h^2}{2r} = n'\frac{h^2}{2r} - n'\frac{h^2}{2i}$$

This simplifies to

$$\frac{n}{o} + \frac{n}{r} = \frac{n'}{r} - \frac{n'}{i} \quad \text{or} \quad \frac{n}{o} + \frac{n'}{i} = \frac{n'-n}{r} \qquad (5\text{-}36)$$

The lens-maker's equation is also a very important and useful relationship in geometrical optics. If the above equations are used for two surfaces,

$$\frac{n}{o_1} + \frac{n'}{i_1} = \frac{n'-n}{r_1}$$

$$\frac{n'}{o_2} + \frac{n''}{i_2} = \frac{n''-n}{r_2}$$

$$\frac{n'}{i_1} = \frac{n'}{o_2} \qquad \text{assuming very thin lens}$$

$$n = n'' \qquad \text{assuming the same initial and final medium, e.g., air}$$

Then

$$\frac{n}{o} + \frac{n}{i} = (n'-n)\left(\frac{1}{r_1} - \frac{1}{r_2}\right) \qquad (5\text{-}37)$$

5.4.4 *Thin-Lens Theory*

So far, the wave theory of light has been approximated by the geometrical theory by using wave normals (rays) and straight-line projections in place of waves. Ray-tracing formulas were derived on the basis of these geometrical considerations, and sines and tangents were replaced by the first terms of their series expansions to get first-order theory. The next useful approximation is to assume that lenses are thin. Derivation of the thin-lens formula is carried out with reference to Figure 5-11; one obtains

$$\frac{y + (-y')}{i} = \frac{y}{f'}$$

$$\frac{y + (-y')}{o} = \frac{-y'}{f}$$

$$\frac{y - y'}{o} + \frac{y - y'}{i} = \frac{y}{f'} - \frac{y'}{f}$$

$$\frac{1}{o} + \frac{1}{i} = \frac{1}{f} \tag{5-38}$$

Note that this equation utilizes the fact that $f = f'$, or that the material is the same on both sides of the lens. One can obtain similar equations in a different way. Consider x and x' and the triangles ABF and $A'B'F'$, which are similar, respectively to FDE and $F'DC$.

$$x = o - f \qquad\qquad x' = i - f'$$

$$\frac{x}{y} = \frac{f}{-y'} \qquad\qquad \frac{x'}{-y'} = \frac{f'}{y} \tag{5-39}$$

$$xx' = ff' \tag{5-40}$$

But from Figure 5-11,

$$xx' = (o - f)(i - f')$$

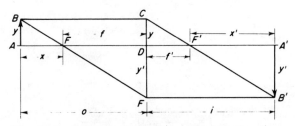

Fig. 5-11. Geometry for deriving thin-lens formulas.

Thus

$$oi - if - of' + ff' = ff'$$

$$\frac{f}{o} + \frac{f'}{i} = 1 \qquad (5\text{-}41)$$

Clearly, if the refractive indices of object and image space are identical, then Eq. (5-41) reduces to Eq. (5-38).

5.4.5 *Thick-Lens Theory*

It is now possible to derive the relationships for thick lenses. The process is to consider imaging by two spherical surfaces in series: the object formed by the first surface is the image for the second. The object formed by the first surface and the image formed by the second are the object and image of the entire thick lens. Then, two surfaces called principal planes can be found such that when distances i, o, and f are measured with these planes as reference, the thin-lens equation applies to thick lenses.

Combine Eqs. (5-34), (5-32), and (5-33)

$$\sin \phi = \frac{r + o}{r} \sin \theta$$

$$\frac{n'}{n} \sin \phi = \frac{r + o}{r} \sin \theta$$

$$\frac{n'}{n} \frac{i - r}{r} \sin \theta' = \frac{r + o}{r} \sin \theta$$

$$\frac{i - r}{o - r} = \frac{n}{n'} \frac{\sin \theta}{\sin \theta'}$$

Applying first-order theory,

$$\frac{i - r}{o + r} = \frac{n}{n'} \qquad \frac{h/o}{h/i} = \frac{n}{n'} \frac{i}{o}$$

$$n'oi - n'or = noi + nir$$

$$\frac{n}{o} + \frac{n'}{i} = \frac{n'}{r} - \frac{n}{r}$$

or, by analogy to Eq. (5-41),

$$\frac{f}{o} + \frac{f'}{i} = 1$$

where

$$f = \frac{nr}{n' - n}, \quad f' = \frac{n'r}{n' - n}$$

Now consider a thick lens in air as the combination of two spherical refracting surfaces. Denote quantities referring to the first surface with a subscript 1, etc.

Thus

$$\frac{f_1}{o_1} + \frac{f_1'}{i_1} = 1$$

But $f_1' = n f_1$, where n is the relative refractive index of the lens. Then

$$\frac{1}{o_1} + \frac{n}{i_1} = \frac{1}{f_1}$$

The image of the first surface is the object for the second, so

$$\frac{n}{d - i_1} + \frac{1}{i_2} = \frac{1}{f_2}$$

where the surfaces are separated by an axial distance d. Therefore

$$i_1 = \frac{n o_1 f_1}{o_1 - f_1}; \qquad i_1 = d - \frac{n f_2 i_2}{i_2 - f_2}$$

Then

$$o_1 i_2 + o_1 f \left(\frac{nd}{f_1} - 1 \right) + i_2 f \left(\frac{nd}{f_2} - 1 \right) = n d f$$

where $(1/f) = (1/f_1) + (1/f_2) - (nd/f_1 f_2)$. To factor, add $(fnd)^2/f_1 f_2$ to both sides of the equation

$$o_1 i_2 + \frac{o_1 fnd}{f_1} + \frac{i_2 ndf}{f_2} + \frac{(fnd)^2}{f_1 f_2} = o_1 f + i_2 f + nd + \frac{(fnd)^2}{f_1 f_2}$$

$$\left(o_1 + \frac{fnd}{f_2} \right) \left(i_2 + \frac{fnd}{f_1} \right) = f \left(o_1 + i_2 + nd + \frac{fn^2 d^2}{f_1 f_2} \right)$$

But

$$nd + \frac{fn^2 d^2}{f_1 f_2} = fnd \left(\frac{1}{f} + \frac{nd}{f_1 f_2} \right) = fnd \left(\frac{1}{f_1} + \frac{1}{f_2} \right)$$

Therefore

$$\left(o_1 + \frac{fnd}{f_2} \right) \left(i_2 + \frac{fnd}{f_2} \right) = f \left(o_1 + i_2 + \frac{fnd}{f_1} + \frac{fnd}{f_2} \right)$$

$$= f \left[\left(o_1 + \frac{fnd}{f_1} \right) + \left(i_2 + \frac{fnd}{f_2} \right) \right]$$

Finally,

$$\frac{1}{f} = \frac{1}{i + (fnd/f_1)} + \frac{1}{o + fnd/f_2}$$

This is the same as the thin-lens equation with a new definition for f, and with the object and image distances reckoned from the principal planes which are located distances of fnd/f_1 and fnd/f_2 from the surfaces of the lens.

It should be clear now that the thin-lens formulas can be used to calculate relationships for thick lenses once the principal planes and focal points have been located. Further, it should not be inferred that these planes are necessarily within the lens. In fact, for some concave-convex lenses of pronounced curvature, both principal planes may be on the same side of the lens. It also can be seen that systems of thin lenses can be treated by thick-lens formulas.

5.4.6 *Spherical Mirrors*

The lens formulas apply to spherical mirrors if the convention is accepted that the refractive index is negative. (This is equivalent to assuming the reverse order of signs for radii.) Further, the focal length will be found to be one-half the radius of curvature. The derivation follows simply; refer to Figure 5-12.

From the law of reflection, $\varphi = \varphi'$; then from the law of sines

$$\frac{\sin \theta}{\sin \varphi} = \frac{MC}{MT} \quad \text{and} \quad \frac{\sin \theta'}{\sin \varphi'} = \frac{M'C}{M'T}$$

But $\varphi = \varphi'$ and $\theta' = \pi - \theta$, and $\sin \theta = \sin \theta'$ so

$$\frac{MC}{MT} = \frac{M'C}{M'T}$$

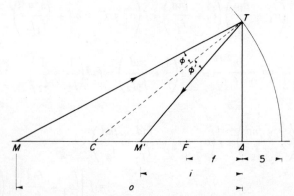

Fig. 5-12. Geometry for deriving spherical-mirror formulas.

For paraxial rays, s is negligible and

$$MC = MA - CA = o - r$$

$$M'C = CA - M'A = r - i$$

$$MT = o$$

$$M'T = i$$

Thus

$$\frac{o - r}{o} = \frac{r - i}{i}$$

$$1 - \frac{r}{o} = \frac{r}{i} - 1$$

$$\frac{1}{i} + \frac{1}{o} = \frac{2}{r}$$

Again, as with lenses, one should insert refractive indices. For mirrors, $-n$ is used for both image and object space.

$$\frac{n}{i} + \frac{n}{o} = -\frac{2}{r} = -\frac{1}{f}$$

5.4.7 *Stops and Pupils*

The stops of an optical system are those irises, diaphragms, and lens and mirror rims which limit the rays passing through the system in one way or another. The aperture stop (see Figure 5-13) is the stop which limits the size of the bundle of rays entering the system; it determines the solid angle over which energy can be integrated and made to fall on a detector. It can be seen in Figure 5-13 that the solid angle of acceptance or the size of the bundle of rays is determined by the aperture stop only. The field stop determines the size of the angle over which such bundles can be accepted by the optical system. The oblique bundle (lines indicated by double arrows) shown in Figure 5-13 cannot be accepted by the optical system; none of the energy in that bundle

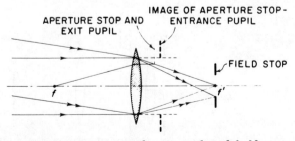

Fig. 5-13. Aperture-stop, entrance-pupil, exit-pupil, and field-stop relationships.

reaches the detector, but the bundle is the same size as the one incident parallel to the optical axis.

Figure 5-13 shows how the aperture stop limits the bundle as it has been altered by all the optical elements preceding the aperture stop. An equivalent method of determining the solid angle of acceptance is to consider the unaltered incident beam and the entrance pupil, which is the image of the aperture stop formed by all the optical elements preceding it. Similarly, the exit pupil is the image of the aperture stop formed by all optical elements following it.

Usually, the method of pupils is used. The image of each iris, lens, and mirror in object space is determined, and the image which limits the size of the entering bundle is designated the entrance pupil. In general, the entrance pupil will be different for different object distances, but good optical design usually requires that the same element should determine the entrance pupil throughout the useful range of the instrument. Figure 5-14 shows the relationship of the aperture to the entrance and exit pupils for a somewhat more complicated system. The diagram shows the stops S_1, S_2, and S_3 and the lenses L_1 and L_2 which, of course, are also stops. The construction of the images S_1', S_3', and L_2' is left to the student. It can be seen from this figure that S_2 is not the aperture stop for all object positions. In fact, it is replaced by S_1 for the object point o_2, and S_1 is the aperture stop for all object distances greater than o_2.

5.4.8 *Field of View*

The field of view is the angle or area from which bundles (whose size is determined by the aperture stop) can be accepted. The field of view is usually specified in terms of a half-angle; that is, the angle between the optical axis and an extreme ray is the half-angle field of view $\alpha/2$. Sometimes, however, the full angle is given. The linear field of view is determined from the angular field of view and the object distance,

$$l = 2 o_2 \tan \alpha/2$$

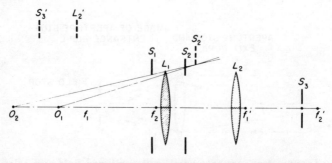

Fig. 5-14. Stops for a more complicated system.

The field angle is determined by the angle the field stop subtends at the entrance pupil, and the field stop is the stop which subtends the smallest angle at the entrance pupil. This is illustrated in Figure 5-15. It can be seen that, for all reasonable arrangements, S_1 is the entrance pupil of the system and L_2' is the image of L_2 formed by L_1. The image S_2' of S_2 formed by L_2 will be very near infinity. In turn S_2'', the image of S_2' formed by L_1, will be near f_1', and total magnification will be near unity. Thus, S_2'' will be about the size and in the position shown in Figure 5-15. Clearly, it is the stop in object space that subtends the

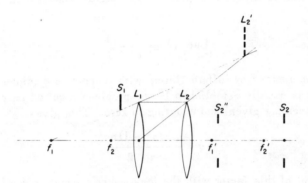

Fig. 5-15. Field-stop geometry.

smallest angle at the entrance pupil. The reader will do well to try other combinations.

5.4.9 *Aberrations*

There are two general types of optical aberrations: chromatic and monochromatic. The latter are also called Seidel aberrations; there are five of these: (1) spherical aberration, (2) coma, (3) astigmatism, (4) curvature of field, and (5) distortion.

Spherical aberration describes the blurring of an image because a ray from an on-axis point which penetrates the lens at height h from the optical axis is bent more than rays close to the axis, so-called paraxial rays. The first-order approximation becomes less good as the height h increases. The next best approximation is to replace sine the function, not by just the first term, but by the first two terms of its series expansion. Such a process yields the so-called third-order theory. The resulting correction to first-order theory thus obtained is

$$\frac{1}{i_m} - \frac{1}{i} = \frac{h^2}{8f^3} \frac{1}{n(n-1)} \left[\frac{n+2}{n-1} q^2 + 4(n+1)pq + (3n+2)(n-1)p^2 \right.$$

$$\left. + \frac{n^3}{n-1} \right] \quad (5\text{-}42)$$

where $p = \dfrac{(i - o)}{(i + 1)}$, and is called the position factor, $q = \dfrac{r_2 + r_1}{r_2 - r_1}$ and is called the shape factor, i_m is the marginal image distance, and i is the meridional image distance.

Spherical aberration can be eliminated by aspherizing—grinding the lens to a prescribed non-spherical curve—but this process is very expensive. The aberration can also be minimized for a single lens by adjustment of the position and shape factors. For a combination of lenses one can correct the aberration of one lens by the aberration of another, or by the use of a corrector plate. The lateral spherical aberration is given as

$$\text{Lat.S.A.} = \frac{1}{i_m} - \frac{1}{i} \tag{5-43}$$

It can be minimized by differentiating with respect to q (since the position factor is usually established by the problem: required image and object distances are given) and equating to zero. This gives

$$q = -\frac{2(n^2 - 1)p}{n - 2} \tag{5-44}$$

Combination of this factor with the lens-maker's equation completes the problem.

It can be shown that the minimum spherical aberration occurs at a shape factor q of about 0.7, which is reasonably close to a convex-plano lens of $q = 1$. It is suggested that the reader try different combinations to determine the range of this minimum.

Coma is the second monochromatic aberration, wherein slightly off-axis objects are focused in cometlike shapes. This aberration is due to the violation of the first-order assumptions because the rays are no longer parallel to the axis. The different zones of the lens no longer magnify equally. The radius of the comatic circle is given by

$$R_c = \frac{yh^2}{f^3} \left[\frac{3(2n + 1)}{4n} p + \frac{3(n + 1)}{4n(n - 1)} q \right] \tag{5-45}$$

By adjustment of the shape factor, one can eliminate coma. It is fortunate that it is zero for a shape factor of about 0.7—about the same q as that required for minimum spherical aberration.

A system which is free of both spherical aberration and coma is said to be aplanatic; it also satisfies the sine condition:

$$ny \sin \theta = n'y' \sin \theta' \tag{5-46}$$

This concept is illustrated in Chapter 7.

A system which does not suffer from astigmatism, the third of the monochromatic aberrations, concerned with the imagery of off-axis points, is said to be anastigmatic. Astigmatism is caused by the fact that wavefront is not incident on the lens symmetrically. Accordingly, there will be two positions where different portions of the object are imaged sharply. These are the sagittal and tangential foci. The position of best focus lies between them, and the spot formed there is called the circle of least confusion. The correction for astigmatism is obtained by a combination of surfaces of different shape.

Curvature of field, the fourth aberration, is not usually serious for infrared systems, since it is not difficult to shape detectors, and since imaging is not always so important.

Distortion is related to the symmetry of optical systems. To avoid having the image of a square appear like a pincushion or a barrel, it is necessary to minimize asymmetry.

There exist two types of chromatic aberration—longitudinal and lateral. The former relates to the change of focal length with color due to the wavelength dependence of the refractive index, and the latter represents the change in distance with color of the focal point for an off-axis image. One might draw an analogy between the combination of these and astigmatism, and visualize an image surface for successive colors that slants toward the axis. Thus, both the focal length and the magnification vary with wavelength. There are a number of ways to correct for chromatic aberration, the most common of which is a multiplet lens of appropriate materials of differing refractive index. A second method utilizes two lenses, both of the same material, separated by an air space.

5.4.10 *Speed of Optical Systems*

It is useful to recall some of the radiometric relationships, and relate them to an optical system. It is known that for extended sources the brightness of an optical system is constant if it is always measured in the same medium. Moreover, the brightness divided by the square of the refractive index is constant no matter what the media. Brightness is equivalent to radiance N, but is limited in the sense that the brightness is normalized to the wavelength-dependent response of the human eye. For infrared usage one can say that N/n^2 is a constant for any optical system. Now, consider Figure 5-16. The total flux (watts) P from the source on the collector is (subscripts s, c, d, represent the source, collector, and detector, respectively; A is area and ω is the solid angle):

$$P = \frac{NA_c A_s}{o^2}$$

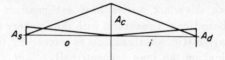

Fig. 5-16. Radiometric relationships.

There must be no loss of flux through the system, and N/n^2 is a constant. Thus

$$P = \frac{NA_c A_s}{o^2} = \frac{N}{n^2} \frac{A_c A_d}{i^2}$$

By consideration of the solid angles involved, one can write

$$P = NAc\omega_s = NA_s \omega_c = (N/n^2)A_d \omega_c = (N/n^2)A_2 \omega_d \qquad (5\text{-}47)$$

This is an interesting relationship, and a useful one. In practice it is also necessary to multiply the last two terms by a transmission factor for the entire optical system.

The radiance and irradiance of the detector can also be written in terms of the numerical aperture and f number ($f/\text{No.}$) of the optical system. Consider Figure 5-17 (on the opposite page); the power relations are written in differential form,

$$dF = NA \cos \alpha \, d\omega$$

$$= NA \cos \alpha \, (2\pi \sin \alpha \, d\alpha)$$

$$F = NA\pi \sin^2 \theta \qquad (5\text{-}48)$$

where θ is the maximum value of α and is determined by the angle the optical collector subtends at the source. If the law of sines, Eq. (5-46), is squared,

$$n^2 A_s \sin^2 \theta = (n')^2 A_d \sin^2 \theta'$$

Thus

$$H = \frac{F}{A_d} = \frac{\pi N' A_d \sin^2 \theta'}{A_d}$$

$$= \pi N' \frac{n^2 A_s}{(n')^2 A_d} \sin^2 \theta$$

$$= \frac{\pi N'(n \sin \theta)^2}{(n')^2 M^2} \qquad (5\text{-}49)$$

where M is the lateral magnification of the optical system. The quantity $n \sin \theta$ is called the numerical aperture (N.A.); it is most useful for

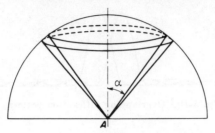

Fig. 5-17. Solid-angle relationships.

microscope systems.   It is less useful for telescopes because it is a function of the distance from the object to the collector.

Recall that $F = NA_d \omega_c$; then ω_c can be given in terms of the focal length and collector size. When infinitely distant objects are considered

$$\omega_c = \frac{A_c}{f} = \frac{\pi d^2}{4 f^2} \tag{5-50}$$

The ratio f/d is called the focal ratio or f number (f/No.). The speed of an optical system is proportional to the square of the reciprocal of the focal ratio—and the proportionality constant is $\pi/4$.

Another way in which the collecting power of an optical system is described is in terms of optical gain, which is defined in either of two ways: it is the ratio of the flux density on a given detector in the optical system to the flux density of the detector,

(1) Considering only geometrical factors,
(2) Considering geometry and reflection and absorption losses.

To compute the energy on the detector if definition (1) is used, one must multiply the optical gain G by what is generally called an instrument transmission factor $\tau(\lambda)$. It should be noted that G is independent of wavelength while transmission factor is not; in fact, it is often a strong function of wavelength.

5.4.11 *Resolution*

The resolution of an optical system is specified in terms of how well it can image two closely spaced point targets as separate points. Recall that, in the limit, the geometrical imaging process is just the formation of many diffraction patterns. Thus the images appear as in Figure 5-18. Two objects will be resolved if the dip of the combined curve is discernible.   Lord Rayleigh observed that this is possible when the maximum of the one pattern falls on the minimum of the next. From the discussion in Section 5.3.6, it can be seen that the one curve must be dis-

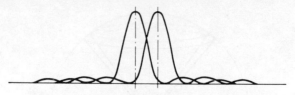

Fig. 5-18. Overlapping diffraction patterns.

placed a distance characterized by $\beta = \pi$. The condition is

$$\beta = \frac{\pi a \, \sin \, \theta}{\lambda} = \pi$$

$$\sin \, \theta = \frac{\lambda}{a}$$

For small-angle approximations, the Rayleigh resolution criterion is

$$\theta = \lambda/a \tag{5-51}$$

where a is the long dimension of a slit. If a circular system is used, it can be shown that the diffraction pattern is described by a Bessel function of the first kind. The first zero of the function is at 3.83, so that

$$\theta = 1.22 \, \lambda/a \tag{5-52}$$

1. F. A. Jenkins and H. E. White, *Fundamentals of Optics.* New York: McGraw-Hill, 1950, Third Edition.
2. J. Strong, *Principles of Classical Optics.* San Francisco: W. H. Freeman, 1958.
3. J. A. Stratton, *Electromagnetic Theory.* New York: McGraw-Hill, 1941.
4. W. K. H. Panofsky and M. Phillips, *Classical Electricity and Magnetism.* Reading, Massachusetts: Addison-Wesley, 1955.
5. M. Born and E. Wolf, *Principles of Optics.* New York: Pergamon, 1959.
6. A. E. Conrady, *Applied Optics and Optical Design.* New York: Dover, 1957.
7. M. Herzberger, *Modern Geometrical Optics.* New York: Interscience, 1958.

CHAPTER 6

OPTICAL MATERIALS FOR USE
IN THE INFRARED

6.1 Introduction

The design of infrared instruments is usually dependent on the appropriate choice of an optical material, for use as a window, lens, prism, or the like. In the visible part of the spectrum, which covers a comparatively small range of wavelengths, relatively little difficulty has been encountered in developing optical materials with desirable properties. Many varieties of glass and transparent crystals are available for the design, for instance, of color-corrected lenses, polarizing prisms, and strong, chemically resistant windows. On the other hand, in the infrared spectrum, which covers an extremely large wavelength interval, the spectrally dependent properties of materials usually vary considerably, and no one substance can be expected to be completely satisfactory over the entire range. Thus, although there are many crystals, glasses, and plastics available, the designers must usually make an engineering decision based on a variety of compromises. A knowledge of the optical, chemical, and mechanical properties is important in optical design, and an understanding of the physical basis of these properties is also valuable.

6.2 Optical Properties

Although it is not possible to establish one hierarchy of properties for all applications, on the basis of the very reasonable assumption that an optical material should have good transmission for any application, the properties of absorption and reflection take positions of dominance. The relationship of transmittance to absorption, reflection, and the other specifications for transmission or attenuation are first discussed. Consider Figure 6-1.

Radiation of intensity I_0 is incident on a plate of absorbing material with plane, parallel sides. The intensity of radiation that is reflected is represented by I_R if there is no multiple internal reflection and by

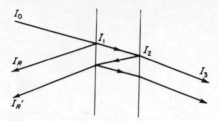

Fig. 6-1. Transmission-absorption-reflection relationships.

$I_{R'}$ if there is. For this simple case, $I_R = \rho I_0$ where ρ is the reflectivity (for intensities). Therefore $I_1 = (1-\rho)I_0$. The ratio of I_2 to I_1, the intensity incident on the second surface divided by the intensity at the first surface (after reflection loss), is called the internal transmittance. The ratio of I_3 to I_2 will be determined by the reflection loss at the second surface, which is here called ρ'. Finally, the external transmittance is the ratio I_3/I_0. Now, I_2 can be related by the Lambert-Bouguer law (see Section 4.4),

$$I_3 = I_2 \exp(-ax) \tag{6-1}$$

where a is the absorption coefficient, a function of λ, and x is the thickness of material. Then

$$I_2/I_1 = \exp(-ax)$$
$$I_3 = (1-\rho)(1-\rho') I_0 \exp(-ax) \tag{6-2}$$

For normal incidence and air as the first and last medium,

$$\rho = [(n-1)/(n+1)]^2. \tag{6-3}$$

Clearly $\rho' = \rho$, and the symmetry and equality are true for non-normal incidence as well. Thus

$$\frac{I_3}{I_0} = (1-\rho)^2 \exp(-ax) \tag{6-4}$$

$$\frac{I_3}{I_0} = (1-\rho)^2 \frac{I_2}{I_1} \tag{6-5}$$

The internal and external transmittance are related by the factor $(1-\rho)^2$. At normal incidence, a case of practical importance

$$\frac{I_3}{I_0} = \frac{4n}{n^2 + 2n + 1} \left(\frac{I_2}{I_1}\right) \tag{6-6}$$

Thus the amount of radiant power that gets through a material is a function of the absorption through the factor $\exp(-ax)$, and a function of the reflection through the factor $(1 - \rho)^2$. These characteristics are discussed below in turn.

6.2.1 Nomenclature

In order that nomenclature may be completely understood, and so that radar and microwave results may be compared to those of the infrared and optical regions, the electromagnetic field equations are used. Maxwell's equations can be written (cf. Chapter 5)

$$\nabla \times E = - \mu \frac{\partial H}{\partial t}$$

$$\nabla \times H = \varepsilon \frac{\partial E}{\partial t} + \sigma E$$

$$\nabla \cdot B = 0, \nabla \cdot D = 0.$$

The wave equation, which is derived from them as before, is

$$\nabla^2 E - \mu\varepsilon \frac{\partial^2 E}{\partial t^2} - \mu\sigma \frac{\partial E}{\partial t} = 0 \tag{6-7}$$

Now a sinusoidal variation of the field quantities is assumed. This is specified either as $\exp(-i\omega t)$ as $\exp(j\omega t)$. Many physicists—and therefore many infrared workers—choose the first expression, and most engineers—and therefore many microwave and radar designers—choose the second. These choices affect the sign of the first but not the second derivative with respect to time. If $e^{j\omega t}$ is chosen, then:

$$\nabla^2 E - j\omega\mu\sigma E + \omega^2\mu\varepsilon E = 0$$

$$\nabla^2 E - (j\omega\mu\sigma - \omega^2\mu\varepsilon)E = 0$$

$$\nabla^2 E + \omega^2\mu\varepsilon[1 + (\sigma/j\omega\varepsilon)]E = 0$$

The solution is of the form

$$E = E_0 \exp\left(j\{\omega t \pm \sqrt{\omega^2\mu\varepsilon[1 + (\sigma/j\omega\varepsilon)]}\,z\}\right) \tag{6-8}$$

This expression may be written, after Ramo and Whinnery[1], as

$$E = E_0 \exp(j\omega t \pm \gamma z) \tag{6-9}$$

or after Stratton[2] as

$$E = E_0 \exp(-i\omega t \pm i\gamma z) \tag{6-10}$$

There is now a choice in defining the complex propagation constant. We choose initially, as do Ramo and Whinnery,

$$\gamma = \sqrt{j\omega\mu(\sigma + j\omega\varepsilon)} \tag{6-11}$$

$$\gamma^2 = -\mu\varepsilon\omega^2 + j\mu\sigma\omega \tag{6-12}$$

$$\gamma^2 = \sqrt{(\omega^2\mu\varepsilon/2)\{[1 + (\sigma^2/\omega^2\varepsilon^2)]^{1/2} - 1\}} \tag{6-13}$$

Thus,

$$\alpha = \sqrt{(\omega^2\mu\varepsilon/2)\{[1 + (\sigma^2/\omega^2\varepsilon^2)]^{1/2} - 1\}} \tag{6-14}$$

$$\beta = \sqrt{(\omega^2\mu\varepsilon/2)\{[1 + (\sigma^2/\omega^2\varepsilon^2)]^{1/2} + 1\}} \tag{6-15}$$

It is also possible to choose, as does Stratton,[2]

$$\gamma = \sqrt{\mu\varepsilon\omega^2 + i\mu\sigma\omega} \tag{6-16}$$

$$\gamma^2 = \mu\varepsilon\omega^2 + i\mu\sigma\omega \tag{6-17}$$

$$\gamma^2 = (\alpha + i\beta)^2 \tag{6-18}$$

Note the difference of sign between Eqs. (6-12) and (6-14). Algebraic manipulation will show that α and β have exchanged their relationship to the physical constants of the problem, i.e, α is given by the right-hand side of Eq. (6-15) and β by that of Eq. (6-14). Then, in this second case β is the amplitude attenuation coefficient and α is the phase constant.

In the optical and infrared case, the solution to the wave equation is usually written in terms of the refractive index.[3,4] A traveling wave may be represented by

$$E = E_0 \exp\{i\omega[t - (z/v)]\}$$

The velocity v is associated with n by the definition of refractive index: the ratio of the speed of light *in vacuo* to speed of light in any medium. Thus, the velocity v in the medium is related to the speed of light *in vacuo c* by

$$v = c/n$$

Then

$$E = E_0 e^{i\omega[t-(n/c)z]} \tag{6-19}$$

It is shown in Chapter 5, and it can be verified here by substitution of Eq. (6-19) in to Eq. (6-7), that

$$(c/n) = v = (\mu\varepsilon)^{-1/2} \tag{6-20}$$

The complex refractive index $\tilde{n}$ can be written $n-ik$ by analogy to the propagation constant $\gamma = \alpha + j\beta$. Then $(n-ik)^2 = (\mu\varepsilon - i\sigma\mu/\omega\varepsilon_0) c^2$. Equating real and imaginary parts, one can obtain

$$n^2 - k^2 = \mu\varepsilon \tag{6-21}$$

$$2nk = \sigma\mu/\omega\varepsilon_0 \tag{6-22}$$

These are the real and imaginary parts of the dielectric constant. Algebraic manipulation then yields

$$n = c\sqrt{\frac{1}{2}\,\mu\varepsilon\,[(1 + \sigma^2/\omega^2\varepsilon^2)^{1/2} + 1]} \qquad (6\text{-}23)$$

$$k = c\sqrt{\frac{1}{2}\,\mu\varepsilon\,[(1 + \sigma^2/\omega^2\varepsilon^2)^{1/2} - 1]} \qquad (6\text{-}24)$$

The amplitude attenuation factor α was found to be

$$\alpha = \sqrt{\frac{1}{2}\,\omega^2\mu\varepsilon\,[(1 + \sigma^2/\omega^2\varepsilon^2) - 1]} \qquad (6\text{-}25)$$

Thus

$$\alpha = (\omega k/c) = (2\pi f k/c)$$

Finally, since the intensity coefficient is twice the amplitude coefficient,

$$\alpha_i = 2\alpha_a = (4\pi f k/c) = (4\pi k/\lambda) \qquad (6\text{-}26)$$

Frequently α is specified as the absorption coefficient or constant[3] (coefficient is more accurate since α is a function of wavelength, temperature, purity, pressure, and several other variables). If no modifiers are used, α usually means *intensity* absorption coefficient for optical problems and *amplitude* absorption coefficient for electric field problems. To avoid confusion and to improve nomenclature, we use α for amplitude coefficient and a for intensity coefficient. The imaginary part of the refractive index is called the extinction coefficient. Three other quantities have also been called extinction coefficient.

If the complex refractive index is defined by

$$\tilde{n} = n - ink_1$$

then

$$k_1 = k/n$$

The term extinction coefficient is also used to describe k_1. This measure is used by the British a good deal, in Ditchburn's excellent work, for instance.[4] Still others have defined the extinction coefficient in terms of standard or common logarithms rather than natural logarithms. Thus,

$$I = I_0\,10^{-Kz}$$

Then $K = 0.4343a$ from the relation that standard logarithms bear to natural logarithms. In chemical work still another definition incorporating the concentration is used!

Radar and microwave engineers have made use of a quantity known as loss tangent, which is quite analogous to the power factor used to evaluate power loss in circuits. The total current associated with a magnetic field is the sum of the displacement current and the conduction current:

$$J_{total} = \frac{\partial D}{\partial t} + \sigma E \tag{6-27}$$

$$= (j\varepsilon\omega + \sigma)E \tag{6-28}$$

Then the loss tangent is defined as the ratio of the conduction current to the displacement current:

$$\tan \delta = \frac{\sigma}{\varepsilon\omega} \tag{6-29}$$

From Eq. (6-25):

$$a = 2\alpha = 2\sqrt{(\omega^2\mu\varepsilon/2)[(1 + \tan^2 \delta)^{1/2} - 1]} \tag{6-30}$$

$$a = (4\pi fn/c)\sqrt{\frac{1}{2}[(1 + \tan^2 \delta)^{1/2} - 1]} \tag{6-31}$$

If $\tan^2 \delta \ll 1$, then

$$a = (4\pi n/\lambda)\sqrt{\frac{1}{2}(1 + \frac{1}{2}\tan^2 \delta) - \frac{1}{2}}$$

$$a = \frac{2\pi n}{\lambda}\tan \delta \tag{6-32}$$

The intensity absorption coefficient is related directly to the loss tangent by a fairly simple expression if the conductivity is small compared to the product of the dielectric constant and the circular frequency. This is an assumption which is good for most infrared optical materials.

6.2.2 *Physics of Absorption and Transmission*

Consider now the processes in a solid which lead to the absorption of incident photons. In Chapter 1 the basic concepts of the Bohr-Sommerfeld and quantum-mechanical models of individual atoms are reviewed. Emission processes are the principal topic, but the Kirchhoff principle also relates emission to absorption. The quantum-mechanical emission transition probability is also directly related to the absorption transition probability. One can conclude, therefore, that electronic transitions from the inner electron shells of atoms will be accompanied by the absorption or emission of very energetic (short-wavelength) quanta

$$hc/\lambda = E_2 - E_1 \tag{6-33}$$

For absorption to occur, an incident quantum must have an energy equal to the energy difference corresponding to permissible transitions. In the very energetic short-wavelength case, the orbital quantum numbers are of prime importance. Thus, there will be in the transmission spectrum a series of sharp dips corresponding to the K-, L-, M-, and N-shell transitions.

Usually, well defined spectra, as described above are found only for gases; liquids and solids exhibit a more complex spectrum because the atoms (or molecules) are packed much closer together. Accordingly, the fields of some atoms influence the electrons of others. What were very sharply defined energy levels for gases become energy bands for solids (see Chapter 9). The most energetic levels, those with low quantum numbers characteristized by the inner electron orbits, will be full of electrons and quite narrow. Further from the nucleus, the bands will be broader but still full of electrons. In a metal, the outermost group of energy levels, the conduction band, is partially filled with electrons; in semiconductors and insulators, the outermost group of energy levels which contains electrons, the valence band, is full, and the first empty one is called the conduction band. Since metals have a partially full conduction band, in which electrons can accept almost any small amount of energy to take on a new state, photons of almost any wavelength can be absorbed. But when a photon is incident on a semiconductor or in-sulator—and the main difference between them is just the size of the energy gap between the valence and conduction bands—it must have a sufficiently high frequency to impart enough energy to valence-band electrons for them to jump the gap to the conduction band. The governing equations are:

$$E_{\text{photon}} \geqslant E_{\text{gap}}$$

or

$$hf \geqslant E_{\text{gap}}$$

or

$$\frac{hc}{\lambda} \geqslant E_{\text{gap}} \qquad (6\text{-}34)$$

$$\lambda \leqslant hc/E_{\text{gap}}$$

Often the wavelength specified by the equality of Eq. (6-34) is called the cutoff or cuton wavelength λ_c. Clearly, all radiation of wavelengths shorter than λ_c will be absorbed by the material. Evaluation of the constants involved yields the useful relationship:

$$\lambda_c = 1.24/E_{\text{gap}} \qquad (6\text{-}35)$$

At still lower energies there are two other effects to be considered: impurity and lattice effects.

The lattice contributions to the absorption process arise from the mechanical motions of the molecules composing the solid. For simplicity, one can consider the so-called dumbbell model of molecules, according to which the molecules consist of rigid spheres bound together by attractive forces that may be thought of as bars. Then the diatomic molecules, e.g., NaCl, have both rotational and vibrational modes of motion. The emission spectra of such bodies are discussed in Chapter 1. The frequencies involved are given by

$$E = \frac{1}{2} I\omega^2$$

$$\omega = \sqrt{\frac{2E}{Md^2}} = \frac{h\sqrt{J(J+1)}}{2\pi Md^2} \tag{6-36}$$

where M is the reduced mass, d the interatomic distance, E the energy, and J the rotational quantum number. There are a number of discrete rotational frequencies allowed. There are also a number of discrete energies allowed, and the absorption of a photon is associated with the transition from one angular momentum state to another. The frequency associated with the change is

$$f = \frac{2h}{8\pi^2 cI}(J+1) \tag{6-37}$$

This equation represents a series of equally spaced lines about a center line characterized by the moment of inertia of the molecule.

An oscillating or vibrating diatomic molecule can be evaluated the same way. The classical frequency is

$$f = \sqrt{k/M} \tag{6-38}$$

where k is the spring constant, and the energy is

$$E = h\sqrt{k/M}\left(v + \frac{1}{2}\right) \tag{6-39}$$

where $v = 0, 2, \ldots$, and is called the vibrational quantum number.

Only the two simplest cases have been considered here; extensions include the anharmonic oscillator, the nonrigid rotator, the symmetric-top and asymmetric-top molecules, and molecules with more than two atoms (which have considerably more complexity). The state of the molecules must also be considered. In the gaseous state most of the modes of motion considered are possible, but in the liquid and solid state many of these modes are "frozen out."

Impurities in the material cause absorption of radiation in regions of the spectrum different from those where intrinsic absorption takes place, and the impurity absorption is usually smaller. The energy levels of the impurities are in the forbidden energy region. For instance germanium, which has an intrinsic band gap of about 0.75 ev at room temperature, can have gold impurity levels at 0.04, 0.20, 0.60, and 0.70 ev from the bottom of the conduction band. Thus, only photons with wavelengths shorter than 1.8 μ can be absorbed by pure germanium, but impure germanium may be absorbing even at 31 μ. In addition, there are fewer electrons in an impurity level than there are in the valence band, so impurity absorption is usually less intense than is intrinsic absorption. The electrons which are raised to the conduction band from the impurity sites are now free to contribute to the conduction of electricity, absorption of radiation and other phenomena. In addition, there are always a few electrons excited to the conduction band from the valence band because transitions are statistical in nature. The transition probability is proportional to exp $(-E_g/kT)$ where E_g is the gap energy, k is Boltzmann's constant and T is the absolute temperature. Thus, although the transition probability becomes very small when the photon energy is less than the gap energy, it is not zero. Both impurity electrons and valence electrons can contribute at wavelengths longer than cutoff.

The complete absorption spectrum and the associated transmission spectrum of a typical solid material can now be understood on a qualitative basis. Below are described the effects first for very short wavelengths (high frequencies, high energies) and then for progressively longer ones. Very short wavelength radiation (1A to 500A) is usually called "gamma rays" and "hard X-rays"; it is of sufficiently short wavelength to be diffracted by the crystal lattice in the same manner as visible radiation is diffracted by a grating. In addition, it is sufficiently energetic to change permanently the chemical composition of the material by dissociation and to strip electrons from low-lying energy levels. In the soft X-ray and far ultraviolet regions (500A to 2000A) the radiation can cause electronic transitions between the K, L, M, and N shells; these transitions give rise a series of sharp lines. The series have been described in Chapter 1.

Many materials have molecular rotation absorptions starting in the near ultraviolet, although this is usually the region characterized by electronic transitions from the valence band to the conduction band. The termination of these transitions usually occurs before 0.4 μ for insulators, but may occur quite far into the infrared for some semiconductors. After the cuton (or cutoff) wavelength is reached, there usually follows a spectral band of good transmission until the lattice vibration bands set in. Then come vibration-rotation bands, and finally pure rotation bands. Free carriers contribute an absorption which is proportional to the square of the wavelength. This can usually be seen toward the long-wavelength end of the region of good transmission. These effects are shown in Figure 6-2 on an absorption coefficient basis. In the region to the left of A in the figure (shorter wavelengths–higher energies) there is a series of absorption bands related to inner-orbit transitions. The region characterized by A is a region of high absorption related to conduction-band

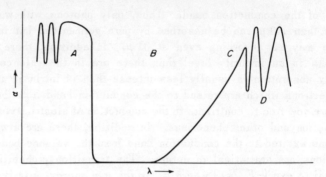

Fig. 6-2. A typical absorption coefficient curve.

electrons which absorb the incident energy. The transition from A to B is usually relatively steep and is determined by the fact that longer wavelength photons are no longer sufficiently energetic to cause band-to-band transitions. B is a region of low absorption. The gradual increase of absorption from B to C is due to the λ^2 dependence of absorption on free carriers, which are there in quantities depending in part on impurity-center concentration and in part on thermal excitation of intrinsic electrons. The region D is characterized by the mechanical motions of the lattice-rotations, vibrations, and combinations of rotations and vibrations.

The external transmittance is related to the absorption coefficient by the expression [see Eqs. (6-1) and (6-6)]:

$$\tau = (1 - \rho)^2 e^{-ax} \qquad (6\text{-}40)$$

Thus, the external transmittance is a sensitive function of the absorption coefficient—as the absorption increases, the transmittance decreases exponentially. It is also a relatively slowly varying function of refractive index. The external transmittance of the sample whose absorption curve is shown in Figure 6-2 is shown in Figure 6-3. The general appearance is a sharp edge at which transmission begins, a region of very high and very uniform transmittance where the only losses are Fresnel

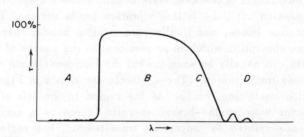

Fig. 6-3. Transmission curve corresponding to Figure 6-2.

reflection losses, then free-electron contributions, and finally lattice-band contributions to the absorption.

6.2.3 Dispersion Theory

The relationship of the absorption coefficient to the refractive index, and these to the physical parameters of the system, is usually termed dispersion theory,

Consider an electron in the orbit of an atom in a crystal; it is attracted to the atom by electrostatic forces. Suppose an incident electromagnetic wave is applied. As a first approximation, the electron undergoes simple harmonic motion, since the restoring force is proportional to the displacement; one can write

$$m\ddot{x} = -kx$$

If damping proportional to velocity is included,

$$m\ddot{x} + mg\dot{x} = -kx$$

$$m\ddot{x} + mg\dot{x} + kx = 0$$

The forcing function is the electrical field of the electromagnetic wave; therefore

$$m\ddot{x} + mg\dot{x} + kx = eEe^{i\omega t}$$

where e is the electronic charge. Assume that x will be of the form $x = x_0 i\omega t$; then

$$-m\omega^2 x_0 + i\omega mg\,x_0 + kx_0 = qE$$

$$x_0 = \frac{gE./m}{(k/m) - \omega^2 + i\omega g}$$

or

$$x = \frac{gE/m}{\omega_n^2 - \omega^2 + i\omega g} \tag{6-41}$$

where the undamped natural frequency is $\omega_n = \sqrt{k/m}$. The polarizability of the material, its inclination to reorient its charges under an applied electric field, is $P = Nex/E$; N is the number of electrons. The dielectric constant is

$$\varepsilon = 1 + \frac{P}{\varepsilon_0}$$

Thus

$$(n - ik)^2 = \varepsilon = 1 + \frac{Ne}{\varepsilon_0} \frac{Ee./m}{\omega_n^2 - \omega^2 + i\omega g}$$

and

$$n^2 - k^2 = \frac{Ne^2}{m\varepsilon_0} \left[\frac{\omega_n^2 - \omega^2}{(\omega_n^2 - \omega^2)^2 + \omega^2 g^2} \right] + 1 \qquad (6\text{-}42)$$

$$2nk = \frac{Ne^2}{m\varepsilon_0} \left[\frac{\omega g}{(\omega_n^2 - \omega^2)^2 + \omega^2 g^2} \right] \qquad (6\text{-}43)$$

If one differentiates the imaginary part of the dielectric constant and sets the result equal to zero, he will find that $2nk$ has a maximum at ωn; the real part $n^2 - k^2$ is found to have a maximum at a frequency somewhat less than ω_n. The absorption maxima do not coincide with the maxima of refractive index. Between any two absorption maxima which are due to the mechanism discussed here, the refractive index behaves as is indicated in Figure 6-4. The behavior throughout the entire electromagnetic spectrum is indicated in Figure 6-5. Several things should be noticed: the curve of Figure 6-4 is repeated between each pair of absorption bands; the curve is higher each time as wavelength increases; the absorption bands are spread further apart as wavelength increases, and the region of almost constant index increases correspondingly.

There are always some free electrons in a material, either from impurity transitions or because of the very small but finite probability of extrinsic transitions at any temperature. The absorption due to these free carriers can be described by dispersion theory. Free carriers have zero restoring force. Then from Equation (6-43)

$$2nk = \frac{Ne^2}{m\varepsilon_0} \left[\frac{\omega g}{\omega^4 + \omega^2 g^2} \right]$$

For a steady field, g is equal to $e/\mu m$ where μ is the electron mobility. Substitution provides a relationship which shows that the absorption coefficient is proportional to the square of the wavelength.

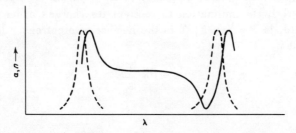

Fig. 6-4. Absorption-refractive index relationships.

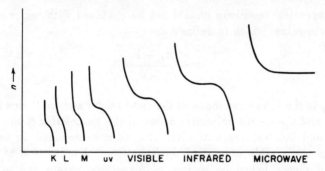

Fig. 6-5. Dispersion throughout the electromagnetic spectrum.

Thus, the dispersion equations tell a great deal about absorption and refraction.

The construction of dispersion equations is also important on an empirical basis for a complete knowledge of refractive index. The dispersion equations relate refractive index to wavelength; if the extinction coefficient is zero, from above, one has

$$n^2 - 1 = \frac{Ne}{m\varepsilon_0} \sum \frac{\omega_0^2 - \omega^2}{(\omega_0^2 - \omega^2) + \omega^2 g^2}$$

where the summation is over the different oscillators. Usually, one has at his disposal values of n for many different values of λ rather than N, ε_0, m, ω_0, and g. Thus, semiempirical equations have usually been developed. Possibly the best known of these is the Cauchy equation:

$$n = A + \frac{B}{\lambda^2} + \frac{C}{\lambda^4}$$

If only the first two terms are used, the equation is sometimes called the Hartmann formula. The Sellmeier equation looks more like the theoretical one derived above:

$$n^2 - 1 = D\lambda^2 / (\lambda^2 - \lambda_0^2)$$

However, these equations can be shown to be equivalent.

There are additional equations, due to Ketteler, Helmholtz, Lorentz, and others, but the above should suffice for most experimental work. If moderate accuracy is needed over a small wavelength interval, the Cauchy formula is generally used; for better fit over a broader range, more and more terms of the series-like expressions are needed. In some cases graphical or computer methods are valuable either for the entire calculation or for final adjustment of the above expressions.

The dispersion equations should not be confused with reciprocal dispersion or ν-value, which is defined as

$$\nu = \frac{n_D - 1}{n_F - n_C}$$

where n_D is the refractive index of the material for sodium D line $(0.59\,\mu)$, while n_F and n_C are the refractive index of the Fraunhofer F and C lines $(0.486\,\mu$ and $0.656\,\mu$, respectively). Nu values are used in designing lenses for the visible portion of the spectrum. A collection of expressions and theory based on reciprocal dispersion exists and is useful. Thus far, however, no such definition has been accepted for the infrared. One might use, for example, these three regions: 1.8–$2.7\,\mu$, 3.0–$5.5\,\mu$ and 8.0–$13.0\,\mu$.

6.2.4 Reflection

Fresnel's laws of reflection can be derived rigorously from electromagnetic theory. They are stated here without proof:

$$\frac{E_s''}{E_s} = -\frac{\sin(\theta - \theta')}{\sin(\theta + \theta')} \qquad (6\text{-}44)$$

$$\frac{E_p''}{E_p} = \frac{\tan(\theta - \theta')}{\tan(\theta + \theta')} \qquad (6\text{-}45)$$

$$\frac{E_s'}{E_s} = \frac{2\sin\theta'\cos\theta}{\sin(\theta + \theta')} \qquad (6\text{-}46)$$

$$\frac{E_p'}{E_p} = \frac{2\sin\theta'\cos\theta}{\sin(\theta + \theta')\cos(\theta - \theta')} \qquad (6\text{-}47)$$

Here E_s represents the perpendicular component of electric field, and E_p the parallel component. Primes (') indicate refracted quantities, and double primes ('') indicate reflected quantities.

From the Fresnel relationships, Eqs. (6-44 and 6-45) immediately above, it can be seen that the ratios $\dfrac{E_s''}{E_s}$ and $\dfrac{E_p''}{E_p}$ are not the same for all angles; there is a polarization effect accompanying reflection. Further, there is an angle called the polarizing angle for which reflected radiation becomes completely polarized: $\dfrac{E_p''}{E_p}$ vanishes for $\theta - \theta' = 0$ and $\theta + \theta' =$

$\pi/2$. But Snell's law and the law of reflection are:

$$n \sin \theta = n' \sin \theta'$$

$$\theta = \theta'$$

For case 1, $n = n'$, which is trivial. For case 2,

$$\frac{\sin \theta}{\sin \theta'} = \frac{\sin \theta}{\sin [(\pi/2 - \theta]} = \tan \theta = n'/n \qquad (6\text{-}48)$$

The polarizing angle is $\tan^{-1}(n'/n)$. If light travels from a medium of high refractive index n to one of low refractive index n', there is an angle of incidence θ such that

$$\sin \theta' = \frac{n}{n'}, \sin \theta = 1 \qquad (6\text{-}49)$$

This value of θ is called θ_c, the critical angle. For all angles of incidence greater than θ_c, light is reflected internally—back into the medium of higher refractive index.

Figure 6-6 illustrates the Fresnel laws of reflection. It shows the reflectivity as a function of angle for different refractive indexes. ρ is defined as $|E''/E|^2$, where either an s or a p subscript may be used, or the light may be considered unpolarized. The lower dashed curve shows $|E''_p|/|E_p|$, the upper dashed curve $|E''_s|/|E_s|$. The curve between them is characteristic of unpolarized light at the angles indicated for $n = 1.5$.

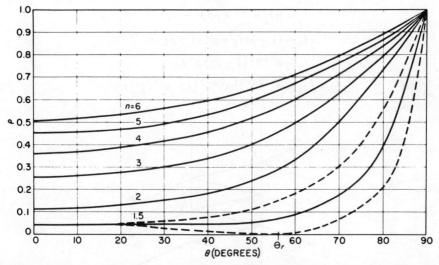

Fig. 6-6. Reflection loss for different incidence angles and different refractive indexes.

The other curves are also for unpolarized light. It can be seen from the equations and the curves that there is a phase change of π (indicated by the minus sign in Eq. (6-44) for E_s vibrations for all angles of incidence. There is a phase change for E_p vibrations only for angles equal to or exceeding the polarizing angle. If radiation is incident normally, the two different polarizations cannot be distinguished, and the expression for reflectivity reduces to the well-known formula:

$$\rho = \left(\frac{n-1}{n+1}\right)^2 \qquad (6\text{-}50)$$

Finally, at grazing incidence angle the reflectivity approaches 100%, and the two orientations are again indistinguishable.

Very often, in the course of optical measurements of dielectrics and semiconductors, one has need for considering reflection losses under the condition of multiple reflection. The following derivations provide such expressions.

Consider the ray shown incident on a plane parallel plate (actually incident perpendicularly, but shown at an angle for clarity). The following expressions (see Figure 6-7) hold:

$$I_1 = (1-\rho)I_0$$
$$I_2 = I_1 e^{-ax} = (1-\rho)I_0 e^{-ax}$$
$$I_3 = (1-\rho)I_2 = (1-\rho)^2 I_0 e^{-ax}$$
$$I_4 = \rho I_2 e^{-ax} = \rho(1-\rho)I_0 e^{-ax}$$
$$I_5 = \rho I_4 e^{-ax} = \rho^2(1-\rho)e^{-3ax}$$
$$I_6 = (1-\rho)I_5 = \rho^2(1-\rho)^2 e^{-3ax}$$
$$I_9 = e^{-5ax}(1-\rho)^2 \rho^4 I_0$$
$$I_{3n} = e^{-(2n-1)}\rho^{2n-2}(1-\rho)^2 I_0$$

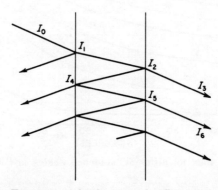

Fig. 6-7. Multiple internal reflections.

If the transmitted intensity is written I_T, then

$$I_T = I_3 + I_6 + I_9 + \ldots = \sum_{n=1}^{N} I_{3n}$$

This is a geometric series with the ratio equal to $\rho^2 e^{-2ax}$. The sum of an infinite number of terms is $S_\infty = I_T/(1-\rho)^2 I_0$

$$I_T = \frac{a}{1-r} = \frac{e^{-ax}}{1-\rho^2 e^{-2ax}} (1-\rho)^2 I_0 \tag{6-51}$$

If $= 0$

$$\tau_\infty = \frac{(1-\rho)^2}{1-\rho^2} = \frac{1-\rho}{1+\rho} \tag{6-52}$$

And for normal incidence

$$\tau_\infty = \frac{1 - [(n-1/n+1)]^2}{1 + [(n-1/n+1)]^2}$$

$$\tau_\infty = \frac{2n}{n^2+1} \tag{6-53}$$

6.2.5 *Emissivity Relations*

Emissivity is a third important optical property of a material. It is defined as the ratio of the radiant emittance of a body to the radiant emittance of a blackbody at the same temperature. McMahon[5] has summarized the relationships among emissivity, transmittance, and reflectivity. He shows that

$$\varepsilon(\lambda, T) + \rho(\lambda, T) + \tau(\lambda, T) = 1$$

the sum of the emissivity, reflectivity (for multiple surfaces), and transmittance is unity. The terms are given below, where the functional dependence of all quantities on temperature and wavelength is suppressed. These are derived much as we obtained the expressions for reflectivity with multiple reflections. The subscript 1 means "for a single surface."

$$\varepsilon = \frac{(1-\rho)(1-\tau)}{1-\rho\tau}$$

$$\rho = \rho_1 + \frac{\rho_1 \tau^2 (1-\rho_1)^2}{1-\rho^2\tau^2}$$

$$\tau = \tau_1 \frac{(1-\rho)^2}{1-\rho^2\tau^2}$$

6.3 Useful Optical Materials

The materials which are most useful in the design and construction of infrared instruments will now be described on the basis of their optical, mechanical, and chemical properties some of which have been discussed above. This is done for three different spectral regions: the lead sulfide region which extends from the visible to 3μ, the near infrared region which extends from 3μ to 6μ and the thermal region from 8μ to 13μ.

6.3.1 *General Characteristics*

There are four general classes of materials which are usually considered for optical instrumentation: glasses, crystals, plastics, and compacts. Each class seems to have its unique advantages and disadvantages, although there are exceptions. The glasses, of course, can be melted, molded, formed, drawn, and worked in many ways. Some glasses which are useful in the shorter-wavelength regions are even hard and reasonably thermal-shock resistant. However, most infrared-transmitting glasses have a severe absorption at the 2.7μ water band, and those which are useful to longer wavelengths are soft. Crystals are usually strong, (although many cleave easily) but they are not easily obtained in desired shapes or sizes, nor can they be drawn. By their very nature, those which are transparent to longer wavelengths are usually soft or subject to attack by moisture. Plastics are very versatile as far as available shapes and sizes are concerned, and they are usually water resistant. However, since they are generally polymers with very complex molecular structure, they also have complex absorption spectra. The dilemma with plastics is this: if they are thick enough to be strong enough, they are too thick to be transparent; if they are thin enough to be transparent, they are not thick enough to be strong enough. Recently there has been some success with pressed or sintered compacts. A powder which has very low absorption is put in a die and heated and pressed. The material is formed in the shape of the mold. The resulting solid can be strong and transparent. The problems which remain are to remove some scattering centers, and to get high enough pressures in large enough sizes and for different shapes.

6.3.2 *Thermal Region*

The far infrared or thermal region, from 8 to $13\,\mu$, is the most critical one as far as satisfactory optical materials are concerned. Windows can be fabricated of rock salt, potassium bromide, and several other "conventional" materials, but these are generally water soluble or even hygroscopic. Silver chloride can withstand moisture and even solarization, if pure enough and properly coated for protection, but its homogeneity leaves something to be desired, and also it is rather soft. The synthetic single crystal commonly called KRS-5 has a melting temperature of 415° C, exhibits cold flow, is sometimes inhomogeneous, is somewhat toxic, is expensive, and is of high specific gravity, so optical elements constructed from it are heavy. Arsenic trisulfide glass, which is often used as a window material, loses transmission significantly in the middle of the 8–13-μ region, and softens at a temperature that is too low for many applications. Crystalline germanium and silicon might be used here except for size restrictions and for the fact that the transmission of germanium drops rapidly with increasing temperature, starting at about 100° C; silicon can be used up to about 300° C, although it is not completely nonabsorbing throughout the 8–13 μ atmospheric transmission "window." Irtran-2—pressed, sintered ZnS—also shows considerable promise.[6]

Some of these materials are useful as corrector plates, lenses, and prisms in optical systems, but are not as satisfactory as they might be because of the limitations that have been indicated. So-called immersion lenses for radiation detectors have been made from germanium and selenium; this is probably the least restricted of the applications in the thermal region, because of the less stringent mechanical and thermal requirements.

6.3.3 The Intermediate Region

In this portion of the spectrum, 3 to 6 μ, the situation is somewhat improved. Of course, the above-listed materials can be used as far as their limitations permit, and in addition, calcium aluminate glass, sapphire, and periclase are available. Calcium aluminate glass still shows absorption in the wide water band centering at 2.8 μ, and this fact should be considered with regard to re-emission problems. Sapphire may soon become available in large enough sizes for many applications, but it is expensive. Flat plates and segmented domes of magnesium oxide, arsenic trisulfide glass, Kel-F, etc., have also been used; but these materials are, at best, usually a compromise because of their mechanical limitations, and Kel-F has the usual absorption bands characteristic of a plastic.

Optical elements for this region can be constructed from germanium, silicon, rutile, sapphire, and the glasses mentioned, plus arsenic-modified selenium glass. Care must be taken to avoid or correct for the problems inherent with a high refractive index, and also to use the high index to advantage in, e.g. lens design. Silicon and germanium not only have very high indexes, but they also have low dispersion; thus they are promising as lens and prism materials that possess high power and little chromatic aberration. The reflection-reducing coating problems, however, must not be overlooked. Selenium, germanium, and strontium titanate have been used for immersion lenses. Other materials are available for this use; they should be chosen to best "match" the physical properties of the particular detector.   One notable new material is Irtran-1, pressed sintered MgF_2.[6]

6.3.4 *The Lead Sulfide Region*

This region, which can be considered as extending from the visible to $3\,\mu$, is by far the most satisfactory one from the optical materials point of view. Most of the materials mentioned above are available for consideration; fused silica and some optical glasses can also be used. Fused silica, because of its excellent thermal, chemical, mechanical, and optical properties, is the usual choice. Thus, satisfactory refractory-type windows or domes can be obtained for this wavelength region, lens systems can replace reflecting or catadioptric systems, and virtually any desired spectral band can be isolated by an interference filter.

6.4 Conclusion

This chapter is concluded by reference to a publication (and its addendum) of The University of Michigan which summarizes the information on optical materials for infrared instrumentation as of the end of 1960. The following figures and tables (Figures 6-8 to 6-11 and Tables 6-1 to 6-8) are taken from that publication.

1. S. Ramo and J. R. Whinnery, *Fields and Waves in Modern Radio.* New York: Wiley, 1953, Second Edition.
2. J. A. Stratton, *Electromagnetic Theory.* New York: McGraw-Hill, 1941.
3. F. A. Jenkins and H. E. White, Fundamentals of Optics. New York: McGraw-Hill, 1957, Third Edition.
4. R. W. Ditchburn, *Light.* New York: Interscience, 1955.
5. H. O. McMahon, "Thermal Radiation from Partially Transparent Reflecting Bodies," J. Opt. Soc. Am., **40,** 376–380 (1950).
6. W. F. Parsons and S. E. Hatch, "Properties of Hot Pressed Materials," *J. Opt. Soc. Am.,* **50,** 1130(A) (1960).

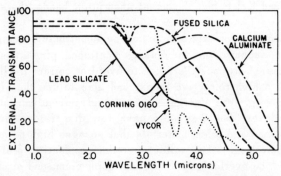

Fig. 6-8. The transmission of several infrared-transmitting glasses: thickness, 2 mm.

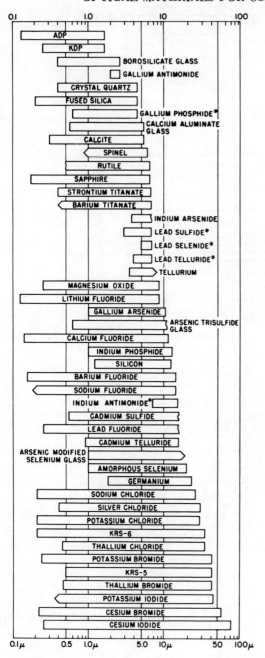

Fig. 6-9. Transmission regions. The limiting wavelengths, for both long and short cutoff, have been chosen as those wavelengths at which a sample 2mm thick has 10 per cent transmission. Materials marked with an asterisk (*) have a maximum external transmittance of less than 10 per cent.

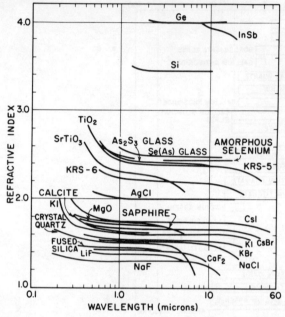

Fig. 6-10. Refractive index versus wavelength for several optical materials.

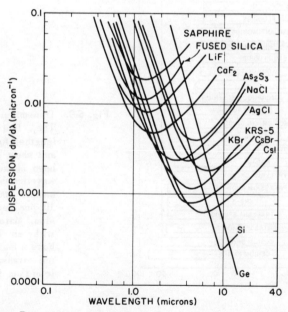

Fig. 6-11. Dispersion versus wavelength for several optical materials.

Table 6-1

Dielectric Constant

Material	Dielectric Constant	Frequency (cps)	Temperature (°C)	Remarks
Fused silica (SiO_2)	3.78	10^2 to 10^{10}	25	
Silica glass	3.81	10^8	20	HCP,[d] p. 2346
Crystal quartz (SiO_2)	4.27^a	10^7	17 to 22	
	4.34^b	10^7	17 to 22	
Potassium chloride (KCl)	4.64	10^6	29.5	
Potassium bromide (KBr)	4.90	10^2 to 10^{10}	25	
Potassium iodide (KI)	4.94	10^6	—[c]	
Cesium iodide (CsI)	5.65	10^6	25	
Sodium chloride (NaCl)	5.90	10^2 to 10^{10}	25	
Amorphous selenium (Se)	6.00	10^2 to 10^{10}	25	
Sodium fluoride (NaF)	6.0	10^6	19	
Selenium crystal (Se)	6.0	10^2 to 10^{10}	—[c]	
Cesium bromide (CsBr)	6.51	10^6	25	
Calcium fluoride (CaF_2)	6.76	10^5	—[c]	
Sodium nitrate ($NaNO_3$)	6.85	10^5	19	
Mica, glass bonded, injection	6.9 to 9.2	10^6	Room	HCP,[d] p. 2344
Barium fluoride (BaF_2)	7.33^b	10^6	—[c]	
Calcite ($CaCO_3$)	8.5^b	10^4	17 to 22	
	8.0^a	10^4	17 to 22	
Sapphire (Al_2O_3)	10.55^a	10^2 to 10^8	25	
	8.6^b	10^2 to 10^{10}	25	
Arsenic trisulfide glass (As_2S_3)	8.1	10^3 to 10^6	—[c]	
Spinel (MgO · 3.5 Al_2O_3)	8 to 9	—[c]	—[c]	
Lithium fluoride (LiF)	9.00	10^2 to 10^{10}	25	
Magnesium oxide (MgO)	9.65	10^2 to 10^8	25	
Cadmium telluride (CdTe)	11.0	10^3 to 10^5	—[c]	5.5×10^{13} carriers/cc
Silicon (Si)	13	10^{10}	—[c]	

(Table continued on page 144)

Table 6-1 (Continued)

Material	Dielectric Constant	Frequency (cps)	Temperature (°C)	Remarks
Silver chloride (AgCl)	12.3	—c	Room	9.0 ohm-cm resistivity
Germanium (Ge)	16.6	10^{10}	—c	
Lead sulfide (PbS)	17.9	10^6	15	
Thallium bromide (TlBr)	30.3	10^3 to 10^7	25	
Thallium bromide-iodide (KRS-5)	32.5	10^2 to 10^7	25	
Thallium chloride (TlCl)	31.9	10^6	—c	
Thallium bromide-chloride (KRS-6)	32	10^2 to 10^5	25	
Potassium dihydrogen phosphate (KDP)	44.5 to 44.3^b	10^2 to 10^8	—c	
	21.4 to 20.2^a	10^2 to 10^8	—c	
Ammonium dihydrogen phosphate (ADP)	56.4 to 55.9^b	10^2 to 10^8	—c	
	16.4 to 13.7^a	10^2 to 10^{10}	—c	
Titanium dioxide (TiO$_2$)	170^a	10^4 to 10^7	25	
	86^b	10^2 to 10^7	25	
Strontium titanate (SrTiO$_3$)	234	10^2 to 10^{10}	25	
Barium titanate (BaTiO$_3$)	1240 to 1200	10^2 to 10^8	25	

[a] Dielectric constant measured parallel to c axis.
[b] Dielectric constant measured perpendicular to c axis.
[c] —Value not indicated.
[d] Handbook of Chemistry and Physics. Cleveland: Chemical Rubber Publishing Company, 1958, 39th Edition.

Table 6-2

Melting or Softening Temperature

Material	Temperature (°C)
Amorphous selenium (Se)	35[a]
Arsenic modified selenium glass Se(As)	70[a]
Arsenic trisulfide glass (As_2S_3)	210[a]
Potassium dihydrogen phosphate (KDP)	252.6
Sodium nitrate ($NaNO_3$)	306.8
Gallium arsenide (GaAs)	400[b]
Thallium bromide-iodide (KRS-5)	414.5
Thallium bromide-chloride (KRS-6)	423.5
Thallium chloride (TlCl)	430
Tellurium (Te)	449.7
Silver chloride (AgCl)	457.7
Thallium bromide (TlBr)	460
Gallium phosphide (GaP)	>500
Indium antimonide (InSb)	523
Cesium iodide (CsI)	621
Cesium bromide (CsBr)	636
Gallium antimonide (GaSb)	720
Potassium iodide (KI)	723
Potassium bromide (KBr)	730
Potassium chloride (KCl)	776
Sodium chloride (NaCl)	801
Borosilicate crown glass	820[a]
Lead fluoride (PbF_2)	855
Lithium fluoride (LiF)	870
Calcite ($CaCO_3$)	894.4[b]
Cadmium sulfide (CdS)	900[c]
Lead telluride (PbTe)	917
Germanium (Ge)	936
Indium arsenide (InAs)	942
Sodium fluoride (NaF)	980
Cadmium telluride (CdTe)	~1040
Indium phosphide (InP)	1050
Lead selenide (PbSe)	1065
Lead sulfide (PbS)	1114
Gallium arsenide (GaAs)	1238
Barium fluoride (BaF_2)	1280
Calcium fluoride (CaF_2)	1360
Silicon (Si)	1420
Crystal quartz (SiO_2)	<1470
Barium titanate ($BaTiO_3$)	1600
Fused silica (SiO_2)	~1710
Titanium dioxide (TiO_2)	1825
Sapphire (Al_2O_3)	2030
Spinel (MgO · 3.5 Al_2O_3)	2030 to 2060
Strontium titanate ($SrTiO_3$)	2080
Magnesium oxide (MgO)	2800

[a] Softening temperature.
[b] Dissociation temperature.
[c] Sublimation temperature.

Table 6-3

Thermal Conductivity

Material	Thermal Conductivity $(10^{-4} \, cal/(cm \, sec \, C°))$	Temperature (° C)	Remarks
Diatomaceous earth	1.3	"Ordinary"	HCP,[c] p. 2255
Arsenic modified selenium glass Se(As)	3.3	[d]	
Arsenic trisulfide glass (As$_2$S$_3$)	4.0	40	
Thallium bromide-iodide (KRS-5)	13	20	
Thallium bromide (TlBr)	14	43	
Lead sulfide (PbS)	16	[d]	
Thallium bromide-chloride (KRS-6)	17.1	56	
Thallium chloride (TlCl)	18	38	
Ammonium dihydrogen phosphate (ADP)	17[a]	42	
	30[b]	40	
Cesium bromide (CsBr)	23	25	
Cesium iodide (CsI)	27	25	
Silver chloride (AgCl)	27.5	22	
Fused silica (SiO$_2$)	28.2	41	
Potassium dihydrogen phosphate (KDP)	29[a]	39	
	32[b]	46	
Barium titanate (BaTiO$_3$)	32	Room	Ceramic material
Calcite (CaCO$_3$)	132[a]	0	
	111[b]	0	
Potassium bromide (KBr)	115	46	
Tellurium (Te)	150	[d]	
Sodium chloride (NaCl)	155	16	
Potassium chloride (KCl)	156	42	
Crystal quartz (SiO$_2$)	255[a]	50	
	148[b]	50	

Material			
Calcium fluoride (CaF$_2$)	232	36	
Lithium fluoride (LiF)	270	41	
Barium fluoride (BaF$_2$)	280	13	
Titanium dioxide (TiO$_2$)	300[a]	36	
	210[b]	44	
Spinel (MgO · 3.5 Al$_2$O$_3$)	330	35	
Cadmium sulfide (CdS)	380	20	
Sapphire (Al$_2$O$_3$)	600[a]	26	
	550[b]	23	
Magnesium oxide (MgO)	600	20	
Indium antimonide (InSb)	850	20	
Germanium (Ge)	1400	20	n-Type, 40 ohm-cm resistivity
Silicon (Si)	3090	40	p-Type
Silver (Ag)	10060	18	HCP,[c] p. 2254

[a] Thermal conductivity measured with heat flow parallel to c axis.
[b] Thermal conductivity measured with heat flow perpendicular to c axis.
[c] Handbook of Chemistry and Physics; see Table 6-1.
[d] Value not indicated.

Table 6-4

Linear Coefficient of Thermal Expansion

Material	Coefficient of Thermal Expansion $10^{-6}/C°$	Average Temperature or Temperature Range ($°C$)	Remarks
Fused silica (SiO_2)	0.5	20 to 900	
Invar	0.9	20	$HCP,^d$ p. 2062
Silicon (Si)	4.2	25	
Cadmium sulfide (CdS)	4.2	27 to 70	
Cadmium telluride (CdTe)	4.5	50	
Indium antimonide (InSb)	4.9	20 to 60	
Indium arsenide (InAs)	5.3	—^{c}	
Germanium (Ge)	5.5 to 6.1	25	
Gallium arsenide (GaAs)	5.7	—^{c}	
Spinel ($MgO \cdot 3.5\,Al_2O_3$)	5.9	40	
Sapphire (Al_2O_3)	6.7^a	50	
	5.0^b	50	
Borosilicate crown glass	9	22 to 498	$HCP,^d$ p. 2065
Titanium dioxide (TiO_2)	9.19^a	40	
	7.14^b	40	
Strontium titanate ($SrTiO_3$)	9.4	—^{c}	
Crystal quartz (SiO_2)	7.97^a	0 to 80	
	13.37^b	0 to 80	
Sodium nitrate ($NaNO_3$)	12^a	50	
	11^b	50	
Magnesium oxide (MgO)	13.8	20 to 1000	
Copper (Cu)	14.09	−191 to 16	$HCP,^d$ p. 2061
Tellurium (Te)	16.75	40	
Barium titanate ($BaTiO_3$)	19	10 to 70	Ceramic
	6.2^a	4 to 20	Single crystal
	15.7^b	4 to 20	Single crystal
Calcium fluoride (CaF_2)	24	20 to 60	
Arsenic trisulfide glass (As_2S_3)	24.6	33 to 165	
Calcite ($CaCO_3$)	25^a	0	
	-5.8^b	0	
Silver chloride (AgCl)	30	20 to 60	
Amorphous selenium (Se)	34	—^{c}	Estimated
Sodium fluoride (NaF)	36	Room	
Potassium chloride (KCl)	36	20 to 60	
Lithium fluoride (LiF)	37	0 to 100	
Potassium iodide (KI)	42.6	40	
Potassium bromide (KBr)	43	20 to 60	
Sodium chloride (NaCl)	44	−50 to 200	
Cesium bromide (CsBr)	47.9	20 to 50	
Thallium bromide-chloride (KRS-6)	50	20 to 100	

(continued)

Table 6-4 (Continued)

Material	Coefficient of Thermal Expansion $10^{-6}/C^{\circ}$	Average Temperature or Temperature Range ($^{\circ}C$)	Remarks
Cesium iodide (CsI)	50	25 to 50	
Thallium bromide (TlBr)	51	20 to 60	
Thallium chloride (TlCl)	53	20 to 60	
Thallium bromide-iodide (KRS-5)	58	20 to 100	

^{a}Thermal expansion measured parallel to c axis.
^{b}Thermal expansion measured perpendicular to c axis.
^{c}Value not indicated.
^{d}Handbook of Chemistry and Physics, see Table 6-1.

Table 6-5

Specific Heat

Material	Specific Heat	Temperature ($^{\circ}C$)
Thallium bromide (TlBr)	0.045	20
Tellurium (Te)	0.0479	300
Cesium iodide (CsI)	0.048	20
Thallium bromide chloride (KRS-6)	0.0482	20
Lead sulfide (PbS)	0.050	—^{a}
Thallium chloride (TlCl)	0.052	0
Cesium bromide (CsBr)	0.063	20
Germanium (Ge)	0.074	0 to 100
Potassium iodide (KI)	0.075	-3
Barium titanate (BaTiO$_3$)	0.077	-98
Silver chloride (AgCl)	0.0848	0
Potassium bromide (KBr)	0.104	0
Potassium chloride (KCl)	0.162	0
Silicon (Si)	0.168	25
Titanium dioxide (TiO$_2$)	0.17	25
Sapphire (Al$_2$O$_3$)	0.18	25
Crystal quartz (SiO$_2$)	0.188	12 to 100
Calcite (CaCO$_3$)	0.203	0
Sodium chloride (NaCl)	0.204	0
Calcium fluoride (CaF$_2$)	0.204	0
Magnesium oxide (MgO)	0.209	0
Fused silica (SiO$_2$)	0.22	—^{a}
Sodium nitrate (NaNO$_3$)	0.247	0
Sodium fluoride (NaF)	0.26	0
Lithium fluoride (LiF)	0.373	10

^{a}—Value not indicated.

Table 6-6

Hardness

Material	Hardness (Knoop Number)	Direction	Indenter Load (gm)	Remarks
Potassium bromide (KBr)	5.9	$\langle 110 \rangle$	200	
	7.0	$\langle 100 \rangle$	200	
Potassium chloride (KCl)	7.2	$\langle 110 \rangle$	200	
	9.3	$\langle 100 \rangle$	200	
Silver chloride (AgCl)	9.5		200	
Thallium bromide (TlBr)	11.9	$\langle 110 \rangle$	500	
	11.9	$\langle 100 \rangle$	500	
Thallium chloride (TlCl)	12.8	$\langle 110 \rangle$	500	
	12.8	$\langle 100 \rangle$	500	
Sodium chloride (NaCl)	15.2	$\langle 110 \rangle$	200	
	18.2	$\langle 100 \rangle$	200	
Sodium nitrate (NaNO$_3$)	19.2	Perpendicular to cleavage planes	200	
Cesium bromide (CsBr)	19.5		200	
Thallium bromide-chloride (KRS-6)	29.9	$\langle 110 \rangle$	500	
	38.5	$\langle 100 \rangle$	500	
Thallium bromide-iodide (KRS-5)	40.2		200	
	39.8	$\langle 100 \rangle$	500	
	33.2	$\langle 110 \rangle$	500	
Barium fluoride (BaF$_2$)	82		500	
Lithium fluoride (LiF)	102–113		600	Vacuum grown
Arsenic trisulfide glass (As$_2$S$_3$)	109		100	
Calcium fluoride (CaF$_2$)	158.3	$\langle 110 \rangle$	500	
	158.3	$\langle 100 \rangle$	500	
Fused silica (SiO$_2$)	461		200	Machined surface

Material				
Strontium titanate (SrTiO$_3$)	595			
Magnesium oxide (MgO)	692	600	Perpendicular to cleavage planes	
Crystal quartz (SiO$_2$)	741	500	Perpendicular to z- and x-cut faces	
Titanium dioxide (TiO$_2$)	879	500	Random	
Spinel (MgO · 3.5 Al$_2$O$_3$)	1140	1000	Random	
Silicon (Si)	1150			7 (Moh Number)
Sapphire (Al$_2$O$_3$)	1370	1000	Random	
Calcite (CaCO$_3$)				3 (Moh Number)
Cadmium telluride (CdTe)				43.4 (Vickers Scale)
Barium titanate (BaTiO$_3$)				200–580 (Vickers Scale)
				Single crystal

Table 6-7

Solubility

Material	Solubility (gm/100 gm water)	Temperature (°C)
Spinel (MgO · 3.5 Al$_2$O$_3$)	Insoluble [a]	
Crystal quartz (SiO$_2$)	Insoluble	
Fused silica (SiO$_2$)	Insoluble	
Titanium dioxide (TiO$_2$)	Insoluble	
Sapphire (Al$_2$O$_3$)	Insoluble	
Silver chloride (AgCl)	Insoluble	
Arsenic trisulfide glass (As$_2$S$_3$)	Insoluble	
Amorphous selenium (Se)	Insoluble	
Arsenic modified selenium glass; Se(As)	Insoluble	
Tellurium (Te)	Insoluble	
Cadmium sulfide (CdS)	Insoluble	
Gallium arsenide (GaAs)	Insoluble	
Germanium (Ge)	Insoluble	
Indium arsenide (InAs)	Insoluble	
Gallium antimonide (GaSb)	Insoluble	
Tellurium (Te)	Insoluble	
Lead selenide (PbSe)	Insoluble	
Silicon (Si)	Insoluble	
Cadmium telluride (CdTe)	Insoluble	
Indium antimonide (InSb)	Insoluble	
Magnesium oxide (MgO)	Insoluble	
Calcite (CaCO$_3$)	0.0014	25
Calcium fluoride (CaF$_2$)	0.0017	26
Thallium bromide (TlBr)	0.05	25
Thallium bromide-iodide (KRS-5)	0.05	Room
Barium fluoride (BaF$_2$)	0.17	10
Lithium fluoride (LiF)	0.27	18
Thallium bromide-chloride (KRS-6)	0.32	20
Thallium chloride (TlCl)	0.32	20
Sodium fluoride (NaF)	4.22	18
Ammonium dihydrogen phosphate (ADP)	22.7	0
Potassium dihydrogen phosphate (KDP)	33	25
Potassium chloride (KCl)	34.7	20
Sodium chloride (NaCl)	35.7	0
Cesium iodide (CsI)	44	0
Potassium bromide (KBr)	53.5	0
Sodium nitrate (NaNO$_3$)	73	0
Cesium bromide (CsBr)	124.3	25
Potassium iodide (KI)	127.5	0

[a]"Insoluble" means less than 10^{-3} gm/100 gm water at room temperature.

Table 6-8

Young's Modulus

Material	Young's Modulus $(10^6 \ psi)$	Remarks
Cesium iodide (CsI)	0.769	Measured in flexure
Thallium bromide-iodide (KRS-5)	2.3	Measured in flexure
Cesium bromide (CsBr)	2.3	Measured in flexure
Arsenic trisulfide glass (As_2S_3)	2.3	
Silver chloride (AgCl)	2.9	Measured in flexure
Thallium bromide-chloride (KRS-6)	3.0	Measured in flexure
Potassium bromide (KBr)	3.9	Measured in flexure
Thallium bromide (TlBr)	4.28	Calculated
Potassium chloride (KCl)	4.30	Measured in flexure
Potassium iodide (KI)	4.57	Calculated
Thallium chloride (TlCl)	4.60	Calculated
Barium titanate ($BaTiO_3$)	4.90	Single crystal
	16.50	Ceramic
Sodium chloride (NaCl)	5.80	Measured in flexure
Indium antimonide (InSb)	6.21	Calculated
Barium fluoride (BaF_2)	7.70	Measured in flexure
Gallium antimonide (GaSb)	9.19	Calculated
Lithium fluoride (LiF)	9.40	Measured in flexure Minimum value
Calcite ($CaCO_3$)	10.50^a 12.80^b	
Fused silica (SiO_2)	10.60	
Calcium fluoride (CaF_2)	11.0	Measured in flexure Minimum value
Crystal quartz (SiO_2)	11.1^b 14.1^a	
Germanium (Ge)	14.9	Calculated
Silicon (Si)	19.0	Calculated
Magnesium oxide (MgO)	36.1	Calculated
Sapphire (Al_2O_3)	50.0	

[a] Young's modulus measured parallel to c axis.
[b] Young's modulus measured perpendicular to c axis.

CHAPTER 7

OPTICAL COMPONENTS AND OPTICAL SYSTEMS

7.1 Introduction

Since infrared instrumentation—both for military and civilian applications—depends upon the proper collection and focusing of infrared radiation and the imaging of objects emitting that radiation, it is important to consider the optical components and systems that can be used in a variety of these applications: prisms, diffraction gratings, interferometers, mirrors, parallel plates, scanning systems, immersion lenses, cone condensers, and fiber optics. First, consider those elements used to separate light into its spectral components.

7.2 Prisms

Prisms may be used for dispersing light or for deviating it. Consider Figure 7-1.

$$n_1 \sin \theta_1 = n'_2 \sin \theta'_1 \qquad (7\text{-}1)$$

by Snell's law,

$$n_1 \cos \theta_1 \, d\theta_1 = n'_2 \cos \theta'_1 \, d\theta'_1 \qquad (7\text{-}2)$$

by differentiation,

$$n_3 \cos \theta_2 \, d\theta_2 = n'_2 \cos \theta'_2 \, d\theta'_2 \qquad (7\text{-}3)$$

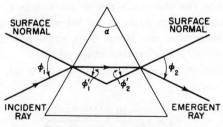

Fig. 7-1. Prism geometry.

155

by application to the second surface. If air is both the first and last medium, then:

$$\frac{\cos\theta_1}{\cos\theta_2}\frac{\cos\theta'_2}{\cos\theta'_1} = \frac{d\theta_2}{d\theta_1}\frac{d\theta'_1}{d\theta'_2} \tag{7-4}$$

But

$$\theta'_1 + \theta'_2 = \alpha; \qquad \text{so} \qquad d\theta'_1 = -d\theta'_2$$

and

$$\frac{d\theta_2}{d\theta_1} = -\frac{\cos\theta_1}{\cos\theta_2}\frac{\cos\theta'_2}{\cos\theta'_1} \tag{7-5}$$

Equation 7-5 gives the angular magnification of a prism.

The deviation of a prism can be represented by the angle between an incident and an emergent ray. If the prism is used to disperse light, the deviation will be different for each wavelength. Clearly, the total angular deviation for any wavelength is the sum of the deviations at each surface:

$$\delta = \theta_1 - \theta'_1 + \theta_2 - \theta'_2$$
$$= \theta_1 + \theta_2 - (\theta'_1 + \theta'_2)$$
$$= \theta_1 + \theta_2 - \alpha \tag{7-6}$$

The conditions for minimum deviation for any wavelength are determined by setting the derivative of the deviation angle equal to zero:

$$d\delta = d\theta_1 + d\theta_2 + 0$$
$$(d\delta/d\theta_1) = 1 + (d\theta_2/d\theta_1) \tag{7-7}$$

For this to be consistent with the expression for angular magnification derived above, one must have,

$$\frac{\cos\theta_1}{\cos\theta_2}\frac{\cos\theta'_2}{\cos\theta'_1} = 1 \tag{7-8}$$

This is true if all angles are zero (a trivial case), or if $\theta_1 = \theta_2$ and $\theta'_1 = \theta'_2$. Thus, the ray traverses the prism symmetrically in the case of minimum deviation. The expression for minimum deviation is also easily obtained, assuming the prism with refractive index n_2 is immersed in a material with a refractive index of n_1.

At minimum deviation, $\theta'_2 = \alpha/2$, $\sin\theta'_2 = \sin(\alpha/2)$, $\delta = 2\theta_2 - \alpha$, and $\theta_2 = (\delta + \alpha)/2$. Thus,

$$n_2 = n_1 \frac{\sin\frac{1}{2}(\delta_{min} + \alpha)}{\sin\alpha/2} \tag{7-9}$$

The minimum deviation condition is important as the basis of one of the most accurate methods of measuring the refractive index of a prism; the prism angle is measured, the minimum deviation condition is determined, δ is measured, and n is calculated.

If a prism is to be used in a spectrometric application, it is necessary to determine its resolution and resolving power—specifications of how well two very close spectral lines can be measured. The two spectral lines will each have a different deviation, as mentioned above, so that the problem of determining the resolution is to determine the dispersion, the change in deviation angle for a small change in wavelength. Thus, one differentiates the angle of deviation with respect to the refractive index of the prism; then by differentiating the refractive index with respect to wavelength the following equations are obtained:

$$\frac{dn_2}{d\delta} = \frac{\cos\left[(\delta + \alpha)/2\right]}{2 \sin \alpha/2}$$

$$\frac{d\delta}{dn_2} = \frac{2 \sin \alpha/2}{\cos\left[(\delta + \alpha)/2\right]}$$

$$\sin^2 \frac{\delta + \alpha}{2} + \cos^2 \frac{\delta + \alpha}{2} = 1$$

$$\cos \frac{\delta + \alpha}{2} = \sqrt{1 - \sin^2 \frac{\delta + \alpha}{2}}$$

$$\frac{d\delta}{dn_2} = \frac{2 \sin \alpha/2}{\sqrt{1 - (n_2/n_1)^2 \sin^2 \alpha/2}}$$

Thus,

$$\frac{d\delta}{d\lambda} = \frac{dn_2}{d\lambda} \frac{2 \sin \alpha/2}{\sqrt{1 - (n_2/n_1)^2 \sin^2 \alpha/2}} \qquad (7\text{-}10)$$

An average value of n_2 is taken. The determination of $dn_2/d\lambda$ is discussed in Chapter 6.

Resolving power is defined as $\lambda/d\lambda$. Such a measure normalizes wavelength effects. The condition for interference is $d\theta = \lambda/a$, where $a =$ beamwidth. Then,

$$\frac{\lambda}{d\lambda} = \frac{\lambda}{d\theta} \frac{d\theta}{d\lambda} = a \frac{d\theta}{d\lambda} = a \frac{d\theta}{dn} \frac{dn}{d\lambda}$$

From above,

$$\frac{d\theta}{dn} = \frac{2 \sin \alpha/2}{\sqrt{1 - (n_2/n_1)^2 \sin^2 \alpha/2}} = \frac{2 \sin \alpha/2}{\cos i}$$

Therefore

$$\frac{\lambda}{d\lambda} = \frac{2a\sin\alpha/2}{\cos i}\frac{dn}{d\lambda}$$

where $a = l\cos i$, $t = 2l\sin\alpha/2$. Then

$$(\lambda/d\lambda) = t(dn/d\lambda) \qquad (7\text{-}11)$$

The resolving power equals the effective thickness of the prism times the dispersion of the prism material.

7.3 Diffraction Gratings

A second method for separating radiation into its component parts includes the use of a diffraction grating. Such a grating consists of a large number of small equal-size equally separated slits; each slit causes a diffraction pattern, and the waves from the individual slits also interfere, and a combined interference-diffraction pattern is formed. The intensity can be written

$$I = A^2\frac{\sin^2\beta}{\beta^2}\frac{\sin^2 N\gamma}{\sin^2\gamma}$$

The distribution described by this equation is illustrated in Figure 7-2. The grating equation, which gives the location of the maximum of each diffraction is $d(\sin\theta + \sin\theta') = m\lambda$. The angle of incidence is θ; the angle of diffraction is θ'; the slit separation is d.

It is now of interest to obtain the angular dispersion and resolving power for the grating, by differentiating the grating equation:

$$d(0 + \cos\theta'\, d\theta') = md\lambda$$

$$(d\theta'/d\lambda) = (m/d\cos\theta') \qquad (7\text{-}12)$$

The dispersion is proportional to the order of the spectrum. High orders (m) provide greater spectral separation, and θ' should be large ($\pi/2$ if this were possible) for high dispersion. Resolving power is defined as before as $\lambda/d\lambda$ and if the Rayleigh criterion of resolution is used, one can write $mN\lambda + \lambda = mN(\lambda + d\lambda)$. This says that, for order m,

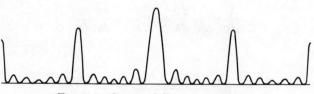

Fig. 7-2. Grating diffraction patterns.

the minimum of the pattern for wavelength $\lambda + d\lambda$ falls on the maximum of the pattern for wavelength λ. Then

$$(\lambda/d\lambda) = mN \qquad (7\text{-}13)$$

The resolving power is just equal to the number of lines in the grating times the order so that gratings with many lines used in a high order have high resolving power.

Gratings present essentially two difficulties for the infrared researcher. The first of these is overlapping of orders, and the second is ghosts. It can be seen from the grating equation that all spectral lines will appear at the same place in the diffraction pattern if they have the same value of $m\lambda$. Thus 1-μ radiation in the first order and 0.5-μ radiation in the second order are both diffracted to the same place in the image plane. Similarly, 2-μ first order, 1-μ second order, 0.5-μ fourth order, and 0.67-μ third order appear there, too. It is easy to see that this overlapping of orders is not very serious in the visible, but presents a considerable problem in the infrared where more intense, visible light in higher orders often masks the infrared radiation, and where many more octaves of radiation are present. This problem can be alleviated by blazing and by filtering the radiation before it reaches the grating. (In some instruments a prism monochromator is used as the filter.) A blazed grating is one in which each line is cut so that it reflects or refracts light to a particular order.

One problem that should not be overlooked with gratings is the appearance of ghosts. Lines must be ruled with great precision because the bump where a pulley belt is joined, or the small but gradual change in line spacing as an entire grating is ruled, is enough to produce a significant change in periodicity—and therefore produce lines which are characteristic of the grating rather than the sample under test. Such lines are called ghosts; they may appear randomly or periodically as satellites of other lines. When grating spectra are interpreted, the ghosts should be kept in mind.

Gratings have also been ruled on concave blanks, thereby producing a grating with focusing properties. Such gratings have some obvious advantages in that they replace part of the collimating or focusing system; but they have the aberrations of these optical systems. These gratings are usually mounted on a Rowland or Eagle mounting—specific arrangements of entrance slit, grating, and exit slit. These mountings and other details of prisms and gratings may be found in References 1 and 2.

7.4 Interferometers

The last of the types of "spectral" instruments considered here is the interferometer. The prism disperses light by selective refraction and the grating disperses it principally by diffraction; the interferometer separates the monochromatic components of light by interference.

There are two very popular types of interferometer: the Michelson and the Fabry-Perot. The Michelson interferometer has as its most frequent use the very accurate measurement of length. Recently, however, the use of interferometric spectroscopy[2] has resulted in an awakened interest in the properties of the Michelson interferometer. It consists of an extended source and a pair of light paths, one of them adjustable in length; see Figure 7-3. The different rays are separated to show the generation of interference. Light travels from the extended source and enters the interferometer which has a partially silvered back surface. The light is "split" so that half goes to mirror M_1 and half to M_2. Each of these rays is reflected from its respective mirror, the one originally reflected by the plate B has a component transmitted to the screen, and vice versa. Thus the two beams should be of equal intensity and with a phase difference governed by the difference in the two paths. A second plate is often placed in path A to compensate for the passage of light through the plate in path B. The light from every point on the extended source interferes with itself according to how much the mirrors are separated, or according to the different length of the arms A and B. Constructive interference will occur when

$$2d \cos \theta = m\lambda \qquad (7\text{-}14)$$

if d is the path difference and θ is the angle to a source element imaged by M_1 or M_2 as seen by the eye.

The Fabry-Perot interferometer is shown diagramatically in Figure 7-4. Light from an extended source is transmitted through plate P_1 and reflected many times between the partially silvered surfaces of P_1 and P_2. The different rays (which exit parallel and must be focused) then interfere with one another, and the condition for interference is the same as that for the Michelson interferometer, $2d \cos \theta = m\lambda$; the same pattern

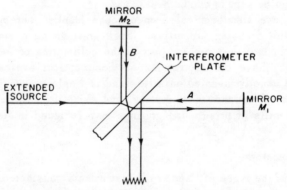

Fig. 7-3. Michelson interferometer.

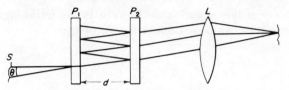

Fig. 7-4. Fabry-Perot interferometer.

should, therefore, be expected. The detailed treatment of either of these interferometers used for obtaining spectra requires background not assumed for this book. Suffice it to say that the principal advantage lies in the fact that an interferogram is obtained from energy of all wavelengths on the receiver at one time—by contrast with a spectrometer—and is more efficient for some spectroscopic applications. Further details on interferometers will be found in References 1, 2, and 3.

7.5 Mirrors

The use of reflecting optics for collecting radiation and focusing it has been widespread in infrared technology, due largely to the problem of finding suitable optical materials. Mirrors, of course, exhibit no chromatic aberration, but they do suffer from the five monochromatic image defects. It is the subject of this and subsequent sections to outline the properties of mirrors and some of the methods used to provide good imagery.

Most mirror surfaces are spherical, and almost all are conic sections, so some of the basic concepts of the analytic geometry of conic sections are important. A conic section is defined as a curve generated by a point which moves such that its distance from a fixed line (the directrix) is equal to a constant (the eccentricity) times its distance from a fixed point; see Figure 7-5. From this definition, $d_1 = ed_2$

$$d_1 = \sqrt{(x - r_0)^2 + y^2} = e(x + k)$$

$$(1 - e^2)x^2 + y^2 - 2(r_0 - e^2k)x + (r_0 - e^2k^2) = 0$$

There are two cases to consider for the solution of this equation: when $e = 1$ and when $e \neq 1$. For $e = 1$,

$$y^2 - 2(r_0 - k)x + (r_0^2 - k^2) = 0$$

To simplify, set $k = -r_0$, placing the vertex midway between the focus and the directrix. Then

$$y^2 = 2r_0x$$

For $e \neq 1$, simplification is obtained by another appropriate substitution. Then

$$(1 - e^2)x^2 + y^2 - 2r_0x = 0$$

The correctness of this equation can be seen by the following: the standard conic equations can be written in the $\xi\eta$ system:

Circle

$$\xi^2 + \eta^2 = r_0^2 \qquad e = 0 \tag{7-15}$$

Ellipse

$$\frac{\xi^2}{a^2} + \frac{\eta^2}{b^2} = 1 \qquad e = \frac{\sqrt{a^2 - b^2}}{a} r_0 \tag{7-16}$$

Parabola

$$\xi^2 = 2\eta r_0 \qquad e = 1 \tag{7-17}$$

Hyperbola

$$\frac{\xi^2}{a^2} - \frac{\eta^2}{b^2} = 1 \tag{7-18}$$

These can now be translated to the (x, y) system and the above equation is verified. When $y/r_0 \ll 1$, the solution can be determined in terms of an infinite series.

$$x^2 - \frac{2r_0}{1 - e^2} x + \frac{y^2}{1 - e^2} = 0$$

$$x = \frac{r_0}{1 - e^2} \pm \frac{1}{2} \sqrt{\frac{4r_0^2}{(1 - e^2)^2} - \frac{4y^2}{1 - e^2}}$$

$$x = \frac{r_0}{1 - e^2} \left[1 - 1 + \frac{1}{2} \frac{y^2}{r_0^2} (1 - e^2) + \frac{1}{8} \frac{y^4}{r_0^4} (1 - e^2)^2 + \dots \right]$$

$$= \frac{1}{2} \frac{y^2}{r_0} + \frac{1}{8} \frac{y^4}{r_0^3} (1 - e^2) + \dots$$

Therefore the shapes for the two most interesting surfaces are:

$$\text{Parabola} \qquad x = y^2/2r_0 \tag{7-19}$$

$$\text{Sphere} \qquad x = (y^2/2r_0) + (y^4/8r_0^3), + \dots \tag{7-20}$$

The significance of the above equations is emphasized if it is recalled that when two bodies are rubbed together in a random fashion, a spherical surface is generated. Thus, a parabola is usually figured by "correcting" a sphere, by removing $y^4/8r_0^3$ amount of material.

7.5.1 *Paraboloidal Mirrors*

A parabolic surface of revolution is the three-dimensional shape obtained by rotating the line described by Eq. (7-19) about the y axis. This is the shape used for many mirrors in infrared technology, and it

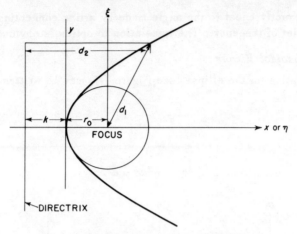

Fig. 7-5. The geometry of conic sections.

is properly called a paraboloid and although three-dimensional geometry is needed for some purposes it is sufficient to consider the properties of the parabola for the present simple treatment. Figure 7-6 shows a parabola with focus F and origin O. The tangent at point $P(x_1, y_1)$ passes through the y axis at Q and the x axis at T, and a line parallel to the x axis through P intersects the y axis at L and the directrix at K.

The equation of the tangent at P is obtained by differentiating Eq. (7-19):

$$2y\,dy = 2r_0\,dx$$

$$y(y_1 - y) = r_0(x_1 - x)$$

when $y = 0$, $x = x_1$, or $TO = LP$. The eccentricity is 1; therefore $KL = OF$. Then, $TF = TO + OF = LP + KL = KP$. By definition, $KP = FP$; thus, $TF = FP$ and TFP is isoceles. But, $TPL = TPF$, $T'PK' = TPL = TPF$, $FPN = K'PN$.

This result stated in words is that any line parallel to the axis of a parabola makes an angle with the normal to the tangent at the point of

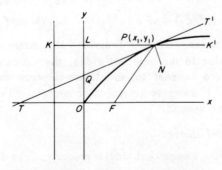

Fig. 7-6. The geometry of the parabola.

tangency exactly equal to the angle made by a line connecting the focus and the point of tangency. The translation to optics is obvious.

7.5.2 *Ellipsoidal Mirrors*

The equation for the ellipse (see Figure 7-7) may be written

$$\frac{\xi^2}{a^2} + \frac{\eta^2}{b^2} = 1$$

or

$$\xi^2 b^2 + \eta^2 a^2 = a^2 b^2$$

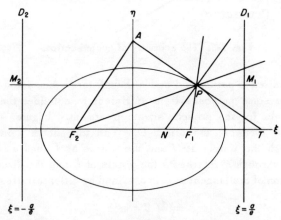

Fig. 7-7. The geometry of the ellipse.

The equations of the directrices are given by $\xi = (a/e)$, $\xi = -(a/e)$. The foci are at $\xi = \pm a/e$. Then by the definition of a conic

$$F_1 P = ePM_1 = e\left[(a/e) - \xi_1\right] = a - e\xi_1$$
$$F_2 P = ePM_2 = e\left[(a/e) + \xi_1\right] = a + e\xi_1$$
$$F_1 T = (a^2/\xi_1) + ae = (a/\xi_1)(a + e\xi_1) = (a/\xi_1)\,F_1 P$$
$$F_2 T = (a^2/\xi_1) - ae = (a/\xi_1)(a - e\xi_1) = (a/\xi_1)\,F_2 P$$

By a theorem from geometry, if PT divides the external side of triangle $F_1 P F_2$ in proportion to the adjacent sides, the external angle $F_1 PG$ is bisected. Thus, a tangent to an ellipse bisects the external angle formed by the radii drawn to its point of contact. Thus, all rays from one focus go to the second.

7.5.3 *Hyperboloidal Mirrors*

The hyperbola has a somewhat similar property. The derivation follows:

$$b^2\xi^2 - a^2\eta^2 = a^2b^2$$

$$F_1P = eM_1P = e[\xi_1 - (a/e)] = e\xi_1 - a$$

$$F_2P = eM_2P = e[\xi_1 + (a/e)] = e\xi_1 + a$$

$$\frac{F_2T}{F_1T} = -\frac{F_2P}{F_1P}$$

As in the case of the ellipse PT, the tangent bisects the angle formed by the focal radii drawn to its point of contact. All rays which are directed initially to a focus F_1 (see Figure 7-8) will be redirected to a focus F_2.

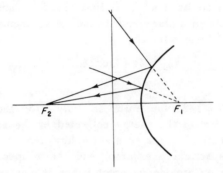

Fig. 7-8. The geometry of the hyperbola.

This is an interesting property, and it leads directly to somewhat more complicated systems.

7.6 Mirror (Catoptric) Systems

A Cassegrain system can be constructed as indicated in Figure 7-9. Mirror M_1 is a parabola. Therefore, all parallel incident rays (from infinity or as collimated by a lens) will be directed to F_1, the focus of the parabola. For convenience it may be desired to have the rays focus at F_2. Thus, mirror M_2 is inserted. It is a hyperboloid which has one focus at F_1, and the conjugate focus at F_2. Thus, all rays directed towards F_1 by the paraboloid will be focused ultimately at F_2. The conjugate hyperboloid is also shown (dotted). Other arrangements might be used: an ellipse with conjugate foci at F_1 and F_2, or a spherical mirror, or even a flat.

The exact arrangement of the mirrors in these combined systems is governed by the nature of the problem. A flat, which is certainly the most simple and does not increase the focal length, may be acceptable if the detector assembly can be extended through the aperture of the primary. To get the focus outside of the paraboloid with this scheme, it

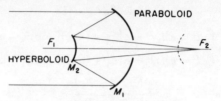

Fig. 7-9. A Cassegrain system.

is necessary to move the flat closer to the primary mirror, thereby requiring a large flat and resulting in more obscuration. The obscuration effects can be seen by calculating the size of the flat necessary; the result is not as drastic as it might at first appear. Consider the ratio of
the area of a circle with diameter D to that of an annulus with inner and
outer radii d and D, respectively.

$$\text{Ratio} = \frac{(\pi D^2/4) - (\pi d^2/4)}{\pi D^2/4} = 1 - (d/D)^2$$

Even when $d/D = 1/2$, the ratio is only .75; the folded system
collects 75 per cent of the energy collected by the unobscured mirror.
The use of a spherical mirror as a secondary, reduces the obscuration,
but introduces spherical aberration, and the ellipse as used in the
Gregorian system to provide an erect image is not as compact as the
hyperbolic Cassegrain system.

It might be noted that "Cassegrain" has been used by various authors
to describe most of the above systems as well as systems which have a
spherical primary (collector) mirror. It seems preferable to call these
"folded systems," and reserve "Cassegrain" for its original meaning:
the combination of a paraboloid and a hyperboloid.

7.7 Lens (Dioptric) Systems

There is a vast number of papers and books on the subject of lens design, and any detailed coverage here would be out of place. It does
seem appropriate to make some fairly general statements about lens design and to compare the performance of lenses with that of mirrors.

If a very simple optical system is assumed, these relationships can
be seen fairly directly. Assume that the detector is the field stop, and
the lens or mirror is the aperture stop; then, the field of view and the
collecting power for the two systems are almost identical. The effective
f/number of the mirror is reduced slightly from the geometrical f/number
by the area of the detector. However, in most systems, the detector is
encased in an evacuated housing which sometimes has a preamplifier
attached, in which case the effective f/number may be reduced appreciably. This is not so for lenses. The systems assumed above will also

require equal space; any folding arrangement will be more difficult with the mirror system than with lenses. Lenses therefore provide considerable convenience in design.

For the arrangement assumed above, and in most cases, it can be shown that a lens provides better resolution than a mirror of the same size and focal length, and it does so over larger fields of view. The reasons lenses have not been used more widely are that the statements above hold for only limited spectral bands (where chromatic aberrations do not become intolerable) and that there is a dearth of substances which have properties desirable for infrared lenses:

1. High transmittance
2. Relatively constant refractive index
3. Hardness
4. Homogeneity

The methods of achromatization have been described in several references. The basic principle is to balance the chromatism of one lens with that of another. The second is usually a low-power lens of a different material.

7.8 Catadioptric Systems

It has been shown how parabolas, hyperbolas, and ellipses can be used alone and in combination to obtain useful reflecting systems. Can spherical mirrors also be used? An affirmative answer may provide a very economical solution to system design. Of course, if the large aberrations are tolerable, a spherical mirror is useful by itself. Frequently, however, spherical or aspherical refractive elements are used to correct for the aberrations of the spherical surface. The most common systems based on such combinations are the Schmidt, Bouwers-Maksutov, and Mangin systems.

7.8.1 *The Schmidt System*

The Schmidt system utilizes a spherical concave mirror with a stop placed at the center of curvature. All rays are on axis, and the system is symmetrical, so spherical aberration and curvature of field are the only aberrations which remain. A reflected wave is advanced a factor of $h^4/4r_0^3$ more by a sphere than the (ideal) parabola; therefore, Bernard Schmidt proposed placing a curved refractive element of thickness $d = \{h^4/[(n-1)4r_0^3]\}$, in the optical system. Such a catadioptic system is often called a Schmidt system of the first kind. The more usual, improved system makes use of a corrector which directs parallel rays to the position of the minimum circle of least confusion rather than the paraxial focal point. An element which does this has a thickness described by the following equation:

$$d = \frac{h^4}{(n-1)\,4\,r_0^{\,3}} - \frac{3}{8}\,\frac{R^2}{r_0^{\,3}}\,h^2$$

where R is the radius of the corrector. This system has less chromatic aberration and provides better correction.

7.8.2 *The Bouwers-Maksutov System*

Bouwers has described the Schmidt system and his own approach to catadioptric systems. He reasoned that a lens could be used to offset the spherical aberrations of spherical mirrors. If this is true, a system using only spherical surfaces could be designed with all the good qualities of the Schmidt system. Maksutov apparently reasoned in about the same way independently. There are several types of Bouwers systems, some of which are shown in Figure 7-10. Clearly, the "Bouwers princi-

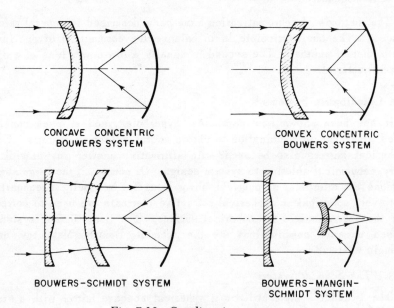

CONCAVE CONCENTRIC
BOUWERS SYSTEM

CONVEX CONCENTRIC
BOUWERS SYSTEM

BOUWERS-SCHMIDT SYSTEM

BOUWERS-MANGIN-
SCHMIDT SYSTEM

Fig. 7-10. Catadioptric systems.

ple" of correcting the spherical aberration of a spherical mirror by the use of a spherical lens of modest power and appropriate shape can be used in conjunction with many optical systems. The reader is referred to Bouwers' work[4] for the details of the technique.

7.8.3 *Mangin Mirrors*

Mangin mirrors, sometimes called Mangin lenses or thick mirrors, consist of a refractive element which is coated on its rear surface with a highly reflecting material like silver. Usually, the Mangin mirror is designed so that there is an equal deviation of the ray on leaving and entering.

7.9 Scanning Systems

Most infrared optical systems have a small flake of semiconductor material as the fundamental detector or transducer. All the energy from a given optical field is translated into a single electrical pulse. If a picture is to be generated, or if any sort of information is to be gained from a large area, some sort of scanning is necessary. It is possible to consider this scanning process as a generalization of a television scan. We consider here a few simple ways to do this optically.

7.9.1 *Plane Parallel Plates*

Figure 7-11 shows a plane parallel plate which, when rotated or oscillated, can cause a beam of light to move in a prescribed direction. The displacement of a single beam in a stationary plate is determined as follows (it is assumed that for air $n = 1$):

$$y = (BD - CD) \cos \phi \qquad (7\text{-}21)$$

$$BD = d \tan \phi$$

$$CD = d \tan \phi$$

$$y = d \cos \phi (\tan \phi - \tan \phi')$$

$$y = d \cos \phi \left(\frac{\sin \phi}{\cos \phi} - \frac{\sin \phi'}{\cos \phi'} \right) \qquad (7\text{-}22)$$

$$n \sin \phi = n' \sin \phi'$$

$$\sin \phi' = \frac{\sin \phi}{n'}$$

Finally,

$$y = d \sin \phi \left(1 - \frac{\cos \phi}{n' \cos \phi'} \right) \qquad (7\text{-}23)$$

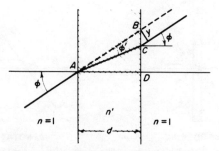

Fig. 7-11. The plane parallel plate.

How is the plane parallel plate used for scanning? Since the displacement y is proportional in a trigonometric sense to the angle of incidence, a point in object space can be made to trace a line in image space if the plate is rocked back and forth. See Figure 7-12(a). Also, an inclined plate can be rotated about an axis through the plate and in the same plane as the incident ray, Figure 7-12(b), and the point will describe a circle, the diameter of which depends on the inclination, the thickness, and the refractive index of the plate.

Although it is not a scanning application, another property of the plane parallel plate might be mentioned at this point: if the plate is placed in a converging beam it affects the focal length of an optical system because each extreme ray of an incident converging beam is refracted at each surface of the plate, and emerges parallel to, but displaced from, its original direction.

From the equations relating to the plane parallel plate, it can be seen that the focus changes by the distance $(y/\sin \phi) = d[1 - (\cos \phi/n \sin \theta)]$. The interior rays of the bundle will be less affected since they meet the surface of the plate more nearly at normal incidence.

7.9.2 Prisms

Prisms may also be used for optical-mechanical scanning applications. The deviation of a prism is given by $\delta = \theta_1 + \theta_2 - \alpha$. For small angles (a good assumption for most optical systems), one can approximate Snell's law by the first terms of the sine expansion. Then,

$$\theta'_1 = n \theta_1 \qquad \theta'_2 = n \theta_2 \tag{7-24}$$

$$\theta'_1 + \theta'_2 = \alpha \tag{7-25}$$

$$\delta = (n - 1) \alpha \tag{7-26}$$

The effect of the rotation of the prism can now be considered. The y-component of deviation will be maximum (positive) when the prism is in its vertical position and there will be no deviation in the y direction

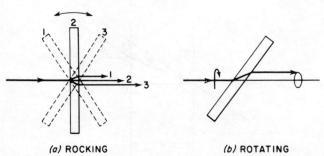

(a) ROCKING   (b) ROTATING

Fig. 7-12. (a) and (b). Scanning with a plane parallel plate.

when the prism is in its horizontal position. Further consideration along these lines leads to the relationship

$$\delta y = (n - 1)\, \alpha \, \cos \phi, \qquad \delta_x = (n - 1)\, \alpha \, \sin \phi \qquad (7\text{-}27)$$

where y is the vertical coordinate, x the horizontal one, and ϕ is the angular measure of prism position ($\phi = 0$ for an upright prism). When the prism is rotated, one can replace ϕ by ωt, where ω is the rotation rate. If two prisms are used, the deviations are additive, two rotation rates must be used, and a phase angle ψ must be included.

$$\delta y = (n - 1)\, \alpha \, [\cos \omega_1 t + \cos (\omega_2 t + \psi)]$$
$$\delta_x = (n - 1)\, \alpha \, [\sin \omega_1 t + \sin (\omega_2 t + \psi)] \qquad (7\text{-}28)$$

Notice that the condition of minimum deviation has not been used. That would be just the wrong thing to do. But minimum dispersion is desired. The deviation for small angles is

$$\delta = (n - 1)\, \alpha \qquad (7\text{-}29)$$

The dispersion is

$$(d\delta/d\lambda) = \alpha\,(dn/d\lambda) \qquad (7\text{-}30)$$

Thus, for a scanning prism, n and α should be large for maximum deviation, and $dn/d\lambda$ and α should be small for minimum dispersion. The compromise is a moderate value of α and an appropriate material (germanium satisfies these conditions remarkably well for a wide spectral range).

The possibilities for scanning devices are far from exhausted. Entire optical assemblies can be moved; one can rotate elements eccentrically; many systems oscillate; some are servo driven; in many cases independent motions in the x and y directions are superimposed. An exhaustive treatment of the possibilities is beyond the scope of this book. The section on scanning is concluded with a description of a number of scan patterns and possible means for their generation.

7.9.3 Scan Patterns [5]

The Palmer scan (see Figure 7-13) is one of the simplest to generate: a prism, flat, or an off-axis mirror is rotated in such a way that a circular scan results, and the entire optical system is translated at a uniform rate; the center (horizontal) line of the Palmer scan represents this translational motion. The amount of overlap, represented by the distance d, is determined by the time it takes for one circle to be scanned and the forward velocity of the system, as well as the size of the circle and the distance from the optical system to the object point. The hypocycloidal scan is generated by the superposition of two eccentric circular motions. A sinusoidal raster can be generated by the two-prism systems

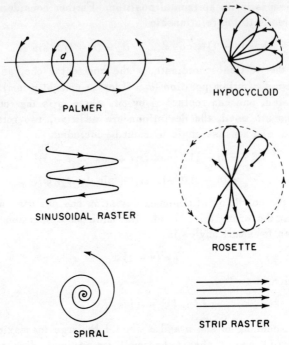

Fig. 7-13. Scan patterns.

described above, or it might be obtained by the use of an oscillating mirror in a translating optical system. The rosette and spiral scans can also be obtained by the prisms. The different patterns generated by prisms are determined by their relative rotational rates and directions resulting in patterns quite analogous to Lissajous figures. Finally, a simple strip raster can be obtained by the use of a rotating element in a translating system, although considerable dead time is inherent in this technique, even though certain stratagems, like using many-sided mirrors, may be employed. More detailed considerations are given to this problem in Chapters 13 and 14; certainly the application will greatly determine the type of scan used. Some of the considerations in the choice of a scan pattern for a given application are: What is the purpose (search, track, etc.)? What is the shape of the field? Is uniform or nonuniform coverage desirable?

7.10 Unusual Optical Elements

The problems which are now approached by infrared techniques are far more complex than in the recent past. Designers of optical instruments have been forced to approach them with ingenuity, and sometimes with inspiration. (These statements, of course, are true also for optical design for the visible spectrum.) Accordingly, some rather unusual techniques have developed, and there are probably innovations to come. This section describes some elements that may be seen more frequently in the future.

7.10.1 *Fiber Optics*

The use of long, thin fibers of material for transmitting and guiding light has recently gained increased attention.[3] Even more recently, some thought has been given to the use of this technique in the infrared part of the spectrum.[6]

A single fiber can be bent and shaped to some extent to direct light in a prescribed way. Many fibers can be placed side by side, and such a bundle can be used, e.g., to transmit crude images, to scramble images, or to correct for spherical aberration in a unique way.[3] The properties of fibers are described below; the applications they have to infrared optics is a fertile field for investigation.

It is important to know the optical limitations of a single fiber; refer to Figure 7-14. A ray of light, which is chosen for convenience as a chief ray, is incident at an angle θ; the angle of refraction is θ'; the angle ϕ is $(\pi/2) - \theta'$ because it and the angle of refraction are two acute angles of a right triangle; the angle ϕ is also the angle of incidence on the surface of the fiber. If ϕ is greater than the critical angle, the ray will be totally reflected. The geometrical path length d of a ray through the fiber can now be determined. Let L be the length of the fiber. Then,

$$d = mAB$$

$$= \frac{mAC}{\cos \theta'} \tag{7-31}$$

$$= \frac{mAC}{\cos \left\{\sin^{-1}\left[(n/n') \sin \theta'\right]\right\}}$$

$$= \frac{mAC}{\sqrt{1 - (n/n')^2 \sin^2 \theta'}}$$

$$= \frac{L}{\sqrt{1 - (n/n')^2 \sin^2 \theta}} \tag{7-32}$$

The external transmittance of a fiber can now be written. There are $m/2$ reflections at the sides and at each end. Thus,

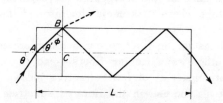

Fig. 7-14. Ray tracing in an optical fiber.

$$\tau = \rho^{m/2} [1 - \rho^2] e^{-\alpha d} \qquad (7\text{-}33)$$

The second two terms represent the external transmittance of a parallel plate, and the first term, representing wall losses, would be equal to 1 if the surfaces were perfect. No analytical expression exists for the reflection factor ρ, which probably varies along the surface. It is clear, however, that the value of ρ has a very strong influence on the transmission, since m will be high. In fact, m is given by

$$m = \frac{L \sin \theta'}{2BC\sqrt{1 - (n/n')^2 \sin^2 \theta}} \qquad (7\text{-}34)$$

$$= \frac{nL \sin \theta}{2BC\sqrt{n'^2 - n^2 \sin^2 \theta}} \qquad (7\text{-}35)$$

The acceptance angle of a single fiber will be determined by the critical angle of the fiber:

$$\theta_c = \sin^{-1} (n/n') \qquad (7\text{-}36)$$

The ray is incident on the side of the fiber at an angle ϕ. From the geometry,

$$\phi + \theta' = (\pi/2)$$

$$\theta' = (\pi/2) - \phi$$

$$n \sin \theta = n' \sin \theta'$$

$$\sin \theta = (n'/n) \cos \phi$$

$$\sin \theta = (n'/n) \cos [\sin^{-1} (n/n')]$$

$$\sin \theta = (n'/n) \sqrt{1 - (n/n')^2}$$

$$\sin \theta = \sqrt{(n'/n)^2 - 1} \qquad (7\text{-}37)$$

The maximum acceptance angle is dependent only on the relative index of refraction.

The two effects that have not been discussed are what happens when the fiber is bent and when a number of fibers are grouped together.[3] There is also the interesting case of propagation of waveguide modes for fibers with diameters of about the wavelength of the light. Theoretical work has been done on the waveguide propagation,[7] but it has not yet reached the stage where it is useful for infrared instrument applications.

The chief problems facing fiber research today are those of drawing, extruding, or in other ways making fibers—and in coating the fibers with an appropriate material of low refractive index. The problem of getting a fiber at all for use in the infrared spectrum is an extremely difficult one. Materials which have been used so far are chiefly the glasses of the arsenic–sulfur system, and some attempt has been made to coat the higher-index fibers with lower-index samples of the glass.

7.10.2 *Cone Condensers*

For nonimaging optical systems, another way to collect energy is to use a cone condenser, a hollow reflecting cone. Williamson has discussed such cones and their applications.[8] Figure 7-15 which illustrates a cone condenser also incorporates Williamson's nomenclature. The length of the cone for a system that has a focal plane with radius s and detector with radius c is x, where

$$x = \left(1 - \frac{c}{s}\right) \frac{s \cos v}{(c/s) - \sin v} \tag{7-38}$$

The method of design is to draw an extreme ray, and construct a circle with center on the optical axis, thereby determining the cone angle and

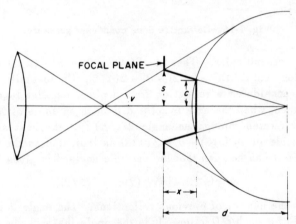

FOCAL PLANE

Fig. 7-15. Cone condenser optics.

the length of the cone. The chief advantages of the cone condenser are that it scrambles light incident on it, thus making the light incident on the detector of uniform intensity, and it permits the use of a smaller detector thus increasing detectivity. In his article, Williamson also showed that the response of a cone condenser is quite uniform and that $f/0.5$ is its theoretical f/number. In practice, the attainable f/number will be larger ($f/0.77$ to $f/1.0$) because reflection losses will decrease the efficiency of the system.

It is also possible to design refracting cone condensers. The situation is more complex. In Figure 7-16 light is shown incident on the front surface of the cone at an angle θ. The angle of refraction is θ'; BC is the normal to the cone side; BD is normal to the cone axis; x is the cone angle. Then, $\angle CBD = \alpha/2$ since the sides of the angles are re-

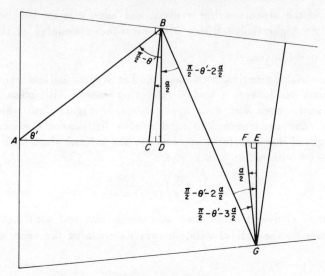

Fig. 7-16. Refractive cone condenser geometry.

spectively perpendicular. Then $\angle CBG = (\pi/2) - \theta' - (\alpha/2)$ by the Law of Reflection, and $\angle DBG = (\pi/2) - \theta' - 2(\alpha/2)$. (Incidentally, this could have been considered a reflection from a plane parallel to the axis of the cone; then, when the axis is rotated through an angle of $\alpha/2$, the reflected ray rotates through an angle $2\alpha/2$.) At the next surface, the angle of incidence is $(\pi/2) - \theta' - 3(\alpha/2)$ as indicated on the figure, and by induction it can be seen that the variable angle ϕ is given by

$$\phi = (\pi/2) - [\theta' + (2m + 1)(\alpha/2)] \qquad (7\text{-}39)$$

where m is the number of previous reflections. The angle ϕ is the incidence angle for each reflection. It is the angle that must be considered to determine whether or not the ray is reflected internally. It is clear that in this case the length of the cone condenser will determine its f/number. Similarly, for short cones the refractive system can provide a greater angular acceptance than the reflective system. A construction similar to that described by Williamson is possible, but now the criterion of use is whether or not the critical angle condition is violated. Kapany[9] has recently given the expression for a "long" cone as

$$n \sin \theta \text{ (max)} = (r_2/r_1)(n^2 - n'^2)^{1/2}$$

7.10.3 *Immersion Lenses*

Many infrared instrument applications require large-aperture, high-speed, optical systems. The straightforward approach to this problem is careful design and painstaking manufacture of precision surfaces—which often must be aspheric. But the straightforward technique has engineering limitations, e.g., maximum obtainable size of refractive elements, and stress and temperature problems with very large reflectors. The requirements for volume and weight reduction imposed by space applications are also an influential factor. Accordingly, optical designers have come upon the idea of using small field lenses in contact with detectors. These lenses provide an engineering advantage over larger optical systems—and provide an additional advantage when used in an already large, high-speed system. The usual arrangement has been a hemispherical button which provides a gain proportional to the refractive index.[1] More recently, it has been shown that the gain for the aplanatic case is proportional to n squared.[2]

There are two general cases for which the gain should be calculated: (1) sources which are small compared to the entrance window of the optical system, and (2) sources which are large compared to or about the same size as the entrance window. It also is important to specify whether the gain is obtained by changing the position of the detector assembly in the optical system (keeping the detector size constant) or by changing the detector size, keeping the position fixed. Finally, the gain will depend upon the configuration of the lens itself. Only the hemisphere and aplanatic hyperhemisphere are considered here.

The inclusion of all these parameters in the analysis requires consideration of eight cases. These cases are listed below:

I. Point Source
  A. Constant-Area Detector
    1. Aplanatic lens
    2. Hemispherical lens
  B. Constant-Position Detector
    1. Aplanatic lens
    2. Hemispherical lens
II. Extended Source
  A. Constant-Area Detector
    1. Aplanatic lens
    2. Hemispherical lens
  B. Constant-Position Detector
    1. Aplanatic lens
    2. Hemispherical lens

7.10.3.1 *Definition of Gain.* Since infrared, immersion, optical systems are the sole subject of this section the gain can be defined as the ratio of the output of an infrared detector which is immersed to the output of an unimmersed detector. The useful output of a detector may be specified as the signal-to-noise ratio S/N generated by a given input power P. This can be written in terms of the detectivity D:

$$S/N = PD$$

Thus the gain G is

$$G = \frac{(S/N)'}{S/N} = \frac{P'D'}{PD}$$

where primes indicate quantities describing the immersed system. The gain is equal to the ratio of the product of the incident power and the detectivity for the two cases. It has been shown[12] that the detectivity of a detector is expected to be inversely proportional to the square root of its area. Thus,

$$G = \frac{P'}{P} \sqrt{\frac{A}{A'}}$$

7.10.3.2 *Point-Source Cases*. If the object to be viewed is a radiating point source, and if reflection losses are ignored, the power received by an immersed detector is the same as the power received by an unimmersed dectector. Then the gain is

$$G = \frac{P'}{P} \sqrt{\frac{A}{A'}} = \sqrt{\frac{A}{A'}}$$

If the detector area is not changed (Cases IA1 and IA2), there is no gain. If the immersion lens is used so that the area of the detector can be decreased, the gain will equal the ratio of the square root of the detector areas. For the aplanatic lens (Case IB1) this ratio is n^2, or

$$G = n^2$$

This relationship can be obtained through the following considerations (Fig. 7-17). A spherical lens of refractive index n and radius r is placed in air (of refractive index 1). Then two hypothetical spheres are constructed concentric with the spherical lens, one with radius nr, one with radius r/n. The lens then has the property that all rays like AB which would

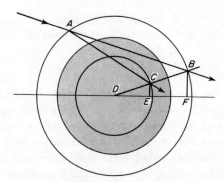

Fig. 7-17. Aplanatic sphere.

have intersected the outer sphere at B now intersect the inner sphere at C. Furthermore, the image is aplanatic—it has no spherical or comatic aberration. The properties of such a sphere are further described in the literature.[13,14] It is easy to see that, if chords are good approximations to arcs, the ratio of the linear dimensions of the images of the optical system is given $\dfrac{CE}{BF}$. Further, the triangles DEC and DBF are similar; thus

$$\frac{CE}{BF} = \frac{DC}{DB} = \frac{r/n}{rn} = \frac{1}{n^2}$$

The linear dimensions of the detectors have the ratio $1:n^2$; the areas have the ratio $1:n^4$. So the gain is

$$G = \sqrt{\frac{A}{A'}} = \sqrt{n^4} = n^2$$

For the hemispherical case with constant area (Case IA2) there is no gain, as noted above for Cases IA. If the area is changed (Case IB2) the magnification expressions for a single spherical surface can be used. The result is

$$G = \sqrt{\frac{A}{A'}} = \sqrt{n^2} = n$$

7.10.3.3 *Extended-Source Cases.*   Next, the extended-source cases may be considered. For an extended source, the radiance divided by the square of the refractive index is constant. Thus

$$G = \frac{P'D'}{PD} = \frac{N'A'\omega'D'}{NA\omega D} = \frac{\omega'n^2}{\omega}\sqrt{\frac{A'}{A}}$$

where ω is the solid angle of the optical system. For constant area (Cases IIA1 and IIA2), the gain is proportional to the ratio of the solid angles of acceptance and n^2. These angles can be determined as follows: the angle ω is the area of the principal optical element divided by the focal length squared. When the immersion lens is introduced, the angle ω' is the area of the image of the principal optical element formed by the immersion lens divided by the distance of the image from the focal plane. Consider Figure 7-18. The image of the optical element h is h', the object and image distances are o and i, respectively. Then from two expressions for magnification it is possible to write

$$\frac{h'}{h} = \frac{1}{o}$$

Fig. 7-18. Solid-angle geometry.

Thus

$$\frac{\omega'}{\omega} = \left[\frac{h/o}{h/f}\right]^2 = \left(\frac{f}{o}\right)^2 = \left(\frac{f}{d-r}\right)^2$$

where $d = 0 + r$. Thus for Case IIA1.

$$G = \left(\frac{nf}{d - r + r/n}\right)^2$$

and for Case IIA2,

$$G = \left(\frac{nf}{d - r}\right)^2$$

The problem then is to determine d. Refer to Figure 7–19. The equation of the edge ray is

$$y = \frac{h}{f}\ x + h$$

where h is the semidiameter of the principal optical element and f is its focal length. The equation for the immersion lens is

$$(x - d)^2 + y^2 = r^2$$

Other relationships can be obtained from the geometry; an explicit equation for d might be derived, but it would not be very useful because of

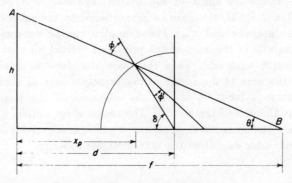

Fig. 7-19. Immersion lens geometry.

its complexity. However, one can also assume reasonable values for f, h, r, n, and d, and solve for the detector height l. These calculations require: (1) simultaneous solution of the two equations above for specific values of f, h, r, n, and d; (2) determination of $\delta = \tan^{-1}\left(\dfrac{y}{d-x}\right)$; (3) determination of $\emptyset = \delta - \theta$; (4) calculation of $\emptyset' = \sin^{-1}\left[\dfrac{(\sin\emptyset)}{n}\right]$ and calculation of $\sigma = \delta - \emptyset'$; and (5) calculation of $l = y - (x-d)\tan\sigma$. These computations can also be done graphically. The results of the graphical computations are shown in Figure 7-20, which is a graph of de-

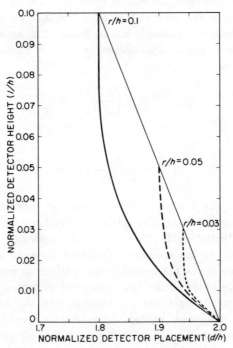

Fig. 7-20. Detector size and position.

tector height as a function of position of the immersion lens for an $f/\dfrac{\sqrt{3}}{2}$ system (chosen close to $f/1$ but so that the half angle is $30°$). All values of the parameters have been normalized to the radius of the immersion lens. The graph can now be used to obtain the results for Cases IIA1 and IIA2.

If the position of the lens in the optical system is kept constant (Cases

IIB1 and IIB2), $o + r$ or $o + r + r/n$ will be equal to f, and $\omega = \omega'$. Then

$$G = n^2 \sqrt{\frac{A'}{A}}$$

For the aplanatic case, the gain is 1; for the hemispherical case, the gain is n. This case also results from a requirement to keep $\omega = \omega'$.

7.10.3.4 *Limitations*. In the gains derived above no losses by reflection or absorption were included. A loss factor K may be introduced;

$$K = (1 - \rho)e^{-ax}$$

where ρ is the intensity reflection coefficient, a is the absorption coefficient, and x is the geometrical path length. Because the radiation falling on the lens will probably not be incident at an angle of more than $40°$, it is reasonable to approximate ρ by the Fresnel expression for normal incidence,

$$\rho = \left(\frac{n - 1}{n + 1}\right)^2$$

Thus,

$$K = \frac{4n}{(n + 1)^2} e^{-ax}$$

In most cases, the reflection losses can be reduced significantly by coatings. In regions of no absorption, K may have values of 0.9 to 1.0.

There is a limitation in the use of an immersion lens in very fast optical systems. As the speed and therefore the solid angle is increased, the marginal rays strike the lens-detector surface at more oblique angles. As the refractive index of the lens compared to that of the detector gets larger, the critical angle also increases, and the size of the bundle which can be accepted by the lens-detector combination decreases.

Thus, it can be seen, that the desirable optical properties of an immersion lens are low absorption and high refractive index. However, if the refractive index of the lens is larger than that of the detector, the speed of the optical system will eventually be affected. Finally, reflection losses should be considered and reduced as much as possible. In this connection, the reflection loss at the curved front surface of the immersion lens may be considerably less than the loss at the flat surface of an unimmersed detector in a high-speed optical system.

7.11 Filters

There are two general kinds of filters which are used in infrared systems: spectral filters and spatial filters. The purpose of the latter is to discriminate objects of a certain angular size from objects of all other sizes. This discrimination and the design of these filters is the subject of Appendix A and Chapter 14. It will be seen there that the design involves certain statistical concepts borrowed from communication engineering, and that the subject is not yet very mature. Spectral filters which discriminate on the basis of the wavelength or frequency of the electromagnetic radiation are the subject of this section.

7.11.1 *Nomenclature*

Filters are usually described as being "high-pass," "low-pass," or "bandpass" according to their transmission characteristics. Electrical filters are usually described in terms of frequency, whereas optical filters are described in terms of wavelength. Thus, a low-pass or short-wave pass optical filter is one which transmits all radiation of wavelength shorter than some cutoff wavelength, and a high-pass or long-wave pass optical filter transmits radiation with wavelength greater than some minimum or cuton value; a bandpass filter transmits radiation within a given band of wavelengths. Since electrical filters are fairly well behaved, it is usually possible to specify a rolloff frequency and slope— e.g., 6 db per octave for a single time-constant system. However, the cutoff characteristics of optical filters are not nearly so regular, because they are dependent on, for instance, the type of filter and absorption and interference characteristics. Accordingly, there has been no uniformity in nomenclature. Several things must be specified in one way or another, and until there is greater agreement, only generalities make sense. There must be a specification of the wavelength of maximum transmission (usually center wavelength); there must be a specification of maximum transmission (usually external transmittance); there must be a description of the width of the bandpass. This is usually given in terms of the cutoff and cuton wavelengths, but these wavelengths are sometimes defined as the points of 50 per cent external transmittance; sometimes for 10 per cent external transmittance, and sometimes as 50 per cent or 90 per cent of maximum transmission. The description of the slope of the cutoff and cuton wavelengths is just as arbitrary. Finally, there must be a description of any transmission the filter may have outside the specified band.

There are several different kinds of filters which have been used or which show promise for use in infrared instruments. These are the absorption, interference, and Christiansen filters and reststrahlen plates. The first two types have been discussed by Wolfe and Ballard.[15]

7.11.2 *Absorption Filter*

Possibly the filter that is first considered by a designer is one that makes use of the characteristic absorption of a material. Indeed such filters have long been used, principally as cuton and cutoff filters because the transmission band is seldom exactly what is required. Almost every one of the optical materials discussed in Chapter 6 can be used as a low-pass filter; rock salt, for instance, has a long wavelength cutoff at about 15 μ. The specification of the cutoff wavelength depends upon the definition and on the thickness of the material. One way to adjust the cutoff wavelength is by choosing an appropriate thickness; this choice is limited to a fairly narrow spectral band, and unfortunately, the long-wave cutoff characteristics are usually not very sharp, since the absorption is due to free electrons and varies as the square of the wavelength (see Section 6.2.2); this effect is usually observed in the transmission curve. Sometimes the effects of lattice absorption assist in increasing the absorption coefficient fairly sharply, but most often the gradual cutoff is observed. For some applications such a gradual slope is acceptable. The cuton or short-wave characteristic is most often quite steep, since the absorption coefficient increases abruptly when $hc/\lambda = E_g$ often the coefficient changes by four or five orders of magnitude in about 0.2 μ. The transmittance which is related to absorption by

$$\tau = Ke^{-\alpha x}$$

has a correspondingly greater change—this is probably as close as one can expect to approach a step function in nature. For cutons in the infrared (say at 4 μ), $E_g = (1.24/4) = 0.31$ ev, an energy is characteristic of semiconductors. Thus, one might hope to choose a number of different materials with appropriate transmission edges, and, although this can be done, it is not possible to always find a material with exactly the right characteristics. In 1956 H. Welker and H. Weiss[16] suggested that, if two semiconductor compounds could be mixed, the energy gap should be a linear function of their percentage composition. More recently, Bube[17] has reviewed the status of mixed crystals. He shows that there are a number of compounds (III-V compounds, ZnS-ZnSe compounds, etc.) that do show this characteristic. It can also be seen by reference to some of the original data that the absorption edge changes almost linearly, with the mole per cent of one component of a compound, for many compounds, and that it remains about as steep as both of the original curves. It is interesting to note in this regard that as early as 1929 F. W. Barth[18] observed the change in cuton wavelength as a function of composition for mixtures of thallium salts.

Little work has been done on this type of filter. The problems which must be surmounted are obtaining better maximum transmission and longer wavelength cutoffs. Clearly, to obtain a cuton at longer wavelengths, a material with a smaller energy gap must be used, the smaller the gap, the more free electrons and the greater the absorption. Also, most of the semiconducting materials have a high refractive index, so reflection losses are high. It is possible to apply a reflection-reducing coating, but this will change the steepness of the transmission edge.

7.11.3 Interference Filters

The most common filter used for infrared instrumentation problems is probably the symmetrical, all-dielectric interference filter. The theory of the thin, quarter-wavelength-thick films which make up the filters is described by Strong,[3] and by Wolfe and Ballard.[15] The reduction of reflection is caused by interference of the incident wave and the waves reflected from the back surface of the filter layer. (A single layer is used as a reflection-reduction coating.) The conditions for interference are:

$$n = \sqrt{n'}$$

$$\Delta\phi = (4\pi n d/\lambda) \cos \theta' = 2\pi\left(m + \frac{1}{2}\right)$$

Thus,

$$nd \cos \theta' = (\lambda/4)(2m + 1) \tag{7-40}$$

where n = the refractive index of the film
$\quad n'$ = the refractive index of the layer material
$\quad \Delta\phi$ = the phase change of the incident light
$\quad \lambda$ = the wavelength of the incident light
$\quad d$ = the thickness of the film
$\quad \theta'$ = the angle of inclination, in film, of the ray to the film surface normal
$\quad m$ = 1, 2, 3, ...

The refractive index of air is assumed to be equal to 1.

The properties of these layers can be inferred from Eq. (7-40), which states that, for best reflection reduction or best transmission, the optical path length in the film must be an odd number of quarter wavelengths of the incident light. Since the variation of refractive index with wavelength in regions of high transmission is small, and since d is a constant, reflection reduction is maximized for only a very narrow spectral band at normal incidence. Equation (7-40) also shows that the wavelength of best transmission varies with the angle of incidence. The all-dielectric filter consists of alternate layers of high H and low L refractive index. Thus, at the first layer, radiation of wavelengths which satisfy Eq. (7-40) for the characteristics of the layer will be transmitted. The process will be repeated layer by layer with a resulting pass band which gets narrower and narrower. Again, by consideration of the equation, it is easy to see that there are other combinations for λ and m which satisfy the interference condition. These result in other regions of transmission—

harmonics, side lobes, or secondary transmission. These can be suppressed by the appropriate use of absorption filters. It is usually possible to obtain a bandpass filter in the region 1–5 μ with a half-width of about 10 per cent of the cuton wavelength. These have maximum transmission of about 90 per cent; the maximum transmission is reduced for narrower bandpasses. The problem is most difficult beyond 5 μ; there are fewer available materials and the thicker layers have a greater tendency to peel.

7.11.4 *Christiansen Filters*

A very different kind of phenomenon is the basis of the Christiansen filter. Consider a continuous medium of refractive index n, in which there are many small particles of refractive index n'. The refractive index curves of the two materials are as shown in Figure 7-21. Radiation which enters the material of index n will be scattered by the particles of index n' according to either Mie or Rayleigh scattering theory. (It is usually possible to assume that the particles are small compared to the wavelength of the radiation, so that Rayleigh theory applies.) If $n = n'$, then there is no optical distinction between the medium and the particles, and there is, therefore, no scattering. Figure 7-21 shows that at wavelength λ_0 the two refractive indexes are equal, so that when these two materials are used as described above, the resulting filter has a transmission maximum at λ_0. The bandpass of the filter is a function of the slope of one index relative to that of the other—the steeper the slope, the narrower the filter bandpass. The early filters were made of liquid and dielectric particles. Since the refractive index of most liquids is a relatively sensitive function of temperature—and the index of solids is not—the filters had spectral responses which were quite sensitive to temperature changes. Theoretically at least, it is possible to design filters of two solid materials, although there are difficulties. Figure 6-10, the collection of refractive index curves, shows that there are very few pairs of materials with characteristics like those shown in Figure 7-21.

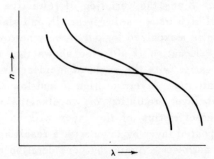

Fig. 7-21. Refractive index characteristics of the materials used in a Christiansen filter.

Further, the discussion of dispersion theory given earlier shows that the refractive index curves are steep only near regions of relatively high absorption of the material. There is little room to compromise.

7.11.5 *Reststrahlen Plates*

Filters can also be based on reflection, in fact, the most useful—and sometimes the only available—filters for the far infrared (15-1000 μ) are based on reflection. Throughout the far infrared, most materials are absorbing because of the free carrier contribution, but the refractive index still has maxima only at lattice absorption bands. It was pointed out in the section on dispersion theory that, in the region of a lattice absorption band, the refractive index goes through a minimum and then a maximum. At each maximum of refractive index, the reflection also has a maximum value. Since the maximum is relatively sharp, a certain amount of reflective spectral filtering can be done. At each reflection the passband is narrowed, so the ratio of reflection coefficients is increased, but the maximum available energy at the peak—the central transmission of the filter—is decreased. The principal restrictions of reststrahlen or residual-ray filters is their low peak transmission, and the fact that there is only a limited number of center wavelengths.

1. F. A. Jenkins and H. E. White, *Fundamentals of Optics.* New York: McGraw-Hill, 1954, Second Edition.
2. R. A. Sawyer, *Experimental Spectroscopy.* Englewood Cliffs, N.J.: Prentice-Hall, 1951, Second Edition.
3. J. Strong, *Principles of Classical Optics.* San Francisco: W. H. Freeman, 1959.
4. A. Bouwers, *Achievements in Optics.* New York: Elsevier, 1950.
5. M. R. Holter and W. L. Wolfe, "Optical-Mechanical Scanning Techniques," *Proc. IRE* 47, 1546-1550 (1959).
6. D. A. Pontarelli and N. S. Kapany, "Infrared Fiber Optics," *J. Opt. Soc. Am.* 50, 1128 (1960).
7. N. S. Kapany and J. J. Burke, "Experimental Studies of Waveguide Effects in Fiber Assemblies," *J. Opt. Soc. Am.* 50, 1128 (1960).
8. D. E. Williamson, "Cone Channel Condenser Optics," *J. Opt. Soc. Am.* 42, 712 (1952).
9. N. S. Kapany, "Fiber Optics. VIII The Focon," *J. Opt. Soc. Am.* 51, 32-34 (1961).
10. R. DeWaard and E. Wormser, *Thermistor Infrared Detectors, Part I, Properties and Developments.* Barnes Engineering Co., Stamford, Connecticut, NAVORD 5495 (April 30, 1958). Unclassified.
11. W. L. Wolfe and J. Duncan, "Immersion Lenses for Infrared Instruments." Presented at the Conference on Optical Instruments and Techniques, London, England, July 1961.
12. T. Limperis and W. Wolfe, "Dependence of Noise Equivalent Power on Area in PbS, PbSe, and PbTe," *J. Opt. Soc. Am.* 51, 482 (1961).
13. M. Born and E. Wolf, *Principles of Optics.* New York: Pergamon Press, 1959, First Edition, pp. 148-149.

14. P. Drude, *The Theory of Optics*. New York: Dover, 1959.
15. W. L. Wolfe and S. S. Ballard, "Optical Materials, Films, and Filters," *Proc. IRE* 47, 1540 (1959).
16. H. Welker and H. Weiss, "Group III–Group V Compounds," *Solid State Physics* 3, 1 (1959).
17. R. Bube, *Photoconductivity of Solids*. New York: Wiley, 1960.
18. F. W. Barth, "Some Immersion Melts of High Refraction," *American Mineralogist* 14, 358 (1929).

CHAPTER 8

PHYSICAL PROCESSES USABLE
FOR DETECTION

8.1 Detector Classification

One may classify infared detectors into two general classes—thermal detectors and quantum detectors—although all infrared detectors are ultimately quantum detectors, since radiation occurs in this form. The distinguishing feature lies in the particular property of the detector which is to perform the transducing action in changing fluctuations of the incoming infrared radiation to some more utilizable form. In the thermal detector, the photon is absorbed; the absorbed energy is spread to the atoms composing the detector by diffusion so that the result is a rise in detector temperature. A temperature-dependent property of the detector is monitored to make evident the change in this property. The action of a quantum detector, on the other hand, does not rely upon the intermediate diffusion of the energy to the atoms composing the detector, but the fluctuation in detector property after the absorption of radiation should be evident whether or not a rise in temperature occurs.

Any object which has a measurable temperature-dependent property can be used as a thermal detector. One commonplace example is the head of a match. The ignition of the match head is a temperature-dependent phenomenon. By focusing the image of the sun onto the head of a match with a two-inch-diameter reading glass, one can ignite the match. If, however, the sunlight first passed through several inches of salt water, then the match head would not ignite, even though the visible brightness of the solar image is not reduced. The head of the match is thus used as an infrared detector in an experiment which demonstrates the attenuation by salt water of infrared radiation. A person's hand is a more sensitive detector of infrared radiation than is the match head. The least detectable increase in infrared power density by the hand is about 0.01 w/cm^2 at room temperature, but this limit is quite variable with other conditions.

189

Any material is a potential quantum detector if the energy distribution of the electron motions can be altered by direct absorption of photons. In infrared quantum detectors, the electrons must be capable of absorbing photons having about 1 ev of energy or less. The search for the means of monitoring these changes in energy distribution is one of the most fascinating challenges to the inventor of new quantum detectors. In some cases, a change in electrical properties occurs—such as resistance change or electric potential difference change across the material—that gives ample evidence of the alteration of electron motions. The familiar photographic light meter is a quantum-detector device.

8.2 Detector Characteristics

Those characteristics which are most useful in infrared detectors will clearly depend upon the requirements of the measurements. The important characteristics of an infrared detector which must be considered are as follows:

1. Responsivity and spectral responsivity
2. Internal detector noise level
3. Response time
4. Dynamic range
5. Stability, or ability to hold a calibration
6. Size and shape
7. Engineering advantages (low cost, simplicity, no need for auxiliary apparatus, uniformity from sample to sample, and long shelf life)

Responsivity is defined as the signal level per watt of incident radiant power on the detector. The responsivity depends upon the spectral distribution of the incident radiant power as well as upon the detector. When a standard radiant source, such as the 500°K blackbody, is used to obtain a responsivity measurement, the responsivity can be considered a characteristic of the detector. When nearly monochromatic radiant power is used to obtain a responsivity measurement, the result is defined as the value of the spectral responsivity for that wavelength. A complete plot of the spectral responsivity for all wavelengths of interest is needed for device design. When the term, spectral responsivity, is used without reference to a particular wavelength, the complete curve is implied. Using the spectral responsivity, the responsivity for any special source with broad spectral distribution can be calculated by integrating the product of the spectral responsivity and the spectral distribution function of the source, and then dividing by the integral of the spectral distribution function of the source.

The responsivities vary over wide limits and become a major consideration in system design. This consideration corresponds to the choice of photographic film types in aerial photographic missions.

The internal noise level of the detector under operating conditions is an important factor in determining the threshold signal level for the detector. The noise is specified in terms of rms (root-mean-square) internal detector noise-level units. The amount of incident radiant power from a given source that will produce a signal level equal to the rms noise level is defined as the NEP (noise equivalent power) of the detector for that source. Here again, reference to a standard source is necessary in order to make the NEP a characteristic of a detector. It is not difficult to see that the NEP is simply the rms internal noise level, divided by responsivity.

The response time is the time required for the monitored property of a detector to achieve a specified fraction of the steady-state value when abruptly illuminated, or a specified fraction of the steady-state value when illumination is abruptly shut off. In some cases the rise time and decay times are different; thus, two numbers may be specified for response times. The common use of the exponential function to describe rise-and-decay characteristics should not be taken to imply that the rise and decay is always a simple exponential function of time, although in many practical cases an exponential function is an adequate approximation.

The dynamic range is usually measured in units of the rms internal noise level of the detector under zero-signal conditions. Usually the dynamic range is not limited by the detector but is limited by the succeeding amplification apparatus. The photographic film, as a special case, is composed of many elemental transducers. Each individual grain of silver halide acts as an irreversible transducer having a dynamic range of only one step. The transducing action of large numbers of these independent detection "channels" within a resolution element provides the dynamic range of photographic film. In this way, the poor dynamic range of the elemental detector can be counterbalanced simply by using huge numbers of parallel detectors that are activated statistically.

The ability to keep a calibration and maintain stability are familiar properties to all engineers, and these properties are self-explanatory.

The characteristic size and shape which a detector takes may sometimes influence other characteristics, such as NEP and response time. In such cases low NEP detectors may occur only in certain configurations which could limit the possible applications. Thermal detectors are frequently limited in this way because their response times depend upon heat capacity and conductance, which are shape- and size-dependent.

The various engineering advantages of low cost and little complexity are sometimes of primary importance. It is interesting to note that the age-old thermocouple is still a popular detector in use in laboratory spectroscopy because it is not high in cost and is simple to use and maintain. In many military device applications the thermocouple is

Table 8-1

Infrared

Name or Class of Detector	Transducing Material
Golay cell	Absorbing solid in contact with an enclosed gas
Rotating or deflecting vane radiometer	Low-pressure gas and adjacent vane with one side absorbing and one side reflecting
Liquid thermometer	Liquid such as mercury or alcohol constrained from a bulb container to move or expand into a capillary
Bimetalic strip	Two dissimilar metal strips fastened together to make a double ribbon
Evaprograph	Thin film of liquid on absorbing solid substrate
Photographic film, (Herschel effect)	Silver halide exposed by visible light to form latent image
Photographic film, (dye-sensitized)	Silver halide mixed with infrared absorbing dye
Stimulated phosphor	Zinc sulfide phosphor (for example) excited by ultraviolet light
Photoelectric emission tubes	Photosensitive cold cathode surface
Thermocouple	Junction of two dissimilar metals
Thermopile	Collection of thermocouples wired together usually in series
Bolometer	Conducting metallic or semi-conducting ribbon or wire
Photo-voltaic detectors	p-n Junction of semiconductor
Photomagnetoelectric detector	Semiconducting ribbon in magnetic field
Photoconducting detectors	Semiconducting ribbon or film

Transducers

Transducing Property	Amplification Method
Thermal expansion in the enclosure displaces a diaphragm	Optical lever and photo-multiplier
Thermal expansion of gas in contact with absorbing surface provides pressure to move the surface.	Optical lever
Thermal expansion of liquid observed by eye	Optical magnification and large ratio of bulb to capillary diameters
Differential thermal expansion causes ribbon to bend	Optical lever
Differential evaporation of the liquid film	Interferometric methods
Bleaching of latent image by near infrared radiation	Densitometer
Production of latent image by near infrared radiation	Densitometer
Stimulation of luminescence by near infrared radiation	Photometer or photographic plate with gamma control
Emission of free electrons which are accelerated by electric field to the anode	Amplification by standard electronic means or directly by electric field acceleration
Voltage generated across junction due to rise in temperature	Standard electronic means
Voltage generated across junctions due to rise in temperature of junctions	Standard electronic means
Change in resistance with temperature	Standard electronic means usually using a bridge circuit
Generation of voltage across junction by free carrier generation interior to the material	Standard electronic means
Generation of Hall effect voltage due to excitation of charge carrier gradient	Standard electronic means
Change in electrical resistance due to free carrier generation interior to the material	Standard electronic means.

most inadequate because of its relatively slow response time and poor sensitivity; nevertheless, its engineering advantages, coupled with broad spectral response and stability, make it one of the most used detectors in the laboratory.

8.3 Summary of Types of Extant Detectors

Because of the advanced state of the art of electrical measurement and amplification techniques of electrical signals, the majority of the most useful infrared detectors are transducers which transform the fluctuations of intercepted radiation into corresponding electric currents or voltages. Almost any amount of amplification can be applied to such electrical signals, so that the lower limit to sensitivity is set only by the random electric noise appearing in the detector along with the signal.

Table 8-1 lists the majority of the useful transducing materials and processes which are currently known and used. One should not be misled into believing that the table includes all possible useful transducing processes, for the number of possible transducing processes is almost limitless.

The recent popularity of research in laser (light amplification by simulated emission of radiation) should be mentioned mainly to point out that the laser is not actually a transducer but is an amplifier. The ability to preamplify the radiation before detection is as valuable as direct detector improvement; over-all detection capability may be achieved either way. The laser is not a panacea, however, since preamplification is not an important factor in applications where the spectral response must necessarily be broad (to receive blackbody radiation) and where the detector is already limited by background radiation noise because of this breadth. The major advantage of the laser in detection systems is the promise of being limited only by background radiation noise in a detection system using very narrow spectral ranges. The laser itself is not restricted to narrowband operation in principle because stagger tuning can always be used. It is simply that the background radiation noise is much lower than internal noise in infrared detectors designed to operate in narrow spectral ranges, whereas the background radiation noise is usually much greater and likely dominant over fixed internal noise in broad-spectrum detectors. For optical communications systems, the laser appears to hold substantial promise not only for preamplification but also for use in generating the transmitted signal.

8.4 Other Possible Detectors

In developing new transducing materials and processes, one should not be guided solely by the amount of response which the transducing material provides; with the present availability of electronic amplification and optical techniques using interferometric measurements, the amplification of almost any effect can be achieved. Therefore, the usefulness of whatever transducing process one should choose is not necessarily governed by its spectacular response to temperature rise or to incident radiation, but is governed by all seven characteristics which were previously mentioned. The spectacular response may be useful only for demonstration purposes, as in the case of the match head.

Some transducing materials which had been investigated very little are organic and biological materials. The pit viper snake can sense infrared radiation by two small pits on either side of its nose. Possibly the pit viper snake does not have suitable amplification means within its body to make full use of the NEP of its infrared detectors, and it does not have the means for obtaining optical gain. Other interesting materials are the organic dyes. Changes in the transmission coefficient, the absorption coefficient, the reflection coefficient, the polarizing effect, or magnetic effects of molecular systems are all possible transducing processes.

The investigation of other optical pumping devices is in its infancy. While the laser shows promise as a narrow-band amplifier, it is limited by internal noise due to spontaneous emission which increases in proportion to the operating frequency. An optical pumping device which operates as a frequency converter-amplifier has a different and possibly lower internal noise limitation.

An important factor which may be overlooked by detector researchers is ease in use, and for many applications this factor may be the governing one. Some transducing processes employ cooling to liquid helium temperature—that is, near $4°K$—but the difficulties and logistic requirements in handling liquid helium may so far overshadow any advantage that one gains that there may be only a few practical uses for such detectors. Only in very special applications, where at least one qualification of such detectors outstrips the corresponding qualifications of every other detector and where that extra qualification is essential to success in the detection process, would the use of such a detector be justifiable. It may appear odd that very significant gains remain to be made in modern detector technology through engineering advances in special cryostats which are only auxiliary to the detector cell. These advances should increase the engineering advantages of cooled detectors and make them applicable in devices which now must employ "uncooled" detectors in many ways less suitable but with low engineering penalty.

CHAPTER 9

QUANTUM DETECTORS

9.1 Summary of the Physics of Semiconductors

Quantum detectors may be classified by their mode of operation. Currently there are photoconducting, photovoltaic, and photomagnetoelectric, photoemissive, photographic, and luminescent modes. It should be pointed out that the first four modes listed here all depend upon gross fluctuating electric currents or potentials. The following summary of the present theory of operation of the quantum detecting modes is based upon the solid-state physics of semiconductors. A fairly brief summary is given, but with sufficient detail to provide insight into the processes which occur interior to the quantum detectors.

9.1.1 *Energy Bands and Electron Motion*

A very useful, though not fully accurate, model of the behavior of electrons in solids is currently used in most engineering literature on semiconducting devices. A number of good references exist.[1-4] The theory is best expounded by the use of an energy-level diagram such as that of Figure 9-1. Here is shown vertically the quantum-mechanical effects in

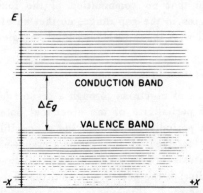

Fig. 9-1. Energy-level diagram of pure crystal. The valence band is normally fully occupied and the conduction band is normally unoccupied at very low temperature.

197

energy, and horizontally, the classical-mechanical effects in spatial distance.

Electrons move about within a crystalline solid. The constants of motion are described by four quantum numbers for each electron. Three quantum numbers specify the three components of the momentum and one quantum number specifies the orientation of the spin of the electron. Within the solid, the momentum quantum numbers describing the electron motion have only discrete and usually closely consecutive values. The total energy is a function of these discrete quantum numbers, and hence will also have only discrete values, closely consecutive (forming energy bands) except in a few important instances as illustrated by the gap in Figure 9-1.

For the purpose of this discussion the Pauli exclusion principle requires that, in any isolated atomic system (a semiconducting crystal in this discussion), no two electrons may take a motion which is specified by the same four quantum numbers. For every permissible set of four quantum numbers there is a value of energy which the electron must have. For an electron to "occupy" an energy level means that an electron has a motion described by the only four quantum numbers that correspond to that energy value.

In a crystal near absolute zero temperature, electrons tend to fall into the motion which provides the lowest total energy. Because of the Pauli exclusion principle, only a few electrons can move at the lowest energy levels and thereby occupy these levels. The others must move at higher energies as long as the lower levels are occupied in keeping with Pauli exclusion principle. In the case of an ideal semiconductor illustrated in Figure 9-1, the lower band of energy levels, "valence band," is fully occupied. A gap of forbidden energies exists between the lower energy valence band and the higher energy unoccupied or empty conduction band. This simply means that no combination of the four quantum numbers correspond to energies in the gap range, so that an electron cannot move through the material with these forbidden total energies.

9.1.2 Thermal Excitation of Electrons

The smooth motion of electrons through a crystal lattice depends upon the perfect spatial periodicity of the electrical potential energy. Any abrupt change from periodicity may provide a possible disruption of the motion. In crystals, even at low temperatures—e.g., liquid nitrogen temperature—the atoms are in constant agitated thermal motion. This agitation tends to disrupt the periodicity and, therefore, could disrupt the smooth motion of electrons. However, a disruption of the motion can occur only to those electrons which can change their motion or quantum numbers by such amounts that the change in electron energy is equal to the energy to be transferred by collision with the displaced atoms. Here the influence of the Pauli principle is important since an electron cannot absorb such energy if the resulting change in energy would bring the electron to an energy level which is already occupied. In this random agitated motion there is an important though infrequent chance that a fairly large energy exchange between electron and lattice atoms will occur such that electrons with energies near the top of the valence band can take on energies near the bottom of the conduction band where occupation of these levels is not likely. Once conduction-band motion is established, the electron is then free to accept even small additional energy increments from lattice atoms because of the low probability of occupation of adjacent energy levels in the conduction band. The resulting motion of the electron is then equivalent to Brownian motion as long as it moves with conduction band energies.

9.1.3 *The Concept of "Holes"*

When an electron in the valence band is excited into conduction band energy levels, a vacancy occurs in the energy level which it left. This vacant level can now be occupied by other electrons in the valence band by only small changes in energy which can easily be supplied by the lattice motion. The net result is that the vacant level may be occupied, leaving a new vacancy at a slightly different energy. This wandering vacancy acts physically as if a positively charged particle were undergoing Brownian motion with a tendency to rise on the energy level diagram to the highest occupied energy level in contradistinction to the electron which tends to fall to the lowest unoccupied energy level. The hypothetical particle is called a "hole" or p-type charge carrier because of the positive effective charge. The electrons in the conduction band in parallel nomenclature are called n-type charge carriers.

9.1.4 *Flow of Charge Carriers*

If the energy levels of the valence band were completely filled and the conduction band empty, there would be as many electrons moving in the $+X$ direction as in the $-X$ direction so that no net current would flow. The application of an external electric field does not alter this situation since the electrons cannot increase in energy by sufficiently small steps to accept acceleration by the field. The Pauli principle forbids small jumps to levels already occupied and the gap of forbidden energies is too large.

However, as soon as a pair on n- and p-type carriers are formed by the chance excitation of an electron from valence band energy to conduction band energy, current can flow, but only as much current as the motion of two charge carriers can provide. The conductivity σ is proportional to the number of such carriers and their mobility in the crystal so that

$$\sigma = e\,(n\mu_n + p\mu_p) \tag{9-1}$$

where e is the magnitude of the electronic charge, μ_n and μ_p are the mobilities respectively—i.e., the average drift velocity per unit electric field, n and p are the carrier concentrations in the mobile condition.

The equations for flow of carriers can be derived from statistical mechanics with the following rather general results

$$\mathbf{i}_n = ne\mu_n\mathbf{E} + e\,D_n\,\mathbf{grad}\ n \tag{9-2}$$

$$\mathbf{i}_p = pe\mu_p\mathbf{E} - e\,D_p\,\mathrm{grad}\ p \tag{9-3}$$

where $\mathbf{i}_n$ and $\mathbf{i}_p$ are the electric current densities carried by n- and p-type carriers, and D_n and D_p are the diffusion coefficients, $[D = (\mu kT/e)]$, and $\mathbf{E}$ is the gross electric field derived from Poisson's equation:

$$\mathrm{div}\ \mathbf{E} = [(4\pi e/\epsilon)]\ (p - n + t^+ - t^-) \tag{9-4}$$

where t^+ and t^- are charged defect concentrations and ϵ is the dielectric constant.

The assumption is always made that $\iiint (p - n + t^+ - t^-)\,dxdydz = 0$. The semi-conductor is electrically neutral over all. The first terms on the right of Eqs. (9-2) and (9-3) are just Ohm's law if $\mathbf{E}$ is largely from an external field. The second terms are thermodynamic terms arising from the fact that, in the absence of any electrical effects, the gradient of the concentrations should tend to vanish everywhere in the crystal—i.e., the most probable distribution of carriers in space is an even distribution. The self- and mutual electric field effects are accounted for by Poisson's equation: the applied field is introduced as the constant of integration of Eq. (9-4).

9.1.5 *Impurities in Semiconductors*

In most cases impurities in semiconducting materials are detrimental to the desirable properties as infrared detectors, but under controlled conditions traces of impurities in otherwise pure semiconductors can provide certain desirable changes in the energy band structure. Concentrations of the order of one part in 10^6 to 10^9 of selected materials are sometimes intentionally introduced for particular effects.

Like any defect in the perfect periodicity of a crystal potential, an atom of an impurity in the crystal tends to disrupt the smooth motion of p- or n-type carriers which may be free to accelerate. In addition, impurities can alter the energy-band picture in various ways, as indicated in Figure 9-2.

The energy levels due to impurities which are of interest fall within the large forbidden-energy gap. The levels are indicated as short in spatial extension implying that the electron is localized in space in the neighborhood of the impurity atom causing this change.

It should be noted that for substitutional impurities (those which take

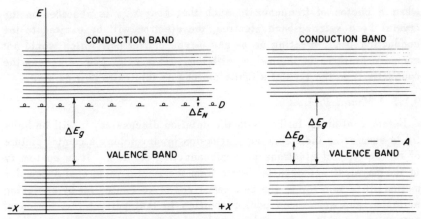

Fig. 9-2. Energy-level diagram of impure crystal. The levels marked D are typical donor levels which can donate electrons to the conduction band. The levels marked A are typical acceptor levels which can accept electrons from the valence band, i.e., donate holes to the valence band.

the same lattice position as the atoms of the pure material), the dashed lines are not additional levels, but represent an alteration of what was there before.

Two important types of alterations may occur. The level marked D, called a donor level, is normally filled at low temperatures, while the level marked A, called an acceptor level, is normally empty at low temperature.

At higher temperatures the thermal excitation is sufficient to excite electrons from donor levels to the conduction band in such numbers that the population of the donor levels is significantly depleted. A semiconductor in this condition will exhibit impurity conductivity having carriers of predominantly n-type. A similar picture applies to p-type conduction and acceptor levels. The empty localized level may be thought of as containing a trapped hole and the excitation of a valence band electron to that level may be viewed as the excitation of a p-type carrier from the localized level to the valence band. In any real crystal there are both types of impurity, although one type usually predominates.

9.1.6 Interaction With Radiation

The excitation of electrons in a solid may be brought about by the mechanical agitation of atoms, or by the absorption of photons which strike the crystal. While both types of excitation are important in infrared detectors, the excitation by photons plays a central role.

Suppose a pure crystal is held at low temperature so that the number of excited carriers (electrons in the conduction band and holes in the valence band) is small. Let the gap of forbidden energy be ΔE_g. Now, when a photon of frequency ν, such that $h\nu \geq \Delta E_g$, is absorbed in the crystal by a valence-band electron, the electron will be excited to the conduction band, creating an n- and p-type carrier pair which would not normally be there in thermal equilibrium. This extra pair increases the conductivity of the crystal slightly as long as this extra pair exists.

9.1.7 A Mental Picture

Before continuing further with the detailed discussion, it will be helpful to summarize the foregoing discussion by developing a mental picture of the activity of electrons in semiconducting crystals. It is customary in the physical sciences to delete from the mental picture of a complex motion all factors which can be summarized or accounted for by assigning suitable (and sometimes odd) properties to that part of the motion of particular interest. A good example of this practice is found in fluid dynamics: If one wishes to calculate the force required to accelerate a solid sphere suspended in an ideal incompressible fluid having the same density as the sphere, he must account for the momentum of the fluid moving around the sphere as well as the momentum of the sphere itself.

After performing the necessary calculation, one will find that the force needed to accelerate the sphere a given amount will be twice the force required to accelerate the sphere the same amount in free space. Now, one can assign an effective mass to the sphere and henceforth ignore the fluid flow problem. Newton's law of motion is preserved in the form

$$F = M^*a$$

where M^*, the effective mass, is twice the free space mass. It is also easy to show that, while the effective inertial mass is twice the free space value, the effective gravitational mass has become zero.

In the same spirit one may attempt to reduce the complexity of the mental image of electron motion in semiconductor crystals. Imagine that a big empty box represents the boundaries of a small electrically neutral semiconducting crystal. This box is filled with electrons moving through a perfectly periodic spatial array of electric potential centers. Recall that near absolute zero temperature with no incident photons an ordinary electric field will have no influence on this motion. We shall, therefore, consider that the box is effectively empty. Now suppose we allow a photon to enter the box with enough energy to excite an electron from the valence band to the conduction band. Suddenly, as if from nowhere in the effectively empty box, a p- and n-type charge carrier pair is created and the photon disappears. These two charged "particles" move freely through the box, bounce off of the walls, and in general obey Newton's laws of motion. To account for the influence of the periodic lattice of potential centers we resort to assigning effective inertial masses to these carriers. The effective masses of the n- and p-type carriers are not usually the same and can be either greater or less than the free-space electron mass. These carriers have an electric charge, $+e$ for the p-type carrier and $-e$ for the n-type carrier. We should expect the carriers to attract each other, and they do, but the force of attraction is reduced by the polarizability of the ion cores which provide the periodic potential. Hence, this "empty" space must have a dielectric constant assigned to it.

Now, consider the picture of the space in the box if a lattice defect is present. When a disruption of periodicity occurs in the periodic potential, that potential may be represented by the sum of two potentials so that

$$V_D = V_P + V_{AP}$$

where V_D is the existing disrupted potential, V_P is the periodic potential that should be there, and V_{AP} is an aperiodic potential.

The part of the potential V_D that causes a disruption of motion is V_{AP}. In order to visualize the potential V_{AP}, represent it by a small luminous volume in this box at the point of disruption such that the brightness of each part of the volume is proportional to the potential V_{AP}. If one of the charge carriers passes near this spot, it will be deflected or possibly captured. In many ways this potential V_{AP} acts as a scattering and binding center for charge carriers just as the pins and holes scatter and capture balls in a pinball machine. Time-dependent disruptions of periodicity occur if the temperature of the crystal is allowed to rise above absolute zero. The thermal agitation of ion cores moves them momentarily from their proper lattice positions, giving rise to a time-dependent potential V_{AP} for each shifting ion. The thermal motion of ion cores in a crystal lattice may be represented by the superposition of very many different high-frequency plane waves of strain moving through the crystal in arbitrary phase, so that the resulting appearance in the box would be a random scintillation of potential spots. The plane waves of strain are also quantized, and each quantum of strain wave is given the appropriate name "phonon." The superposition of some of these waves of disruptive potential may accidentally become large at some point in the box such that an n- and p-type carrier pair appear from "nowhere," and the disruptive potential or phonon disappears. This is the visualization of the thermal generation of charge carrier pairs. Naturally, if a charge carrier is trapped near a fixed defect, it is also possible for phonons to shake the carrier loose and free it by a momentary distortion of the potential at the fixed defect.

The motion of charge carriers in the space which is now represented by fixed and scintillating potential spots is anything but simple straight-line motion. The motion of the charge carriers is essentially Brownian. Application of an external electric field will cause the carriers to drift in the appropriate direction while undergoing many deflecting collisions.

As fast as the external field accelerates the charge carriers, collisions with phonons take away the added energy with a subsequent increase in phonon energy. This is the visualization of Joule heating.

The mobility of a charge carrier is the down-field drift speed per unit electric-field strength. Clearly a reduction in temperature will increase the mobility by reducing the number of collisions deflecting the down field motion of the carrier. As soon as the temperature is so low that only the permanent defects or potential disruptions remain, then the mobility will be limited by what is called impurity scattering.

With this picture of activity one can see that n- and p-type carriers along with traps or permanent defects can be treated by statistical mechanics in the usual manner as a special type of gas where the chemical mass-action law and Le Chatelier's principle apply. The reaction rates are quite parallel to those of ordinary chemical reactions, and the types of reactions can be neatly classified by the use of familiar chemical notation.

For example, the final recombination of carriers can occur by direct collision of p and n carriers so that the process can be written as

$$p^+ + n^- \longrightarrow \text{photon} \qquad (9\text{-}5)$$

However, the reaction rate is very small. Certain traps generally reside in semiconductors which have energy levels with relatively large energy differences from the valence band or conduction band. The probability that a carrier should be re-emitted to the conducting condition by thermal agitation, after being trapped here, is small compared to the probability that the recombination with the opposite carrier will occur at that site. Such recombination sites are sometimes called "ground states" or "recombination centers." The following reaction can take place:

$$r + n^- \longrightarrow (r, n)^- + \text{phonon} \qquad (9\text{-}6)$$

$$(r, n)^- + p^+ \longrightarrow r + \text{phonon} \qquad (9\text{-}7)$$

where r represents the recombination site, and the phonon represents mechanical motion of the lattice atoms. Actually a great variety of reactions can occur, depending upon the nature of the trapping levels. In luminescent materials a reaction such as

$$\text{photon}_1 \longrightarrow p^+ + n^- \qquad (9\text{-}8)$$

$$r + n^- \longrightarrow (r, n)^- + \text{phonon} \qquad (9\text{-}9)$$

$$(r, n)^- + p^+ \longrightarrow r + \text{photon}_2 \qquad (9\text{-}10)$$

describes the emission of longer wavelength light than the wavelength of the exciting light.

9.1.8 *Reaction Rates*

The rate at which pairs are created will be proportional to the number of suitable quanta incident upon the crystal. Usually, the extra electrons and holes do not stay separated for long. They recombine by the aid of at least two means, but the end result is the same regardless of the mechanism, i.e., a conduction band electron finds a hole in the valence band sooner or later and loses energy to return to the original lower energy level. The rate at which extra *n-* and *p*-type carriers recombine will determine the average time extra carriers can spend in the conducting state of motion.

In a pure crystal the average time spent by the charge carriers in the conducting condition and the average time required for recombination are the same. However, if localized energy levels exist in an impure crystal then a portion of the time of the charge carriers may be spent in these levels (called traps) and only intermittantly are the carriers free to conduct. The "lifetime" of the carriers is defined as the average time which the charge carrier spends in the conducting condition while the "recombination time" is defined as the average time the charge carrier stays in the excited states of motion, which includes the time spent in temporary localized positions at traps. Thus, the recombination time is always greater than, or equal to, the lifetime.

In many cases a trap energy level can be "occupied" by only one charge carrier so that the average population of carriers in all trap levels can never exceed a certain maximum number. As the population of carriers in trap levels increases, the number of unoccupied traps becomes significantly sparse so that the influence of traps tends to become inert. The rate at which charge carriers are trapped depends upon the "cross section" for capture by the traps *t*, for a particular charge carrier. Hence for

$$n^- + t_1 \rightleftarrows (t_1, n)^- + \text{phonon}; \qquad p^+ + t_2 \rightleftarrows (t_2, p)^+ + \text{phonon} \quad (9\text{-}11)$$

the rates are

$$R_n = \Sigma_N \bar{v}_n \, N\Delta n; \qquad Rp = \Sigma_p \bar{v}_p P\Delta p \qquad (9\text{-}12)$$

where R is the number per cubic centimeter per second of extra carriers trapped, Σ is the corresponding capture cross section, $\bar{v}$ is the average speed of the charge carrier, N and P are the concentrations of the respective empty traps, and n and p are the concentrations of the respective extra charge carriers in the conducting state of motion.

The reverse reaction rate at which extra carriers are re-emitted into the conducting state of motion from traps depends mainly upon the size of the energy jump required to get away. Hence,

$$G_n = \nu_N N' \exp\left(-\Delta E_N / kT\right); \qquad G_p = \nu_p P' \exp\left(-\Delta E_p / kT\right) \quad (9\text{-}13)$$

where G_n and G_p are the number per cubic centimeter per second breaking free of traps, ν_N and ν_P are characteristic frequencies of the traps, N' and P' are the concentrations of traps occupied by extra carriers, ΔE_N and ΔE_P are the energy jumps required to break free again, k is the Boltzmann constant, and T is the absolute temperature.

Consider the possible set of reactions causing a photoresponse:

$$\text{photon} \rightarrow p^+ + n^-; \qquad \text{rate, } \eta \alpha I$$

$$p^+ + r_1 \rightarrow (p, r_1)^+ + \text{phonon}; \qquad \text{rate, } \Delta p / \tau_p$$

$$n^- + r_2 \rightarrow (n, r_2)^- + \text{phonon}; \qquad \text{rate, } \Delta n / \tau_n \qquad (9\text{-}14)$$

$$\left. \begin{aligned} n^- + t_1 &\rightleftarrows (n, t_1)^- + \text{phonon} \\ p^+ + t_2 &\rightleftarrows (p, t_2)^+ + \text{phonon} \end{aligned} \right\} \text{rates as in Eqs. (9-12) and (9-13)}$$

Now we may write a relation for the generation and recombination of extra carriers including primary photoeffect and recombination center reactions.

$$\frac{\partial \Delta n}{\partial t} = \eta \alpha I - \frac{\Delta n}{\tau_n} + \nu_N N' \exp\left(-\frac{\Delta E_N}{kT}\right) - \Sigma_N \bar{v}_n N \, \Delta n \qquad (9\text{-}15)$$

$$\frac{\partial \Delta p}{\partial t} = \eta \alpha I - \frac{\Delta p}{\tau_p} + \nu_p P' \exp\left(-\frac{\Delta E_P}{kT}\right) - \Sigma_P \bar{v}_p P \, \Delta p \qquad (9\text{-}16)$$

where η is the fraction of absorbed photons which produce carriers, α is the absorption coefficient, and I is the number of photons per square centimeter incident upon the section of semiconductor under consideration. The first term on the right is the generation rate of carriers by photoexcitation. The second term is the rate of recombination by recombination centers and direct p-n collisions. The third term is the rate of regeneration of free carriers from shallow traps, and the fourth term is the rate of combination of free carriers with shallow traps. If a number of different kinds of shallow traps exist, additional terms similar to the third and fourth must be added.

It should be pointed out that Eqs. (9-15) and (9-16) are simply special cases of the more general continuity equations where div i = 0. These equations in their general form for semiconductors are

$$\partial n / \partial t = (1/e) \, \text{div} \, i_n + G_n - R_n \qquad (9\text{-}17)$$

$$\partial p / \partial t = - (1/e) \, \text{div} \, i_p + G_p - R_p \qquad (9\text{-}18)$$

The first term on the right represents the net rate of increase in concentration due to the influx of carriers at some position in space. The second term represents the rate of increase in concentration due to excitation or generation of carriers into the conducting condition at that position from all sources. The last term represents the rate of decrease of concentration due to recombination or capture of carriers at that position for all sinks.

The further analysis of this model will not be covered here. Certain important consequences should be pointed out. Notice that the lifetimes of the two types of carriers need not be the same and, in fact, are usually significantly different. The extra charge carrier concentrations need not be equal, and in general are significantly different. Recall that, by definition, Δn and Δp are the extra carriers which are in the conducting state. Those stuck temporarily in traps are not counted. Since the crystal is expected to be electrically neutral at all times, the balance of extra charge carriers must reside in traps when $\Delta p \neq \Delta n$.

In the simple trap model which is discussed here, only one carrier is required for occupation. So the concentration of empty traps, plus the concentration of traps occupied by extra carriers, must just equal the concentrations N_0, P_0 of traps normally unoccupied during thermal equilibrium—i.e.,

$$N + N' = N_0$$
$$P + P' = P_0$$

Thus the above relations may be written as

$$\frac{\partial \Delta n}{\partial t} = \eta \alpha I - \frac{\Delta n}{\tau_n} + \nu_N N' \exp\left(-\frac{\Delta E_N}{kT}\right) - \Sigma_N \bar{v}_n (N_0 - N')\Delta n \quad (9\text{-}19)$$

$$\frac{\partial \Delta p}{\partial t} = \eta \alpha I - \frac{\Delta p}{\tau_p} + \nu_P P' \exp\left(-\frac{\Delta E_P}{kT}\right) - \Sigma_P \bar{v}_p (P_0 - P')\Delta p \quad (9\text{-}20)$$

In thermal equilibrium the quantities Δn, Δp, N', and P' are zero by definition. Hence, Δn and Δp will both increase at the rate of $\eta \alpha I$ when proper illumination is abruptly started. When the steady state has been reached under illumination,

$$\partial \Delta n/\partial t = \partial \Delta p/\partial t = 0 \quad (9\text{-}21)$$

Moreover, it can be demonstrated by straightforward reasoning that the terms on the right must balance in pairs.

$$\eta \alpha I - (\Delta n/\tau_n) = 0, \quad \nu_N N' \exp[-\Delta E_N/kT] -$$
$$\Sigma_N \bar{v}_n (N_0 - N')\Delta n = 0 \quad (9\text{-}22)$$

and similarly for the p-type carrier. Since the trapping has now balanced itself by supplying as many free carriers as it traps, the population of extra carriers is simply

$$\Delta n = \tau_n \eta \alpha I, \qquad \Delta p = \tau_p \eta \alpha I. \qquad (9\text{-}23)$$

The effect of shallow temporary traps on the response time is usually to lengthen the rise and decay times. In order to establish a steady state, additional carriers must be generated to populate the traps, as well as to supply the usual loss of carriers through recombination. The decay time is also delayed by the time required to empty the population in temporary traps.

Since the lifetime of a carrier is measured only by the average time extra carriers remain in the conducting condition, the trapping of a carrier by a recombination center ends the life of the carrier even though that carrier may have to wait for a carrier of opposite type to complete the recombination reaction; so it is not unexpected to find the lifetimes of the two carrier types differing by significant amounts. One type of carrier usually waits for the other in a recombination center.

9.2 Detection Modes

The operation of infrared quantum detectors is based upon the monitoring of the extra carriers generated in the above fashion. The means by which this monitoring is performed determines the mode of operation of the detector. A detailed analysis of the operation of the photoconducting, photovoltaic, and photoelectromagnetic modes is given in Chapter 10. A qualitative discussion of the photographic, luminescent, and photoemissive modes is given in the remaining sections of this chapter.

9.2.1 Photographic Film

One of the best references for applications and a brief description of the process occurring in infrared photographs can be seen in *Photography by Infrared*, by Walter Clark.[5] In order to describe the infrared effects on photographic film, it will be necessary first to describe the formation of the latent image by ordinary visible radiation. The photographic emulsion is formed by mixing the silver halide salt crystallites with a gelatin. The exact process of mixing and laying down these gelatins is an art. But we can examine the essential features of the formation of the latent image by neglecting the effects of the gelatin and aging processes which are usual for speeding the photographic film or making it more sensitive. Consider a silver halide crystallite. It is a fairly good insulator. The energy-level diagram will appear as if it were an ordinary semiconductor, but the energy gap is quite large. Photons having wavelengths in the blue region of the spectrum are required to excite electrons across the energy-band gap. Another important property of silver halide crystals is the ability of the silver ion itself to wander through the crystal.

The photographic process begins by the absorption of a blue wavelength quantum of light by the valence electron. The valence electron is excited to the conducting state. It then wanders about in Brownian motion until it finds a trap or metastable state slightly below the conduction band. This electron forms a negative charge center and attracts a positive interstitial silver ion somewhere in the lattice. The silver ion eventually finds its way by Brownian motion to the trap where the electron combines with the ion to produce metallic silver. The process can be written as

$$\text{photon} \longrightarrow n^- + p^+ \tag{9-24}$$

$$t + n^- \rightleftarrows (t, n)^- + \text{phonon} \tag{9-25}$$

$$(t, n)^- + Ag^+ \rightleftarrows Ag + \text{phonon} \tag{9-26}$$

which leaves a p-type carrier which is removed as follows

$$p^+ + Br^- \rightleftarrows Br + \text{phonon} \tag{9-27}$$

The excitation of a second electron also can find a similar trap, perhaps in the neighborhood of the first, or perhaps even the same trap after the electron has satisfied the silver ion. A second silver ion will proceed by Brownian motion to come to the electron in the trap. Thus, a few silver atoms may be formed at a particular locality in this crystal. This nucleus of silver atoms forms a part of the latent image. This nucleus is not observable by microscopic investigation. Upon bringing the developing solution into contact with the silver halide crystal, the silver ions precipitate around the nucleus forming a silver deposit in the gelatin. Those crystals which do not have a nucleus do not deposit their silver in this manner. The fixing solution dissolves the unprecipitated silver halide out of the gelatin.

In the infrared dye-sensitized film, a dye which can absorb infrared radiation is placed in the gelatin along with the silver halide crystal. Actual atomic contact is made by this dye with the silver halide crystal. Infrared radiation having a longer wavelength than that which will be needed to excite the latent image in the parent silver halide crystal can be absorbed in the infrared dye, and this absorbed energy is, in some way as yet unknown, passed on to the silver halide crystal. A hypothesis about this action is that the infrared radiation can ionize this dye in contact with the silver halide so that an electron can proceed from the dye into the crystal, and form the first part of the sensitizing speck by finding a trap in the crystal. The spectral absorbtivity of the dye, therefore, specifies the spectral sensitivity of the infrared film. In order to use infrared film it is necessary for obvious reasons to filter out the blue radiation; otherwise, the film will be sensitive both to infrared as well as to the visible blue. The reaction for the dye-sensitized film could be considered as:

$$photon + dye \longrightarrow dye^+ + n^- \tag{9-28}$$

$$t + n^- \longrightarrow (t, n)^- + phonon \tag{9-29}$$

$$(t, n)^- + Ag^+ \longrightarrow t + Ag + phonon \tag{9-30}$$

A second infrared effect is obtained without any sensitizing dye. This is called the Herschel effect. While the latent image is being formed by the electron located in a remote trap in the crystal, infrared radiation of the proper wavelength may be able to dislodge this electron from that trap, and with sufficient luck can keep that electron from finding its way to another trap before it recombines by falling across the energy gap back to its parent position. The reaction of Eqs. (9-25) and (9-26) may be reversed by photons with the recombination being achieved by

$$n^- + r \longrightarrow (n, r)^- + phonon \tag{9-31}$$

$$p^+ + (n, r)^- \longrightarrow r + phonon \tag{9-32}$$

Thus, if a photographic plate is exposed to visible blue light, a large portion of the crystals have a latent image formed in them, that is, a small speck wherein an electron is trapped slightly below the conduction band. Now, if we expose the plate to a near-infrared source we will find that, before development, the latent image can be bleached out again. This effect is unfortunately not a very sensitive one. However, it has been used in the past for certain interesting applications in spectroscopy.

The question is properly asked why infrared photography is apparently limited to the near infrared. Certainly if one can find organic dyes which can absorb near-infrared radiation then perhaps one can find dyes that can absorb radiation a little bit longer. This is certainly the case; however, practical problems arise in handling or even preparing the film. If the film is to be reasonably sensitive, then only a slight exposure to infrared radiation of the proper wavelength should be required to form an image. If we should prepare a film which is sensitive to wavelengths out to 3 μ, we can show by a small amount of calculation that storage of the film, or even the preparation of the film at room temperature, would be sufficient to fog the film before it could be used. The problem is not one of creating the film, but one of making unexposed film. Since all of the current photographic art is done at room temperature with chemical solutions, gelatins, and such, which require room-temperature operation in order to keep things fluid, there is little chance of a simple approach to the extension of infrared photography to longer wavelengths. What is apparently required here is a new sensitizing means. We must have a sensitizer which can be introduced into the gelatin along with the silver halide so that the property of sensitization can be triggered from an external magnetic, electric, or acoustic field, or other influence, when one is ready to employ the film. If one could obtain such a triggered sensitizer, then one could prepare the film by the usual process at room temperature. When the exposure is ready to be made, or the sensitization is ready to be applied, then the photographic film should be reduced in temperature, let us say to liquid air temperature, exposed there; and then sensitization must be removed before the film can be raised to room temperature, and developed and fixed as usual. Only one defect exists in such a process: Recall that the formation of the latent image requires the ionic diffusion of a silver ion to the captured electron. This diffusion process will be substantially slowed at reduced temperatures. Thus, the speed of the film will not be very high.

9.2.2 Infrared Stimulation of Phosphors

If a phosphor such as zinc sulfide is illuminated with ultraviolet light and the phosphor is sufficiently activated by impurity atoms, the phosphor will glow with a particular color. After the ultraviolet light is extinguished the phosphor will continue to glow, but with steadily reducing intensity. If now one should expose this to infrared radiation of the proper wavelength, one would find that the glow would suddenly brighten and then disappear at a more rapid rate than would normally occur. The occurrence of this stimulation is quite similar to the stimulation of the photographic latent image in the Herschel effect. Consider the following reactions:

$$\text{photon (u.v.)} \longrightarrow p^+ + n^- \tag{9-33}$$

$$n^- + t \rightleftarrows (n, \, t)^- + \text{phonon} \tag{9-34}$$

$$n^- + r \longrightarrow (n, \, r)^- + \text{photon (visible)} \tag{9-35}$$

$$p^+ + (n, \, r)^- \longrightarrow r + \text{phonon} \tag{9-36}$$

$$p^+ + (n, \, t)^- \longrightarrow t + \text{photon (visible)} \tag{9-37}$$

When the ultraviolet light illuminates the phosphor, an electron is excited from the valence band to the conduction band, and is lodged eventually in a metastable state t, slightly below the conduction band. This metastable state will be an unstable position for the electron to maintain for any length of time. At random intervals such electrons will be kicked out of these states by thermal agitation of the lattice, and eventually decay back via recombination centers to the valence band, as in the fast reaction [Eq. (9-35)], or by the slow direct process [Eq. (9-37)]. While the process of luminescence is usually somewhat complicated, this description will suffice to describe the effect. The exposure to infrared radiation of a phosphor having electrons situated in metastable states will speed the decay of the electrons back to their former states by reversing the reaction of Eq. (9-34) with photons, and hence explain the sudden brightening of luminescence through Eq. (9-35) with a subsequent decrease in further luminescence.

A phosphor in the form of a sheet can then be used as an image plate very much like the photographic plate itself. The phosphor plate can be placed in very close contact with the photographic plate after the exposure of the phosphor has been made to infrared radiation. The stimulation effect will then provide a darkened image in contact with this photographic plate, and hence expose the photographic plate in the visible region in accordance with the infrared image that was seen.

9.2.3 *Photoemissive Tubes*

The action of the photoemissive tube is somewhat similar to the action of other photodetectors. An incident photon ejects an electron from a metal cathode into an evacuated space. A potential difference between the cathode and metal anode draws the electron to the anode with a consequent measurable flow of current. If no electrons are ejected into the evacuated space then no current can flow. The minimum energy which a photon must have to eject electrons from the cathode is determined mainly by the work function of the cathode surface. The lowest work functions which have been achieved are close to 1 ev. Hence, the wavelengths which can be detected by photoemissive tubes are restricted to the near infrared.

One might think offhand that, if it takes only one electron volt to remove an electron from the surface, then the application of just one volt from anode to cathode would permit all electrons to pour out freely. As is well known, that will not happen. The reason lies in the requirement that the one-volt potential drop shall occur within a few atomic distances from the cathode surface; otherwise, the electrons must be continually reflected back into the interior of the cathode. It is certainly true that, if the electron could actually get out of the surface, then it would not return; but the probability that an electron can get out at all depends upon the electric field strength at the surface and not on the total potential drop it would experience once it is released.

1. L. P. Hunter, *Handbook of Semiconductor Electronics*. New York: McGraw-Hill, 1956.
2. N. F. Mott and R. W. Gurney, *Electronic Processes in Ionic Crystals*. New York: Oxford University Press, 1948, Second Edition.
3. C. Kittel, *Introduction to Solid State Physics*. New York: Wiley, 1956, Second Edition.
4. E. U. Condon and H. Odishaw, *Handbook of Physics*. New York: McGraw-Hill, 1958, Part 8.
5. Walter Clark, *Photography by Infrared*. New York: Wiley, 1946, Second Edition.

CHAPTER 10

DETECTOR PARAMETERS

This chapter deals primarily with the processes of signal and noise generation in quantum and thermal detectors. In addition, discussion is included to describe a detector's speed of response and spectral response characteristic. However, additional information pertinent to these last two parameters is found in Chapter 12 on measurement procedures.

The mechanisms involved in signal and noise generation are described in substantial detail, accompanied generally by quantitative treatments that hopefully exemplify appropriate analysis procedures. The intention here is to establish the necessary background for Chapter 11, which deals with theoretical concepts for evaluating performance capability of detectors.

10.1 Signal Generation in Quantum Detectors

The quantum detector absorbs electromagnetic radiation (or photons), and generates from this absorption new, internal charge carriers. The mechanism of this process requires that the quantum of energy associated with the photons ($E_{ph} = h\lambda/c$) be greater than some critical energy corresponding to allowed transitions between energy levels in the forbidden-energy region, the conduction band, and/or the valence band of the semiconducting detector. This process is carried out without any significant temperature change. The additional carriers that are generated appear in a form suitable for measurement as a voltage or a current.

10.1.1 *Photoconductive Detectors*

The photoconductive detector is generally operated with the simple circuitry of Figure 10-1. The voltage drop across the detector is given by:

$$V_C = \frac{V}{r_L + r_C} \cdot r_C \qquad (10\text{-}1)$$

213

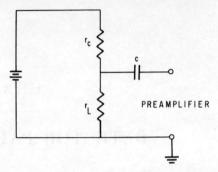

Fig. 10-1. Photoconductive detector circuit.

where V is the bias battery voltage, r_L is the load resistor, and r_C is the resistance of the photoconductive detector.

The signal voltage is the variation in the voltage drop caused by the change in r_C, when the detector is exposed to signal radiation. Therefore:

$$\Delta V_C = I \cdot \Delta r_C + \Delta I \cdot r_C$$
$$= I \cdot \Delta r_C$$

where I (the bias current) $= V/(r_L + r_C)$, and $\Delta I = 0$ when photoconductive detectors are operated under constant current conditions.

The change in resistance is due to the change in the number of carriers created by the absorption of signal photons. For the simplest kind of analysis, consider the intrinsic photoconductor whose hole and electron mobilities are approximately equal. The geometrical configuration shown in Figure 10-2, where the electrodes are placed across the wd end faces, and the lw surface is exposed to radiation, will be used for all discussions that follow, unless otherwise specified. The cell resistance is given by:

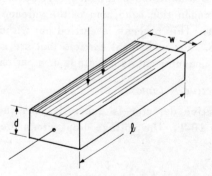

Fig. 10-2. Detector geometry.

$$r_C = \rho \frac{l}{dw} = \frac{l}{\sigma dw} = \frac{l}{2ne\mu dw}$$

where ρ is the electric resistivity

σ is the electric conductivity $= ne\mu_n + pe\mu_p = 2ne\mu$

μ is the mobility equal to $(\mu_n = \mu_p)$,

n is the density of electrons

p is the density of holes

l is the detector length

w is the detector width

d is the detector thickness

When radiation strikes the detector, it causes a change in the density of carriers, and therefore a change in conductivity. The change in resistance is then given by:

$$\Delta r = \frac{dr}{dn} \cdot \Delta n_S = -\frac{\rho l}{dw} \cdot \frac{\Delta N_S}{N} \qquad (10\text{-}2)$$

where $N_s = n_s \cdot wld$. The signal voltage is then

$$V_s = I \cdot \Delta r_C = \frac{V}{r_L + r_C} \cdot \frac{\rho l}{dw} \cdot \frac{\Delta n_s}{n} \qquad (10\text{-}3)$$

or

$$V_s = \frac{V}{r_L + r_C} \cdot \frac{\rho l}{dw} \cdot \frac{\Delta N_s}{N} \qquad (10\text{-}4)$$

The small photodetector signal properties are governed by[1]

$$\frac{d}{dt}\Delta N_s = A\eta_s J_s - \frac{\Delta N_s}{\tau} \qquad (10\text{-}5)$$

$$\Delta N_s = N(t) - N$$

where A is the area wl, N is the equilibrium number of electrons in the absence of the signal radiation J_s, η_s is the responsive quantum efficiency, and τ is the electron-hole lifetime. The solution of this equation for a sinusoidal signal of modulation frequency $f = \omega/2\pi$ is

$$\left| \Delta N_s(f) \right| = \frac{A\eta_s J_s \tau}{\sqrt{1 + (\omega\tau)^2}} \qquad (10\text{-}6)$$

The fractional change in conductivity is:

$$\frac{\left| \Delta N_s(f) \right|}{N} = \frac{\eta_s J_s \tau}{nd\sqrt{1 + (\omega\tau)^2}} \qquad (10\text{-}7)$$

The signal voltage is now

$$V_s = \frac{V}{r_L + r_C} \cdot \frac{\rho l}{dw} \cdot \frac{\eta_s J_s \tau}{nd \sqrt{1 + (\omega \tau)^2}}$$ (10-8)

It is clear that signal response improves with longer lifetimes, improved quantum efficiencies, and decreasing equilibrium density of carriers.

10.1.2 *Photovoltaic Detectors*

The infrared photovoltaic detector is generally made of a single crystal of some semiconductor, with distinctive n- and p-type regions. These regions are separated by a barrier called the "depletion" layer, across which a strong electric field exists. Similar layers can also be formed at a metal-semiconductor contact, a p-type surface on an n-type bulk crystal, and a junction between two semiconductors with unequal band gaps. They all can be used to generate photovoltages.

Consider two crystals which are identical except that one crystal has impurities which make it n-type and the other has different impurities which make it p-type. The first crystal has a greater density of electrons than has the second, while the reverse is true for holes. If these two crystals are connected together with perfect alignment of the atoms so as to make one large single crystal, then the higher concentration of electrons in the n region causes a diffusion of electrons into the p region, and vice versa for holes.

However, this process does not go on until equal densities of electrons and holes prevail throughout the crystal, the reason being that each region of the crystal initially is independently electrically neutral, even though they have opposite types of conductivity. Thus, when an electron diffuses from the n to the p side of the crystal, it gives the p side a negative charge. The next charge to diffuse over does so with more difficulty since the first charge has created an opposing electric field. Each successive charge that diffuses over experiences increased opposition, and requires more energy to get over to the p side. Those that do get over have an increased potential energy corresponding to the charge build-up. Exactly the opposite situation prevails for holes. A negative charge layer is built up on the p side, while a positive charge layer is built up on the n side. This is shown in Figure 10-3. Finally, an equilibrium situation is reached where electrons diffusing from the n- to the p-type region are balanced by a flow of carriers drifting in the opposite direction because of the electric field. A corresponding situation applies to holes. This explains why a current flow is not observed when the two regions of the crystal are connected to an ammeter. At first glance, an examination of Figure 10-3 would lead to the impression that

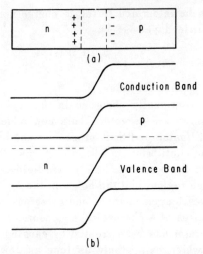

Fig. 10-3. P-N junction. (a) Simplified charge distribution across the barrier.
(b) Energy level diagram.

the charge distribution should cause the crystal to behave like a battery,
since obviously an electrical potential difference exists. However, the
total current is the sum of the currents caused by this potential difference and that due to the imbalance in the charge densities of the two
regions. At equilibrium, these currents are equal and opposite, resulting
in a net current flow equal to zero. Mathematically, this situation can
be described for the one-dimensional case as follows:

$$i_n = \sigma E = -ne\mu_n \frac{dV}{dx} \tag{10-9}$$

$$i_d = D_n \frac{dn}{dx} = \frac{kT}{e}\mu_n \frac{dn}{dx} \tag{10-10}$$

where the p-n surface junction is taken perpendicular to the x direction,
i_n and i_d are the electronic drift and diffusion current densities respectively, D_n is the diffusion coefficient for electrons, given by the Einstein
relationship

$$D = (kT/e)\mu \tag{10-11}$$

and the other quantities as noted earlier. At equilibrium, these two
current densities are equal and opposite, so that:

$$ne\mu_n \frac{dV}{dx} = D_n \frac{dn}{dx} \tag{10-12}$$

This expression can be integrated to relate charge density and potential distribution in the barrier layer as:

$$n(x) = A e^{(\mu_n/D_n)V(x)} \qquad (10\text{-}13)$$

A similar derivation applies for holes.

When photons are continually absorbed in the region of the p-n junction, electron-hole pairs are created. This new added concentration of carriers alters the diffusion and drift processes established in the dark, and results in a new equilibrium condition. A new, lower potential difference exists across the barrier. The electric field causing electrons to drift toward the n-type region, and the holes in the opposite region create negative and positive charges in the n and p regions respectively. This results in the generation of a photovoltage measured across the junction. Thus a voltage generator has been created by causing a new distribution of charge carriers, which exists only as long as new carriers are continually being generated by the absorption of photons.

Another approach to understanding the basic process is to think of the device as a kind of current generator, in which the new carriers generated are forced by the new nonequilibrium conditions to move out of the crystal junction. The n side of the crystal, now with too many electrons, becomes the negative electrode, and electrons exit through its electrode. The situation is reversed for holes on the p-type side, with the understanding that the exiting of holes corresponds to electrons entering the p crystal.

A quantitative treatment describing this situation can be arrived at by utilizing the theory of the p-n junction diode. We shall not try to develop the theory here, but to describe its results and the physical mechanisms involved.

The p-n junction is a diode whose voltage-current characteristic depends on the bias direction and the magnitude of the bias. The modern theory of the p-n junction derives from Shockley.[2] The evolution of the theory is described by Moll.[3] According to Shockley, the current-voltage relationship in the simplest case of a low applied field, with steep concentration gradients in going from the n- to the p-type regions, is given by:

$$I = I_s \left[\exp\left(eV/kT\right) - 1 \right] \qquad (10\text{-}14)$$

where

$$I_s = \left[\frac{p_n D_h}{L_p} + \frac{n_p D_e}{L_n} \right] \cdot e \qquad (10\text{-}15)$$

where L_n and L_p are the diffusion lengths of minority carrier electrons and holes in p- and n-type materials respectively, and D_e and D_h are the corresponding diffusion constants. The diffusion constants and length are related by the Einstein equation:

$$L = \sqrt{D\tau} = \sqrt{(kT/e)\mu\tau} \tag{10-16}$$

where τ is the minority carrier lifetime and D is the diffusion coefficient for either electrons or holes as indicated by a subscript.* In this treatment, the current of holes flowing in one side of the junction is the same as that flowing out the other, while the current of electrons is also equal at both surfaces of the junction, but moving, of course, in the opposite direction. The net current flow is then simply the sum of the hole and electron currents. One assumes further that charge carrier flow of electrons into the p region and holes into the n region (after passing through the junction) is essentially a diffusion process. That is, the n and p type regions are more highly conductive than the junction, and, therefore, that practically all of the voltage drop is across the junction.

It is clear, from examination of Eq. (10-14) in the case of an applied voltage sufficiently large, that I is exponentially dependent on the voltage. When the applied voltage is negative, then the current flow approaches the saturation value I_s. The first case exists when the n region is attached to the negative electrode of a dc supply, while the p region is made positive. This reduces the potential difference across the junction from its original equilibrium value, and facilitates current flow. When the bias is applied in the reverse direction, and the current reaches its saturation value, the current flow is due entirely to the number of minority carriers able to cross the junction. It is now the electrons originating in the p material, within a diffusion length of the barrier L_p, and the holes in the n material within a diffusion length of the barrier (L_n), which constitute the carriers for current flow. These carriers are created by the G-R (generation-recombination) process whereby electron-hole pairs are created in the lattice from phonon (thermal) interaction between atoms that make up the lattice. The saturation arises when all possible minority carriers from either side of the junction region are contributing to the current flow.

The theory and experimental results, however, differ somewhat, even after all sources of error such as surface leakage and crystalline imperfections are included in the analysis. To resolve this difference an extra current component is distinguished, which is attributed to charge carrier generation by the absorption of photons in the barrier region. The p-n junction equation then becomes:

$$I = I_s \left[\exp\left(eV/kT\right) - 1\right] - I_{sc} \tag{10-17}$$

*For basic treatment of this material, see References 4 and 5.

where I_{sc} is the current induced by the incident background radiation. Derivations of I_{sc} are given by Cummerow[6] and Rittner[7] in treatments of the solar battery.

The treatment of the p-n junction is still not complete in that, account has not yet been taken of the facts that carriers are created by phonon interaction in the generation recombination process within the barrier region, and, that there is a shunt conductance leakage for practical diodes. The equation has to be further modified in the form:

$$I = I_s \left[\exp (eV/\beta kT) - 1 \right] - I_{sc} + G_{sh}V \qquad (10\text{-}18)$$

where β is a constant that provides the measure of the extra charge carriers, and G_{sh} is the conductance in shunt with the diode. The factor β is unity for an ideal diode, but in practice is about 2 to 3.

Equation (10-18) can be used to derive an expression for the output open-circuit voltage generated from a p-n junction photodetector, or an expression for the short-circuit current. When used as a photodetector, without any biasing, V in Eq. (10-18) becomes simply the generated voltage. For the open-circuit case no current can flow, and the output voltage becomes:

$$V = \frac{\beta kT}{e} \ln \left[\frac{I_{sc} - G_{sh}V}{I_s} + 1 \right] \qquad (10\text{-}19)$$

while for the short-circuit case, where $V = 0$,

$$I = I_{sc} \qquad (10\text{-}20)$$

In the case where

$$\frac{I_{sc} - G_{sh}V}{I_s} \ll 1$$

the logarithm above reduces to

$$\frac{I_{sc} - G_{sh}V}{I_s}$$

and

$$V = \frac{\beta kT}{e} \cdot \frac{I_{sc}}{I_s} \left[\frac{1}{1 + (\beta kT/e) \cdot (G_{sh}/I_s)} \right] \qquad (10\text{-}21)$$

For the case where a periodically modulated signal is superimposed on a steady background, a correspondingly modulated voltage of amplitude

V_M, and current I_M, are added to the background V_B and I_B. The modified expression is:

$$I = I_s \left\{ \exp \frac{e}{\beta k T} [V_B + V_M \exp i\omega t] - 1 \right\} - (I_B + I_M \exp i\omega t) \\ + G_{sh} (V_B + V_M \exp i\omega t) \tag{10-22}$$

Consider only the simple case where the total voltage generated is sufficiently small so that:

$$\exp \frac{e}{\beta k T} [V_B + V_M \exp i\omega t] - 1 = \frac{e}{\beta k T} [V_B + V_M \exp i\omega t]$$

then

$$I = I_s \left[\frac{e}{\beta k T} (V_B + V_M \exp i\omega t) \right] - [I_B + I_M \exp i\omega t] \\ + G_{sh} [V_B + V_M \exp i\omega t]$$

The short-circuit current becomes:

$$I_{sc} = - (I_B + I_M \exp i\omega t) \tag{10-23}$$

The open-circuit voltage becomes:

$$V_B + V_M \exp i\omega t = \frac{I_B + I_M \exp i\omega t}{I_s (e/\beta k T) + G_{sh}} \tag{10-24}$$

The steady voltage is given by

$$V_B = \frac{I_B}{I_s (e/\beta k T) + G_{sh}} \tag{10-25}$$

and the ac component is

$$V_M = \frac{I_M}{I_s (e/\beta k T) + G_{sh}} \tag{10-26}$$

Often, the p-n junction photodetector is operated in a manner similar to that of the photoconductive detector. A bias voltage is applied to the detector in series with a load resistance, with the photosignal picked off using the same kind of circuitry as for the photoconductive detector. The bias is applied to the junction diode in the reverse direction and effectively shows increased impedance to the preamplifier circuit. Radiation is absorbed creating carriers that reach the junction region, causing changes in the value of I_{sc}. As pointed out by Pruett and Petritz,[8] the response of the photodiode to a small radiation signal ΔJ_s is obtained from the differential of Eq. (10-18):

$$\Delta I = \left[-\frac{dI_{sc}}{dJ_s} + \frac{e}{\beta k T} \left(I_s \exp \frac{eV}{\beta k T} \frac{dV}{dJ_s} \right) + G_{sh} \frac{dV}{dJ_s} \right] \cdot J_s \qquad (10\text{-}27)$$

The small-signal short-circuit current generator for a Norton representation is found by holding V constant:

$$i_s = \Delta I \bigg|_{v = \text{constant}} = -\frac{dI_{sc}}{dJ_s} \cdot J_s$$

This term represents the increase in current due to signal superimposed on background radiation photons. Thus:

$$\frac{dI_{sc}}{dJ_s} = e\eta A$$

and

$$i_s = -e\eta A J_s \qquad (10\text{-}28)$$

where J_s is the number of photons per unit area per unit time falling on the detector of area A, and where the efficiency of conversion to electron-hole pairs is given by η. Thus the signal current is directly proportional to signal radiation.

10.1.3 Photoelectromagnetic Detectors

PEM or PME (photoelectromagnetic and photomagnetoelectric) are names used in reference to the same effect. It may be described with reference to the more familiar Hall effect (see Figure 10-4). In both Hall and PEM effects, a sample of the semiconducting material (usually in the form of a parallelepiped) is placed in a magnetic field and oriented so that its length is perpendicular to the direction of the magnetic field. The sides are arranged so that the magnetic field also passes perpendicularly through a parallel pair of faces. In the Hall effect, a current is made to flow through the sample by the application of a potential difference across its ends. Electrons and holes drift in opposite directions while they travel along the sample's length. The PEM effect, however, initiates current flow by the absorption of photons at the sample's front surface. Photon absorption creates an excess concentration of electrons and holes. The existence of extra carriers at the front surface and their absence at the rear, leads to a diffusion of carriers from the front to the rear to equalize the inhomogeneous distribution. This diffusion process obeys the same law as described for the photovoltaic detector above, that is, Eq. (10-10).

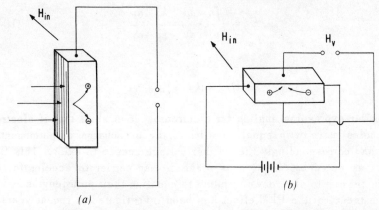

Fig. 10-4. Circuit configurations to observe (a) PEM effect, (b) Hall effect.

The motion of the carriers in both samples is influenced by their inter-action with the magnetic field. In the Hall effect, electrons and holes, usually of different densities, drift along in opposite directions, and under the influence of the magnetic field, tend to accumulate a net charge on one side of the sample. This results in a potential difference between this side and the opposite face. Electrodes placed on these surfaces permit the measurement of this Hall voltage. The diffusion current in the PEM effect has both electrons and holes moving from the front to the rear faces of the sample. Charge carrier interaction with the magnetic field causes the holes and electrons to be deflected in opposite directions, and a potential difference between the sample ends develops. Electrodes placed across the ends permit the measurement of the PEM voltage. This voltage persists as long as the diffusion current flows, which in turn persists as long as the detector is irradiated.

Another phenomenon that might be noted here is the Dember effect. Let us consider Figure 10-4(b) without the magnetic field. Electron-hole pairs created at the front surface move toward the rear surface, in a manner dependent not only upon the carrier concentration at the front surface but also upon their mobilities. If the mobilities are significantly different, one type of carrier moves ahead of the other. This results in a potential difference between the front and rear surfaces, referred to as the Dember voltage. The resultant electric field creates a force in op-position to the diffusion force. The equation expressing this relation-ship for holes is:

$$\frac{I}{e} = -D_p \frac{dp}{dy} + \mu_p \, p \cdot E_y \qquad (10\text{-}29)$$

Under equilibrium conditions, the electric field current component equals the diffusion current and $I = 0$.

$$E_y = -\frac{D_p}{\mu_p} \cdot \frac{dp}{dy} = \frac{kT}{ep} \cdot \frac{dp}{dy} \tag{10-30}$$

since

$$D_p = (kT/e)\mu_p$$

A similar expression applies for electrons. It is clear that if electrons and holes move with equal mobilities, the net charge displacement is zero and correspondingly the Dember voltage ceases to exist. This field effect as noted by Moss[9] causes the slower carrier to accelerate, and the faster one to slow down, tending to equalize their path lengths.

The theory of the PEM effect has been investigated in recent years by a number of authors, who have contributed to its continuous refinement and complexity.[10-18] Moss[9] suggests a readily understandable approach which provides a useful expression for the PEM signal voltage. Assume that the mobilities are sufficiently close so that no appreciable electric field develops. The charges created at the front surface diffuse inward a distance given by their diffusion length.

$$L_n = \sqrt{D_n \tau} \tag{10-31}$$

where τ is the average carrier lifetime. The distance moved by the carrier toward the electrodes is given by:

$$L \sin \theta \approx L \tan \theta \approx \theta$$

for small angle θ. An estimate of the angle θ can be derived using the force components acting on the carrier. The diffusion force per carrier is given by

$$F_D = \frac{kT}{ep} \cdot \frac{dp}{dy}$$

The force created by carrier interaction with the magnetic field is given by:

$$F_B = e[\mu \times B] = e\mu B$$

where μ is the carrier velocity:

$$\mu = \frac{kT}{ep} \cdot \frac{dp}{dy} \cdot \mu_p$$

Therefore

$$F_B = \frac{kT}{p} \frac{dp}{dy} \mu_p B$$

and

$$\tan \theta = (F_B/F_D) = e\mu_p B \tag{10-32}$$

Hence the displacement toward the electrodes is given by

$$\sqrt{D_p \tau} \, e\mu_p B \tag{10-33}$$

The effective charge recorded by the meter in the circuit is:

$$(1/l)\sqrt{D_p \tau} \, e\mu_p B \tag{10-34}$$

The factor $1/l$ can be explained simply by considering one lead of the crystal attached to an electrometer, and the other attached to ground, as in Figure 10-5. Consider a "hole" infinitesimally close to the grounded electrode. The potential energy recorded at the electrometer is given by:

$$\phi_l = (p/\kappa l)$$

where κ is the dielectric constant. Displace the charge a distance r toward the electrometer, so that

$$\phi_{l-r} = \frac{p}{\kappa (l - r)}$$

The increase in potential energy at the electrometer due to the charge movement is given by

$$V = \phi_{l-r} - \phi_l = p \frac{r}{\kappa l (l - r)}$$

The charge induced in the electrometer P can be expressed in terms of V by:

$$V = (P/C)$$

The capacity between two points in space is given by the distance between them. Thus:

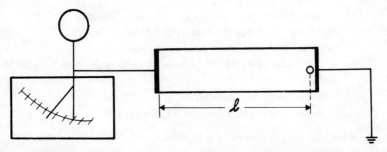

Fig. 10-5. Effective circuit charge as a function of charge displacement in detector.

$$V = \frac{p}{\kappa(l - r)} = p \frac{r}{\kappa l (l - r)}$$

$$P = p(r/l) \tag{10-35}$$

A similar contribution arises from the electrons so that the net current derived if both electrodes were placed directly across an ammeter would be:

$$i_s = \frac{\eta e B J_s}{l} \{\mu_e \sqrt{D_e \tau} + \mu_h \sqrt{D_h \tau}\} \tag{10-36}$$

where J_s is the number of photons per unit time absorbed by the detector element, and η gives the efficiency for conversion of photons to electron-hole pairs. The equivalent open-circuit voltage can be obtained by multiplying i_s by the magnetoresistance of the detector.

The mobilities μ_e and μ_h determine the complexity of the PEM signal. For the simplest case, where $\mu_e = \mu_h$, i_s reduces to

$$i_s = \frac{\eta e B J_s}{l} \cdot \mu^{3/2} \cdot \left(\frac{kT}{e} \tau\right)^{3/2} \tag{10-37}$$

The more complicated general cases, where μ_e, μ_h, p, and n are independent variables, have been treated by many authors including Pincherle,[14] Kurnick and Zitter,[12, 13] and Kruse.[18] Zitter[17] has shown that the short-circuit PEM current can be expressed as:

$$i_{PEM} = \left(1 + \frac{1}{b}\right) e \mu B J_s L_D^* \tag{10-38}$$

where

$$L_D^* = \left[\frac{D \tau_{PEM} (1 + c)}{1 + \mu^2 B^2 + bc \left(1 + \frac{\mu^2 B^2}{b^2}\right)}\right]^{1/2} \tag{10-39}$$

and L_D^* is the effective ambipolar diffusion length, which for zero magnetic field reduces to the diffusion length of the minority carrier in an extrinsic semiconductor;

  c is the ratio of electron to hole densities for the crystal in the dark;

  b is the ratio of electron to hole mobilities.

τ_{PEM} is the time constant for the PEM effect.

It is clear, for small values of μB, that

$$L_D^* = \left[\frac{kT}{e} \cdot \frac{(\mu_e + \mu_h)(1 + c) \tau}{1 + bc}\right]^{1/2}$$

and that for $\mu_e \approx \mu_h \approx \mu$ and $b \approx 1$

$$L_D^* = \sqrt{\frac{kT}{e}\mu\tau_{PEM}}$$

and i_{PEM} is proportional to $\mu^{3/2}$. Therefore, in these limits, Zitter's Eq. (10-38) reduces to the form suggested by Moss.[9]

In the case of μB large:

$$L_D^* = \left[\frac{kT}{e} \cdot \frac{(\mu_e + \mu_h)\tau_{PEM}(1+c)}{\mu^2 B^2(1+c/b)}\right]^{1/2}$$

such that $\mu^2 B^2 \gg b^2$. Then i_{PEM} approaches a value given by:

$$i_{PEM} = \left(1 + \frac{1}{b}\right)J_s\left[kTe\left(\frac{1+c}{1+c/b}\right)\right]^{1/2} \; [\tau(\mu_e + \mu_h)]^{1/2} \qquad (10\text{-}40)$$

and it is clear that the PEM signal goes as the square root of the effective combined mobilities.

The time constant appearing in the PEM effect is a complicated quantity. It is defined by Zitter,[17] and compared with the time constant for the photoconductive effect as:

$$\tau_{PEM} = \frac{\tau_n + c\,\tau_p}{1+c} \qquad (10\text{-}41)$$

$$\tau_{PC} = \frac{\tau_n + \tau_p/b}{1 + 1/b} \qquad (10\text{-}42)$$

In extrinsic material, τ_{PEM} is just the lifetime of the minority carrier, which corresponds to the fact that minority carriers control the diffusion process in this kind of material. However, τ_{PC} is based on the fact that both carriers contribute to photoconductivity, regardless of the type of material. Since the time constant τ_{PEM} appears as a part of L_D in the expression for the short-circuit current i_{PEM}, it is clear that

$$i_{PEM} \sim \sqrt{\tau_{PEM}} \qquad (10\text{-}43)$$

A comparison of the signal generated by the PEM effect to the photoconductive effect can well be made here. The photoconductive current density i_{PC} can be expressed in the form:

$$i_{PC} = [1 + (1/b)]eJ_s\mu E_x\tau_{PC} \qquad (10\text{-}44)$$

where E_x is the applied electric field along the crystal. An examination of the dependence on time constant reveals for the simple intrinsic case (assuming negligible trapping of excess carriers where $\tau_n = \tau_p = \tau_{PC} =$

$\tau_{PEM} = \tau$) that the PEM signal is proportional to the square root of τ, whereas i_{PC} is proportional to τ. Thus the fast, short-time constant detector provides a larger signal in the PEM mode. Second, the magnetic field increases the effective resistance of the detector. Thus in the case of the low resistivity, short-time constant ($\tau < 10^{-6}$ sec) detector such as InSB (indium antimonide) these two factors favor the PEM effect in improving signal output and the ability to match detector impedance to a preamplifier. Other factors favor the PEM detector. The PC detector is thinner than the PEM detector and, therefore, is generally more difficult to fabricate. In the fabrication of detectors, care has to be exercised to avoid damaging its surface. This is to prevent an increase in the surface recombination velocities. Yet, in mounting the detector, the back surface is almost always made to adhere to a cell mount. Thus the back surface is likely to have an increased recombination velocity compared to the front. This effects the PC detector adversely in that the effective density of carriers is reduced, whereas the PEM detector benefits because the diffusion force increases as the concentration gradient of carrier densities from front to back is made steeper.

A complete comparison of the different photodetectors cannot be made until their noise properties are understood. Further discussion is deferred until Chapter 11, where all the necessary factors will be examined.

10.2 Signal Generation in Thermal Detector

This section discusses the thermocouple, the bolometer, and the Golay cell. The first two detectors will be described in some detail, including a mathematical treatment aimed at showing the important factors that govern thermal detector performance. The third cell is described briefly.

To understand the workings of thermal detectors, it is best to review briefly some thermal properties of materials that will appear and the mathematics required to describe them. They are:

1. *Heat capacity.* Suppose a body of some substance is connected to a source of heat (by being placed in an oven, or over a flame, or a heating jacket) and allowed to warm up. The amount of thermal energy gained by the body Q is related to its temperature change ΔT by

$$\overline{C} = (\Delta Q / \Delta T)$$

where $\overline{C}$ is called the mean heat capacity of the body. The true heat capacity at the temperature is expressed in the derivative form

$$C = (dQ/dT) \tag{10-45}$$

corresponding to the changes in temperature becoming infinitesimally small.

2. *Thermal conductance.* This quantity describes the ease or difficulty with which heat flows through a body. Heat flow has the following

characteristics: it flows from a higher to a lower temperature region of the body, and the rate of flow is proportional to the area through which it passes, and to the temperature gradient. These properties are described by:

$$(dQ/dt) = -K'A \, (dT/dx)$$

where K' is the conductivity. For any one body of a specific dimension l across which the temperature change ΔT exists, this relationship can be simplified to:

$$\frac{dQ}{dt} = -K \Delta T \qquad (10\text{-}46)$$

where K is the thermal conductance given by

$$K = K'(A/l)$$

and the minus sign corresponds to heat flow in a direction opposite to the gradient. The reciprocal of the conductance is called the thermal resistance R. For those who are more familiar with the electrical quantities there are the following analogies:

1. Temperature difference (ΔT) corresponds to electromotive force.
2. Heat flow dQ/dt corresponds to current flow.
3. Thermal impedance corresponds to electrical impedance.
4. Thermal capacity corresponds to electrical capacity.

Suppose now, that a thermally isolated mass is made to undergo a temperature rise ΔT. The heat absorbed would be given by:

$$\Delta Q = C \Delta T$$

Now, let a thermal conducting path be connected between this body and a thermal reservoir at the original temperature of the body. Thermal power (P') flows out of the body to the reservoir at a rate given by

$$P' = -K \Delta T$$

This energy outflow can also be described by

$$\frac{d \Delta Q}{dt} = C \frac{d \Delta T}{dt}$$

Therefore:

$$C \frac{d \Delta T}{dt} = -K \Delta T = -\frac{\Delta T}{R}$$

or

$$\frac{d \Delta T}{dt} + \frac{\Delta T}{RC} = 0 \qquad (10\text{-}47)$$

The solution to this differential equation is given by:

$$\Delta T = \Delta T_0 \, e^{-t/\tau} \tag{10-48}$$

where $\tau = RC$ is the time constant for the process.

The next step of complexity consists of allowing radiant power P to be absorbed by the body at the same time heat flow out is permitted as above. This situation is described by:

$$C\frac{d\Delta T}{dt} + K\Delta T = P \tag{10-49}$$

If P is constant and equilibrium conditions are established, the derivative is zero and

$$\Delta T = (P/K) = RP \tag{10-50}$$

Therefore, the equilibrium temperature established by the body is ΔT above the reservoir, and given by the product of the thermal resistance between the body and reservoir and energy flow into the body. If the energy inflow is a sinusoidally varying function, then it can be described by:

$$P = P_0 \, \exp i\omega t \tag{10-51}$$

and our differential equation takes the form

$$C\frac{d\Delta T}{dt} + K\Delta T = P_0 \, \exp i\omega t \tag{10-52}$$

This is a linear first-order differential equation and can be solved using the integrating factor

$$\exp \int (K/C)\,dt = \exp (K/C)t$$

The solution is:

$$\Delta T = [RP_0/(1 + i\omega RC)] \, \exp i\omega t \tag{10-53}$$

where the amplitude of the sinusoidal variation in temperature is given by:

$$\frac{RP_0}{\sqrt{1 + (\omega RC)^2}} = \frac{RP_0}{\sqrt{1 + (\omega \tau)^2}}$$

For sufficiently low frequencies, such that $\omega\tau \ll 1$, the amplitude is the same as for a steady flow of heat input, but for high frequencies it will fall off as the reciprocal of the frequency.

In this simple treatment describing temperature changes of a body of heat capacity C, connected to a reservoir via a thermal leak K, and allowed to absorb radiation energy P, we have the rudiments of the thermal detector. These detectors generally consist of a thin film of metal or semiconductor mounted on a substrate, which in turn is connected to the detector enclosure, usually at room temperature. Thus, the film has a heat capacity C, and is connected to its enclosure through a substrate of conductance K. The only remaining factors to be discussed are those relating the physical process by which the different detectors permit a temperature measurement, and the way in which these factors modify our differential Eq. (10-49). Once the equation applicable to a detector is established, its solution permits analysis of detector behavior.

10.2.1 *The Thermocouple*

The thermocouple is a device which operates because of an important discovery made by T. J. Seebeck about 1821. This discovery consisted of the observation that when dissimilar metals were placed in contact in a series manner and their junctions maintained at different temperatures, an electromotive force was generated. If the metals were made to form a closed loop, a current was observed to flow.

The simplest arrangement consists of a couple of wires, each made of a different metal, joined together at their ends to form a closed loop called a thermocouple. If a temperature difference is maintained at the two places where the wires are joined together, then an electromotive force is generated with a corresponding current flow whose magnitude depends upon the value of the temperature difference. If one of the junctions is held at some constant reference temperature, such as $0°C$, and the other junction allowed to be variable, then it would be found that the electromotive force developed corresponding to the temperature at the variable junction would behave in a quadratic manner; that is, one could write an approximately correct expression for E as a function of T in the form

$$V_{ab} = A_{ab} T^2 + S_{ab} T \qquad (10\text{-}54)$$

where a and b designate different metals. A more precise expression describing this relationship is often found, which would include these two terms plus a cubic term. [19]

In practice it has been found wise to select one metal as a reference metal to which all other metals might be compared. The reference metal is lead. Therefore, in a test circuit for some metal we would have a thermocouple consisting of one metal, the unknown, and the other metal, lead. Suppose, then, we write the expression above in terms of two different metals compared to lead. Then we would have

$$V_a = A_a T^2 + S_a T \qquad (10\text{-}55)$$

$$V_b = A_b T^2 + S_b T$$

Subtracting V_b from V_a provides the expression

$$V_{ab} = V_a - V_b = (A_a - A_b)T^2 + (S_a - S_b)T \tag{10-56}$$

We see then that $(A_a - A_b)$ is equal to the constant A_{ab}, and $S_a - S_b = S_{ab}$. It is clear that we can compare all different thermoelectric materials to lead, then obtain their behavior with respect to one another by simply taking the differences of their constants determined with respect to lead. If we differentiate E with respect to T,

$$(dV/dT) = A'T + S \tag{10-57}$$

ignoring subscripts for the moment. In examining values obtained for A' and S, one finds in general that A' is a small number compared to S, and this derivative can often be well approximated by the constant S. This constant is called the thermoelectric power. The thermoelectric emf can then be approximated by

$$V_{TH} = S_{ab} \cdot \Delta T$$

In designing a thermocouple of two different materials then one would try to obtain a combination of materials such that S was as large as possible, thereby providing as large a voltage generation as possible for some particular value of T. A typical arrangement of a practical thermocouple is shown in Figure 10-6. Here we see a thermocouple metal wire a joined to another thermoelectric wire b. Their ends are, respectively, at the temperature of a receiver of radiant energy and a reference temperature maintained by some reservoir, such as an ice-water bath. The temperature attained by the receiver depends upon the radiation received and its own thermal characteristics. Usually, the receiver consists of some blackened metal foil arranged to have as high an absorption characteristic as possible.

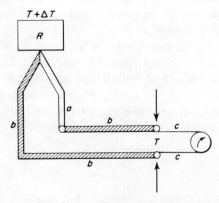

Fig. 10-6. The thermocouple.

In addition to the wires that make up the thermocouple there are also the wires necessary to complete the circuitry incorporating a meter (see Figure 10-6). Usually these wires are made of highly conductive metal such as copper. In order that they may not contribute any thermoelectric effect, the two points where they are joined to the thermocouple must be maintained at the same temperature.

Another factor important in the operation of the thermocouple is referred to as the Peltier effect, after its discoverer. When a current is made to flow in a thermocouple, its junctions will change in temperature. They will get warmer or cooler depending upon the direction of current flow. The rate at which energy is absorbed or given off by a junction is given by

$$P = -\pi_{ab} \cdot i \tag{10-58}$$

where π_{ab} is called the Peltier coefficient. This coefficient is related to the thermoelectric power by:

$$\pi_{ab} = TS_{ab} \tag{10-59}$$

The thermocouple detector, when warmed on absorbing radiant energy, causes a current to flow in the thermoelectric circuit. This current always flows through the receiver junction in such a direction that the receiver always experiences a cooling effect. Thus, the actual temperature increase of the detector is less than would be expected from a simple analysis. It is fortunate however, that the effect opposes a temperature increase, since if the opposite case were to exist, a regenerative effect would prevail with continually increasing current, and the receiver getting correspondingly warmer to self-destruction.

The next step is to find out how the Peltier effect appears as an electrical circuit quantity. Consider now a battery E_b and a series resistor r_g placed in one arm of the thermocouple. Let the cold junction be fixed in temperature by connection to a large icewater reservoir at $0\,^{\circ}$C and examine the effect on the hot junction, with the current directed to provide a cooling effect. From Eqs. (10-58) and (10-59) we see that the hot junction is cooled at a rate given by

$$P = -iTS_{ab} \tag{10-60}$$

We have found from Eq. (10-50) that for a constant rate of energy exchange

$$\Delta T = RP = -iRTS \tag{10-61}$$

where ΔT now is the temperature drop in the hot junction due to the current flow. This drop ΔT causes a thermal emf to be generated given by

$$V_{TH} = S\Delta T = -iRS^2T \tag{10-62}$$

The total voltage in the circuit then is

$$V_T = V_B - V_{TH} = V_B - iRS^2T$$

and the current is

$$i = \frac{V_T}{r + r_g}$$

Therefore one can write

$$V_B = i[r + r_g + S^2RT]$$

and it becomes immediately apparent that the Peltier effect provides an additional resistance to the circuit called the thermocouple dynamic resistance given by:

$$R_D = S^2RT \tag{10-63}$$

The next stop in the analysis is to consider the differential equation applicable to the thermocouple, and obtain its solution. Eq. (10-49) is applicable here, excepting an additional term is required to include the Peltier effect. Accordingly we have:

$$C\frac{d\Delta T}{dt} + K\Delta T = P - SiT \tag{10-64}$$

where SiT describes the rate of energy loss at the detector because of the Peltier effect.

For the equilibrium condition and constant P, the energy balance equation becomes:

$$\frac{\Delta T}{R} = P - SiT \tag{10-65}$$

Now

$$i = \frac{V_{TH}}{r + r_g} = \frac{S\Delta T}{r + r_g} \tag{10-66}$$

Substituting for ΔT in Eq. (10-65), and using the dynamic resistance R_D leads to:

$$i = \frac{PRS}{r + r_g + R_D} \tag{10-67}$$

If we substitute this current back into Eq. (10-66), one obtains

$$\Delta T = \frac{RP \, (r + r_g)}{r + r_g + R_D} \qquad (10\text{-}68)$$

For the open circuit condition, where $i = 0$

$$\Delta T_0 = RP$$

Therefore, one can rewrite Eq. (10-68)

$$\Delta T = \Delta T_0 \frac{r + r_g}{r + r_g + R_D} \qquad (10\text{-}69)$$

and the actual voltage generated by the thermocouple will be $V_{TH} = P \Delta T$. An expression for the current flow can be found since

$$V_0 = S \Delta T_0 = SRP$$

and

$$i = \frac{V_0}{r + r_g + R_D} \qquad (10\text{-}70)$$

Thus, we have found that the current through the thermocouple can be found by dividing the open-circuit thermoelectric voltage by the total circuit resistance, which includes the unique dynamic resistance R_D. Furthermore, the effective temperature change ΔT at the receiver is less than one would expect on open circuit, and that it can be computed knowing R_D.

Now, consider the case where the radiation falling on the receiver is modulated in a sinusoidal manner, so that

$$P = P_0 \exp i\omega t$$

For the open circuit, general case, it was found from Eq. (10-53) that

$$\Delta T = \frac{RP_0}{1 + i\omega\tau} \exp i\omega t$$

and, therefore, the thermocouple voltage generated will be:

$$V = S \Delta T = \frac{SRP_0}{1 + i\omega\tau} \exp i\omega t \qquad (10\text{-}71)$$

where $\qquad \tau = RC$

The closed-circuit condition results in a current of the form of Eq. (10-70), but with the thermal dynamic impedance replacing the resistance R_D; that is:

$$i = \frac{V}{r + r_g + Z_D} \qquad (10\text{-}72)$$

where $Z_D = R_D/1 + i\omega t$, and V is given by Eq. (10-71). Substituting this value of V provides

$$i = \frac{SRP_0}{r + r_g + Z_D} \cdot \frac{\exp i\omega t}{1 + i\omega RC} \qquad (10\text{-}73)$$

The responsivity of the thermocouple can be defined as the ratio of the amplitude of the open-circuit voltage generated to the amplitude of the incident power. This can be obtained from Eq. (10-73), and written as in

$$\gamma = \frac{V}{P} = \frac{SR}{(1 + \omega^2\tau^2)^{1/2}} \qquad (10\text{-}74)$$

Notice that this responsivity is proportional to the thermal impedance of the detector and the thermoelectric power of the materials used, and also that for sufficiently high frequencies that the response falls off with the reciprocal of the frequency. Finally, note that if a thermocouple with rapid response is required, then the receiver must be selected or designed so that the thermal capacity is small, and therefore that the time constant equal to RC be made as small as possible.

10.2.2 The Thermistor Bolometer

The bolometer, like the thermocouple, is a device that can be used to measure radiation or temperature. Its operation is based upon the variation of resistance with temperature of materials such as electrical conductors and semiconductors. Radiation is allowed to fall on a blackened material, causing a temperature rise with an associated change in resistance. This resistance variation is reproduced in the form of an electrical signal which is monitored by some meter device.

The change in electrical resistance on heating depends on a quantity known as the temperature coefficient of resistance, which is defined in

$$\alpha = (1/r) \cdot (dr/dT) \qquad (10\text{-}75)$$

where r is the resistance of the element at temperature T. The resistance of most metals over a wide temperature range is approximately proportional to the temperature, so that $r = MT$, substituted in Eq. (10-75), provides a temperature coefficient of resistance equal to the reciprocal of the temperature.

These values for most metals are approximately the same, being approximately 0.003 to 0.006 (°K). For semiconductors a resistance temperature relationship is described by Eq. (10-76) where β is a constant over a moderate range of temperatures. A typical value is $\beta = 3400\,°\mathrm{K}$.

$$r = r_0 \exp \beta \left[(1/T) - (1/T_0) \right] \qquad (10\text{-}76)$$

Substituting Eq. (10-76) in Eq. (10-75) provides an expression for the temperature coefficient of resistance given by

$$\alpha_S = -(\beta/T^2) \qquad (10\text{-}77)$$

Using the value of β noted above, and $T = 300\,°\mathrm{K}$, one finds that the temperature coefficient of resistance for semiconductors is about ten times greater than that for metals. The thermistor bolometer is the name given to the bolometer made of a semiconducting material.

The usual arrangement of the bolometer detector is shown in Figure 10-7. In this figure the resistance r_L is a load resistance. In practice it is often a thermistor matched to the detector and arranged so that any temperature fluctuations in ambient conditions affect the detector and the load in the same manner, and the bridge remains balanced. It is hidden from signal radiation. The voltage across the active element is given by

$$v = \frac{r}{r + r_L} V \qquad (10\text{-}78)$$

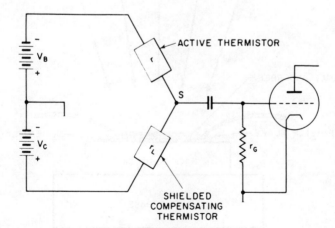

$V_B = V_C \quad r = r_L \quad r_G = \gg r$

Fig. 10-7. The thermistor (by permission of Barnes Engineering Co., from Reference 21).

The variation of this voltage with respect to the detector resistance is given by

$$\frac{dv}{dr} = \frac{V}{r + r_L} \cdot \frac{r_L}{r + r_L} \tag{10-79}$$

The quantity described in $[r_L/(r + r_L)]$ is often called the bridge factor and usually is one-half when the load is matched to the detector or is approximately one when the load is much larger in resistance than the detector.

A typical arrangement for the mounting of a thermistor is shown in Figure 10-8.[20,21] The thermistor has a metal base on which rests a backing block, then a cement layer on top of which is the thermistor flake coated with some black absorbent material. Radiation is absorbed by the blackened surface, and warms the thermistor to a temperature ΔT above the ambient condition. The cement layer provides a regulated thermal leak to the backing block and to the metal base, which represents a thermal reservoir usually at the ambient temperature. Accordingly, the bolometer detector, like the thermocouple, has heat capacity, and loses heat by radiation and conduction. In addition, however, Joulean heat is generated in the bolometer with passage of the bias current. Our basic differential eq. (10-49) must be modified to include this effect, and

$$C_e(d\Delta T/dt) + K_0 \Delta T = P + (dP_H/dT)\Delta T \tag{10-80}$$

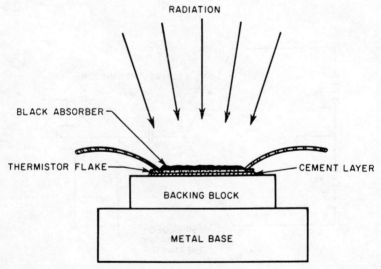

Fig. 10-8. Support construction of thermistor detector (*by permission of Barnes Engineering Co., from Reference 21*).

Reading from left to right, the rate of heat storage in the flake is given by the first term, the rate of heat flow out by conduction and radiation on absorption of power is given by the second term, P is the radiant heat flow incident on the bolometer, and the last expression provides for the variation in Joule heat flow caused by the variation in resistance induced by the absorption of P. The quantity C_e is called the dynamic heat capacitance and K_0 is the static thermal conductance.

To simplify this equation, and put it in a form to which we are accustomed, it is necessary to evaluate dP_H/dT. The Joule heating is given by:

$$P_H = \frac{V^2}{r_t} = \frac{V^2}{r + r_L} \tag{10-81}$$

Therefore:

$$dP_H/dr = -(V^2/r_t^2) \tag{10-82}$$

or for the matched load condition:

$$dP_H = -(V^2/4r^2)dr \tag{10-83}$$

The differential of Eq. (10-76) provides:

$$dr = -(\beta/T^2)rdT \tag{10-84}$$

Thus:

$$dP_H = (V^2/4r^2)\,(\beta/T^2)\,dT \tag{10-85}$$

$$= (P_H/2)\,(\beta/T^2)\,dT$$

The electrical Joule heating forces an equilibrium operating temperature T' where the outflow of heat balances the inflow. This can be expressed as:

$$P_H = 2K_2\,(T' - T_0) \tag{10-86}$$

where T' is the temperature acquired by the thermistor under steady current flow (without radiation heating), and K_2 is the thermal conductance of each flake through the bolometer support. The factor 2 accounts for two thermistors mounted thermally in parallel. Substituting Eq. (10-86) in Eq. (10-85) gives:

$$dP_H/dt = (\beta/T^2)K_2(T' - T_0) \tag{10-87}$$

Substituting this expression in our Eq. (10-80), and simplifying, gives:

$$C_e(d\Delta T/dt) + K_e \Delta T = P \qquad (10\text{-}88)$$

where

$$K_e = K_0 - (\beta/T^2)K_2(T' - T_0) \qquad (10\text{-}89)$$

Notice that K_e can be positive or negative. A negative value provides a solution to the equation which is exponentially increasing with time. The bolometer is unstable; it heats up until it burns out. Therefore the bias voltage has to be kept low enough so that T' remains sufficiently close to T_0 to keep K_e positive.

The solutions to this equation for $P = 0$, $P =$ constant, and $P = P_0$ exp $i\omega t$ are discussed in Section 10.2. We only point out here that, for sinusoidally modulated signal radiation, the complete solution is

$$\Delta T = \Delta T_0\, e^{-t/R_e C_e} + \frac{R_e P_0 \exp i\omega t}{1 + i\omega R_e C_e} \qquad (10\text{-}90)$$

The first term represents a transient that rapidly dies out for positive value of K_e. After the transient has died out, we are left with the oscillatory term whose amplitude is given by

$$\Delta T = \frac{R_e P_0}{[1 + (\omega R_e C_e)^2]^{1/2}} \qquad (10\text{-}91)$$

The responsivity of this detector again is the ratio of the voltage derived to the incident radiation exciting that voltage. Substituting Eq. (10-84) in Eq. (10-79) provides

$$dv = -V \cdot \frac{r}{r + r_L} \cdot \frac{r_L}{r + r_L} \cdot \frac{\beta}{T^2} dT \qquad (10\text{-}92)$$

Substituting Eq. (10-91) in Eq. (10-92) provides an expression for the responsivity in

$$\frac{\Delta v}{P_0} = \frac{\beta V}{4T^2} \cdot \frac{R_e}{[1 + (\omega R_e C_e)^2]^{1/2}} \qquad (10\text{-}93)$$

For the case of removal of radiation as in a step function, the appropriate solution to Eq. (10-88) is

$$\Delta T = \Delta T_0 \exp (t/R_e C_e) \qquad (10\text{-}94)$$

By definition, the time constant τ is

$$\tau = R_e C_e$$

and corresponds to the time for ΔT to increase to $e^{-1}(\Delta T_0)$. Generally, the measurement of τ is made, however, by observing responsivity as a function of frequency. At the half-power point, we obtain τ from the relationship $2\pi f = 1/\tau$.

Referring back to Eq. (10-93), we see that, in order to obtain a high responsivity, a low thermal conductivity must be maintained corresponding to high thermal impedance. If a short-time constant is required, then RC must be small, thereby requiring small thermal capacity of the thermistor flake and/or low thermal impedance. This latter requirement is then associated with reduced responsivity.

A final note with regard to the operating characteristics of the thermistor: Voltage-current characteristics are shown in Figure 10-9. We see that, for low voltage and current, the thermistor resistance is ohmic. As the voltage is increased, the resistance becomes nonlinear because of heating of the thermistor. Finally, the current voltage curve maximizes at a peak voltage V_p. The thermistor would burn out if this condition were maintained unless the point was determined with a constant current source. The thermistor is usually operated over a range of ambient temperatures with a bias voltage usually limited to 60 per cent of the peak voltage determined at an ambient of $25\,^{\circ}$C.

10.2.3 *The Golay Cell*

This cell is one of the pneumatic-type detectors. In its simplest form, it comprises a small gas-filled chamber equipped with an infrared trans-

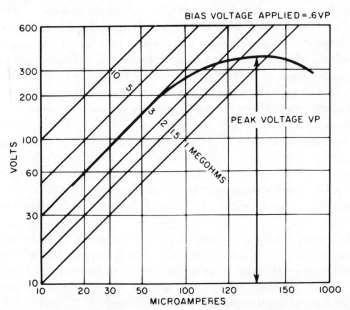

Fig. 10-9. Voltage-current characteristics of thermistor detector (*by permission of Barnes Engineering Co., from Reference 21*).

mitting window, some means for absorbing radiation admitted to the chamber, and finally a method for transposing pressure change in the chamber into a measurable signal output.

Figure 10-10 shows the basic components of a Golay cell,[22],[23] as manufactured by the Eppley Laboratory, Inc. It consists of an optical system on the left and a pneumatic system on the right. We see on the

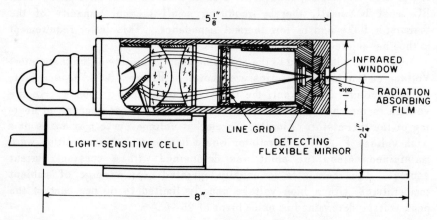

Fig. 10-10. The Golay cell (*as manufactured by Eppley Laboratory, Inc., from Reference 23*).

right an infrared window behind which is a small chamber. The front surface of this chamber consists of a radiation-absorbing film or membrane. Usually this membrane is a blackened thin foil acting as an infrared receiver. At the other end of the chamber is a detecting membrane always under tension which functions as a flexible mirror. The gas in the chamber on expansion due to the absorption of infrared energy by the blackened receiver causes the flexible mirror to change shape.

The optical system to the left consists of a light source and lenses whose rays are permitted to pass through another optical system containing a lined grid, and to be focused onto the flexible mirror. The rays reflected from the mirror fall onto the other half of the grid in a slightly off-focused manner so that a small amount of light is allowed to pass into the optical system and then reflected into a light-sensitive cell.

Infrared energy falling on the receiver causes the flexible mirror to change shape in such a manner that the light falling on the grid is made to become further diffused in image quality or to be sharpened up. This results in the passing through the grid to the sensitive photocell an amount of light proportionate to the radiant energy.

The standard receiver element has a $\frac{3}{32}$ inch diameter absorbing disc. Time constants can be made to range from about 2 to 30 milliseconds.

10.3 Noise

There are essentially five sources of electrical noise that appear in the output of thermal detectors and semiconducting photodetectors. They are called:

(1) Johnson noise
(2) Current or excess noise
(3) Generation-recombination noise
(4) Shot noise
(5) Background radiation

These noise types are treated in the order listed, describing where possible the basic mechanisms contributing to the noise sources, and noting generally accepted analytic expressions that apply to them.

10.3.1 *Johnson Noise*

This type of noise is often referred to as Nyquist noise, since both Nyquist and Johnson treated this noise problem in 1928.[24,25] An ohmic resistance can be pictured as a material which contains a number of free-charge carriers which move about in a crystalline lattice bumping into one another, and into the atoms which make up the lattice. The motion of these carriers is random; the average kinetic energy is a function of temperature (the greater the temperature the greater their average kinetic energy). If a sufficiently sensitive ammeter or voltmeter were placed across a resistor, it would indicate fluctuating voltages or currents corresponding to the motion of the charge carriers. These fluctuations represent a noise whose behavior is evolved purely from thermodynamic considerations, and not from the nature of charge carriers.

Johnson or Nyquist noise can be expressed as:

$$\overline{v^2} = 4kTr\Delta f \tag{10-95}$$

where k is Boltzmann's constant, T is the absolute temperature, Δf is the electrical bandwidth, r is the ohmic resistance, and v is the voltage fluctuation given by the difference between the instantaneous and average values of the voltage, where

$$v = v(t) - v_{Av} \tag{10-96}$$

10.3.2 *Current, 1/f, Modulation, or Excess Noise*

All of the names above have been used at various times for the same kind of noise. It is a noise that appears commonly in photodetectors, in addition to the Johnson noise already discussed, and is generally found to have characteristics that can be described by the expression:[26]

$$\overline{i^2} = C \frac{I_{dc}^2}{fAd} \cdot \Delta f \tag{10-97}$$

where I_{dc} is the total current through the sample, f is the frequency, and C is a constant.

Actually Eq. (10-97) is not universal in that cases have been cited where the current exponent has been found as small as 1.25 and as large as 4,[27] while the frequency exponent has ranged from 1 to 3.[28] However, these extreme exponential variations are not particularly common, and can usually be associated with a particular material, or to some unique treatment and physical condition of a material.[27]

The physical mechanism of this noise is the least understood of all the types of noise found to date. Petritz[29] introduced the name "modulation" noise to identify the mechanism as something quite different from the carrier-density fluctuations described in the generation-recombination (G-R) process (see Section 10.3.3). An effect is assumed that causes the occurrence of a magnitude of conductivity modulation far larger than that obtained from simple carrier-density fluctuations. This effect might well be related, however, to the electronic transitions involved in the G-R process. A simple mechanism that has been proposed involves electrons (while undergoing the transitions involved in the G-R process) falling into electrical lattice pits or wells called "traps," and being temporarily immobilized. While the electrons are in this trapped condition, the local electronic structure of the crystal lattice is changed. This may well result from some shuffling about of lattice particles to some new equilibrium conditions, and to a new electric field pattern. The net effect is presumed to be a marked change in the mobility of the carriers through the localized lattice, and/or a change in recombination velocity, and therefore conductivity modulation. The electronic traps are represented in the band picture as energy levels located in the forbidden energy gap. They are usually due to impurities in the crystal lattice and to crystalline imperfections from edge dislocations and plastic deformation. The energy level below the conduction band then represents a localized condition, which attracts a free electron or hole to a site where an energy well exists. Thus a conduction band electron or valence band hole moving in the vicinity of an electron or hole trap, respectively, is suddenly caught and immobilized in a bound state. Escape is then possible by absorption of phonon energy. The probability of escape increases with increasing temperature, but decreases with the depth of the trap.

The modulation suggestion offered by Petritz, however, can still be only a part of the picture. Brophy and Rostoker,[30] Brophy,[31] and Bess[32] found with direct experimental evidence that the noise fluctuations in Hall voltage followed the same frequency-dependence pattern as the noise from a conductivity measurement. It must be concluded, therefore, that, like conductivity, $1/f$ noise follows the fluctuation in the density of the majority current carriers.

The location of a major source of $1/f$ noise (at least in the case of germanium filaments) has been found to be the surface of the crystal. Recent studies by MacRae and Levinstein[33] noted that a surface inversion layer (a p-type surface on an n-type crystal, or vice versa) is necessary to generate significant $1/f$ noise. A qualitative picture of what is happening involves assuming a set of two surface states, one fast and the other slow. The slow states are associated with the majority carrier traps discussed above, and located in the outermost surface layer of the filament. The fast states are assumed to exist in the interface region between the surface and bulk materials and are primarily responsible for the recombination velocity of the carriers at the surface. Corresponding to the fluctuating density of majority carriers, there is a fluctuating population of slow traps, which causes the enhanced conductivity modulation in the bulk.

Although the surface provides $1/f$ noise, it is quite clear that this kind of noise can also be generated in the bulk material. Brophy[34] finds that by plastic deformation he can create noise sources, and cause an increase of excess noise by orders of magnitude. These sources are uniformly distributed throughout the crystal, and also contribute an unusual I^4 dependence. Bess[35] assumed that the noise was due to edge dislocations with impurities diffusing along the edge. Such distributions throughout the bulk can provide noise spectra similar to that obtained by inversion surface layers.[36]

When surfaces are treated so that their noise contribution is minimized, residual $(1/f)$ noise may still exist. This noise has been associated with non-ohmic contact regions, probably due to minority carrier drift across the contacts. It appears that the fluctuating population of traps causes the capture cross section of the surface recombination centers to be modulated, in turn causing a fluctuating current of minority carriers, resulting in current modulation.

The discussion of $1/f$ noise has shown that the sources of this noise can be found at the surface, in the bulk, and at the contacts. A suitable theory has yet to be found which will provide a quantitative expression for the carrier-density fluctuation and the modulation effect.

10.3.3 *Generation-Recombination Noise*

This type of noise is inherent in the electronic system of semiconducting materials. The basic mechanism responsible for it can be described easily in terms of the band picture of solids.

All atoms in a lattice vibrate in a well-organized manner to the extent that their vibrations are quantized and can be described in particle terminology as "phonons." The energy of the phonon is given by

$$E = \hbar \omega$$

where $\hbar = h/2\pi : \omega = 2\pi\nu$

h is Planck's constant

ν is the vibration frequency.

Valence-band electrons are continually jostled by the vibrations of the lattice atoms. Every so often, the nature and phasing of vibrations between atoms is such that an electron in their midst is able to gain enough energy to be freed from its bound (valence band) state, and to move about in the conduction band. The electron is said to have suffered a phonon collision, and to have undergone an energy change according to:

$$E(k') = E(k) \pm \hbar \omega_{\text{lattice}}$$

where k and k' define the energy states before and after phonon absorption.

Recall from Chapter 9, that when electrons leave the valence band for the conduction band, charge carriers (electrons and holes) become available for the purposes of current flow. The number of carriers created increases with material temperature, and for any one temperature will be greater for diminishing energy gap. The thermal (phonon) excitation process is statistical in nature, and the rate at which electrons are excited to the conduction band fluctuates.

In addition to the statistical pulses of generation, a similar situation exists on the recombination of carriers. The electrons and holes wander about the crystal lattice with some thermal motion, and during a "lifetime" characteristic of the semiconductor, get close enough together to recombine directly, or indirectly through a recombination center. The lifetime is a statistically fluctuating quantity, as is the instantaneous number of electrons and holes. Current carrier fluctuations are therefore inherent in any semiconductor. When a sample is placed in a constant-current electric circuit, one should expect and, in fact, does observe conductivity fluctuations causing electrical noise completely described by the generation-recombination process.

Since this noise is a bulk property of the crystal, and is due to conductivity fluctuations caused by carrier-density changes, it follows from Eq. (10-2) that

$$\Delta r = \frac{dr}{dn} \Delta n = -\frac{\rho l}{d\omega} \cdot \frac{\Delta n}{n} = -\frac{\rho l}{d\omega} \cdot \frac{\Delta N}{N}$$

and

$$\overline{v^2} = I_{\text{dc}}^2 \cdot \overline{\Delta r^2} \qquad (10\text{-}98)$$

It can be shown that:[1,26]

$$\frac{\overline{\Delta N^2}}{N} = \frac{2\tau}{1 + (\omega\tau)^2} \cdot \Delta f \tag{10-99}$$

Therefore

$$\overline{v^2} = I_{dc}^{2} \cdot r^2 \cdot \frac{2\tau}{N[1 + (\omega\tau)^2]} \tag{10-100}$$

or

$$\overline{i^2} = I_{dc}^{2} \cdot \frac{2\tau}{N[1 + (\omega\tau)^2]}$$

as shown by van Vliet.[37]

10.3.4 *Shot Noise*

This noise is usually associated with vacuum tubes, and is described as the electrical noise that appears in the output of a vacuum tube when the grid, if any, is held at a fixed potential. However, it is more precisely described in what is usually called the temperature-limited condition. By temperature limited is meant that the anode voltage on the tube is sufficient to collect all of the electrons emitted from the cathode. Consider a temperature-limited diode connected to a resistance r. Because of the discreteness of the electronic charge, the number of electrons emitted at equal time intervals will fluctuate around an average value. The fluctuating current causes a fluctuating voltage across r which can be amplified and measured. The mean square current fluctuation turns out to be constant up to frequencies of approximately the reciprocal of the transient time, and can be described by[38]

$$\overline{i^2} = 2eI_{dc}\Delta f \tag{10-101}$$

where e is the electronic charge and I_{dc} is the average current. Semiconductor photovoltaic detectors also exhibit shot-type noise. In the case of the vacuum tube, the electrons are taken as independent in the temperature-limited case, and it follows that the current through the resistance will consist of a series of short pulses, each pulse corresponding to the passage of an electron from cathode to anode. In the case of the semiconductor, a similar situation prevails. In a p-n junction diode, a space-charge region is developed across the barrier and an associated electric field. Electrons or holes created by phonons or background photons, diffusing into the barrier region, are swept from the n-type material to the p-type material, or vice versa. This results in current pulses appearing across the diode with the same characteristics that are observed for the vacuum tube.

Petritz[26] has developed a theory applicable to the lead chalcogenide (PbS, PbSe, PbTe) photoconductive films, which is suitable for discussion here. These films are composed of a system of tiny crystallites separated by intercrystalline barriers, where space-charge regions exist. The barrier regions contribute both Johnson and shot noises, while the crystallites generate the usual Johnson noise. For thin barriers, compared to the carrier-diffusion length, the barrier-noise contribution can be determined by using the expression noted by Weisskopf[39,40] for the short-circuit noise generator:

$$\overline{i^2} = \left[\frac{4kT}{r_B} + 2eI_B \right] \Delta f \tag{10-102}$$

The total noise due to the aggregate of crystallites that make up the film is found by properly summing the contributions from each of them. Petritz finds that the macroscopic short-circuit current generator provides a noise given by

$$\overline{i^2} \left[\frac{4kT}{r} + \frac{2eI_{dc}}{n_l l} \right] \Delta f \tag{10-103}$$

where n_l is the number of crystallites per unit length of the detector, r_B is the resistance of a barrier, and r is the macroscopic detector resistance, or expressed as a voltage

$$\overline{v^2} = \left[4rkT + \frac{2er^2 I_{dc}}{n_l l} \right] \Delta f \tag{10-104}$$

10.3.5 Background Radiation Noise

Background radiation can be thought of as a stream of photons originating from the detector environment. The cell walls surrounding the detector, its window, and the media viewed by the detector through the cell window all contribute to this radiation. The extent of the individual contributions is determined by their respective temperatures, emissivities, and geometry.

Photons, originating from the background and impinging on the detector, arrive in a statistically fluctuating manner. In addition, the detector radiates in a manner dependent on its temperature and emissivity, obeying the same statistical law as the background. The net fluctuation in radiant-energy exchange causes a corresponding fluctuation in temperature, and provides the mechanism for the limiting noise process in thermal detectors. This limiting process is called "temperature noise."

The photodetector is insensitive to this temperature effect. However, the radiation fluctuation causes charge carriers to be liberated in varying amounts, causing corresponding changes in the photoelectric effect utilized. When the cause of the electrical noise observed in a photo-detector is due to this radiation, the detector is said to be "background radiation noise limited."

Photons obey Bose-Einstein statistics,[41] and their fluctuation can be described by:

$$\overline{\Delta n_r{}^2} = n_r \{1 + [\exp{(h\nu/kT)} - 1]^{-1}\} \tag{10-105}$$

This expression reduces to the classical case

$$\overline{\Delta n_r{}^2} = n_r \tag{10-106}$$

for values of

$$\exp{(h\nu/kT)} \gg 1$$

Substituting $\nu = c/\lambda$, and considering a room-temperature condition ($\approx 300\,^\circ$K), reveals that the exponential becomes sufficiently large for photons of wavelength less than 10 μ, that classical statistics can be applied. Fellgett[42] clearly shows the relationship between the number of photons and their fluctuation in Figure 10-11.

10.3.5.1 *Contribution to G-R Noise.* In the derivation of the expression for G-R noise, it was assumed that the thermal generation of carriers

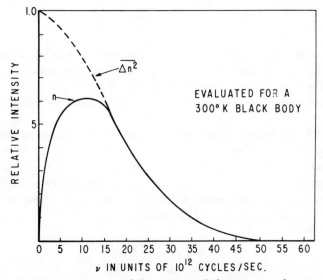

Fig. 10-11. Relative intensity and fluctuation of photons as a function of wave-length and temperature (*prepared by J. Mudar, from Reference 42*).

followed the same statistical process as carrier generation from the absorption of background photons. Therefore the expressions in Eqs. (10-99) and (10-100) are applicable here. The only difference that arises is in the calculation of N_r, that is the contribution to N by the radiation. The complete expression used to derive Eq. (10-99) is given by Petritz[1,26] as:

$$\overline{\Delta N^2} = \frac{4\tau^2 \cdot \Delta f \cdot A(\eta_r J_r + \eta_l J_l)}{1 + (\omega\tau)^2} \tag{10-107}$$

where J_l is the lattice phonon flux

J_r is the background radiation photon flux incident on the detector

η_r, η_l are the efficiency factors for conversion of photons and phonons to carriers.

The number of carriers created by the absorption of photons is of the form $N_r \alpha A \eta_r J_r \tau$, where

$$\eta_r J_r = \frac{c}{4} \int_{E_g/h}^{\infty} \eta(\nu) N_r(\nu, Tr) \, d\nu \tag{10-108}$$

where $\eta(\nu)$ is the responsive quantum efficiency at frequency ν

c is the velocity of light

$N_r(\nu, Tr)$ is the density of photons in the background, and

$$N_r(\nu, T_r) = \frac{8\pi\nu^2}{c^3[\exp(h\nu/kT) - 1]}$$

and similar expressions hold for lattice processes. It is clear, then, that reducing the temperature of the background or of the detector causes a reduction in N and the carrier fluctuation. When N_r is greater than the number contributed by phonon processes, the detector is G-R background noise limited.

10.3.5.2 *Contribution to Thermal Detector Noise.* There is a continual interchange of radiant energy between the detector and its surroundings. The statistical fluctuations in the density of photons exchanged (under equilibrium conditions) causes fluctuations in the energy or heat content of the detector. These thermal fluctuations become apparent in the form of temperature noise, which can be described by:[43,44]

$$\overline{\Delta T^2} = \frac{4kT^2 K \Delta f}{K^2 + \omega^2 C^2} \tag{10-109}$$

where all symbols have the same meaning as in Section 10.2.

10.4 Speed of Response

The speed of response of a photodetector depends upon the mechanism by which charge carriers recombine after their generation by the absorption of radiation. Various recombination mechanisms are possible, and are described by Smith[4] and Bube.[45] Generally these mechanisms fall into two categories: (1) radiative recombination, or recombination of electrons and holes by transitions of electrons from the conduction band directly to the valence band; (2) recombination of electrons and holes through "recombination centers." The decay rate depends upon the type of mechanism, the concentration of carriers generated by the signal, the concentration of recombination centers, and often the existence of electron and hole traps whereby the carriers are temporarily immobilized and unable to participate in the kinetics of recombination.

In simple processes such as (1) above, the photosignal decay after the removal of signal radiation follows a simple exponential decay law. For more complicated mechanisms, the decay might be described by a sum of exponential terms, or possibly a power law. Frequency-response measurements follow a similar pattern in complexity.

10.4.1 *Pulse Response*

When the photon-generated carriers in the semiconductor decay in an exponential manner, the photoresponse to a pulse of light can be described as follows.

During the time of exposure to the light pulse, the detector signal will increase according to:

$$v = v_0 [1 - \exp(-t/\tau)] \tag{10-110}$$

where v_0 is the maximum value of the signal obtained for a light pulse sufficiently long that $\exp(-t/\tau) \ll 1$. For a pulse of short time duration t_0, the rise of the signal will follow Eq. (10-110) to a maximum value of

$$v_{t_0} = v_0 [1 - \exp(-t_0/\tau)] \tag{10-111}$$

The decay that follows the end of the light pulse is given by:

$$v = v_{t_0} \{\exp[-(t - t_0)/\tau]\} \tag{10-112}$$

or

$$v = v_0 [1 - \exp(-t_0/\tau)] \cdot \{\exp[-(t - \tau_0)/\tau]\} \tag{10-113}$$

The signal rise and fall are shown in Figure 10-12. Notice the asymmetry in the rise and decay parts of the trace. The rise is shorter in time than the decay, and the initial slopes of rise and decay are signifi-

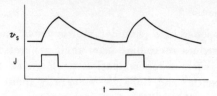

Fig. 10-12. Periodic pulse photoexcitation and detector response.

cantly different in their absolute magnitude. To illustrate the latter, differentiate Eqs. (10-110) and (10-113) and examine their slopes at time $t = 0$, and t_0, respectively.

$$\frac{dv}{dt} = \frac{v_0}{\tau}\left[\exp\left(-\frac{t}{\tau}\right)\right] = \frac{v_0}{\tau}\Big|_{t=0} \qquad (10\text{-}114)$$

$$\frac{dv}{dt} = -\frac{v_0}{\tau}\left[1 - \exp\left(-\frac{t_0}{\tau}\right)\right]\Big|_{t=t_0} \qquad (10\text{-}115)$$

It is clear that the decay and rise curves cannot look alike unless the light pulse $t_0 \gg \tau$. The time constant τ can be obtained from a semi-logarithmic plot of Eq. (10-113) (the decay curve), whereas it cannot be obtained readily from Eq. (10-110).

10.4.2 Frequency Response

When the detector response is observed for excitation by sinusoidally modulated radiation, rather than pulses of light, the response is frequency dependent and behaves as:

$$v(\omega) = \frac{v_0}{[1 + (\omega\tau)^2]^{1/2}} \qquad (10\text{-}116)$$

where $\omega = 2\pi f$, f is the frequency of the exciting signal, and τ is the time constant for the decay mechanism. Fortunately many of the detectors in present usage follow the exponential law of decay, and an effective time constant is easily reported. The measurement techniques used to determine the time constant are described in Chapter 12. From a response versus frequency plot, τ can be calculated easily from the selection of ω when the response is down by $1/\sqrt{2}$, for then:

$$\frac{v}{v_0} = \frac{1}{\sqrt{2}} = \frac{1}{\sqrt{1 + (\omega\tau)^2}} \qquad (10\text{-}117)$$

when

$$\omega\tau = 1$$

or

$$\tau = (2\pi f)^{-1}$$

Another approach is to measure the response at two different chopping frequencies, and take the ratio of the two signals as follows:

$$\frac{v_1}{v_2} = \left[\frac{1 + (\omega_2 \tau)^2}{1 + (\omega_1 \tau)^2} \right]^{1/2} \tag{10-118}$$

and solving for τ, obtain:

$$\tau = \frac{1}{2\pi} \left[\frac{v_1^2 - v_2^2}{(f_2 v_2)^2 - (f_1 v_1)^2} \right] \tag{10-119}$$

for the time constant. From this relationship and assuming that small signal changes about 5 per cent can be recorded, a chopping frequency of about 100 kcs permits a determination of time constant in the region of a half-microsecond.

10.4.3 Multiple Time Constants

When the speed of response does not depend on frequency according to Eq. (10-116), there does not appear to be any clear definition of the time constant τ. This situation prevails particularly when multiple electronic transitions of a carrier are involved so that two or more time constants exist. The decay processes may follow two or more successive exponential processes, or possibly combinations of power and exponential laws. The frequency response characteristic curves will then show two or more peaks (or plateaus), while the decay curve following a pulse of light will exhibit sectors which will follow different decay laws. Time constant has been defined in a number of different ways. Generally the definitions take the form $\tau = \frac{1}{2\pi f}$, where f is the frequency at which the responsivity is 0.707 times the zero frequency responsivity, at which the low- and high-frequency asymptotes intersect, at which the slope of the responsivity versus frequency curve is minus 3 decibels per octave, and at which the phase lag is $45°$.[46] All of these definitions are equal when the photosignal decay follows a simple exponential decay law, or the process is described in terms of the frequency response by an equation in the form Eq. (10-116).

When the response curve to a long pulse of radiation is available, sufficient for the photosignal to reach its maximum value, estimates of time constant are attempted by noting the time for the response signal to decay down 67 or 90 per cent from its maximum value.

A frequency-dependent measurement will follow an expression of the form:

$$v = \frac{K_1 \sin(\omega \tau_1 - \varphi_1)}{[1 + (\omega \tau_1)^2]^{1/2}} + \frac{K_2 \sin(\omega \tau_2 - \varphi_2)}{[1 + (\omega \tau_2)^2]^{1/2}} \tag{10-120}$$

A general solution permitting an evaluation of the two time constants is possible, but is a complicated matter. According to Levinstein,[47] a completely general solution requires for solving four unknowns: they are K_1, K_2, τ_1, and τ_2. It is necessary to measure response at four different frequencies to obtain sufficient information for a solution. If the frequencies are chosen properly, then the two time constants are given by an equation of the form

$$\tau_1, \tau_2 =$$

$$\left\{ \frac{(ed - ah)^2 \pm [(ed - ah)^2 - 4(bh - fd)(eb - af)]^{1/2}}{2(bh - fd)} \right\}^{1/2} \tag{10-121}$$

where a, b, d, e, f, and h are lengthy frequency-dependent measurements. The expression is complicated but does offer recourse when exact analysis from frequency-response data becomes necessary.

The selection of a universal time constant for this complicated case is necessary, but unlikely to be made in the near future. The reader is advised to understand the different definitions noted above, and adjust to their usage as they arise in his work.

10.5 Spectral Response

A discussion of the fundamental mechanisms responsible for photodetector response is presented in Section 10.1. However, a summary of the important aspects relating to spectral response is presented here for continuity. Detailed discussions of the experimental procedures and the calculations required to determine a detector's spectral response are found in Chapter 12.

The spectral response of a photodetector depends upon the energy required by a photon to free a charge carrier. If the photon energy is sufficiently large, charge carriers can be freed, with the new carrier concentration providing photoeffects suitable for measurement.

A plot of responsivity versus wavelength may be drawn in two ways, depending upon the units used in the evaluation of responsivity. It may be expressed as the amount of signal voltage obtained per unit of incident photon flux at a given wavelength, or as the amount of signal voltage obtained per unit of incident power at a given wavelength. The former is the equivalent of a plot made directly with a monochrometer capable of providing detector illumination with a constant unit flux density of photons at all wavelengths, while the latter is that for a constant unit of power exposure. Since a photodetector responds directly to the number of photons per second that are absorbed, an idealized detector would provide a spectral responsivity plot like that in Figure 10-13. Usually, however, the radiation output of monochrometers is measured by a "black" detector, such as a thermocouple. The thermocouple has a constant responsivity as a function of wavelength (at least in the wavelengths of interest here) and is a device which responds to the radiation power. Thus, the photodetector responsivity is readily measured in terms of power rather than photon flux density, and the resultant ideal plot is shown in Figure 10-14. The difference in the shapes of the curves in

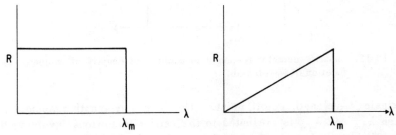

Fig. 10-13. Intrinsic detector response to a constant density of photons, as a function of wavelength.

Fig. 10-14. Intrinsic detector response to constant energy exposure, as a function of wavelength.

Figures 10-13 and 10-14 is readily explained on examining the expression for a photon's energy:

$$h\nu = hc/\lambda \qquad (10\text{-}122)$$

The photons of shorter wavelengths have higher energies. Therefore, fewer photons per second are required to maintain a constant unit of power with decreasing wavelength. Since a photodetector signal is proportional to the photon flux, the detector signal falls off with decreasing wavelength.

The sharp drop-off point at the position indicated as λ_m determines the minimum energy a photon must have to free a charge carrier. If the energy is in electron volts, and the wavelength in microns, then the relationship between them is:

$$\lambda_m = \frac{1.24}{\text{Energy } (ev)} \qquad (10\text{-}123)$$

Impurity-type photoconductors such as gold-doped germanium are designed to extend the spectral response of the material to longer wavelengths than possible with the pure material. The impurities introduce new energy levels in the forbidden gap region of the intrinsic material, and therefore permit lower energy carrier transitions corresponding to longer wavelength response. An idealized spectral response curve for the impurity photodetector is shown in Figure 10-15. The short wavelength response up to λ_{1m} is associated with intrinsic absorption and carrier transitions across the complete energy gap; λ_{2m} refers to the

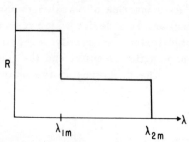

Fig. 10-15. Impurity detector response to a constant density of photons, as a function of wavelength.

extrinsic wavelength cutoff point. The long wavelength response between λ_{2m} and λ_{1m} is attributed to the carrier transitions involving the "impurity levels:" λ_{2m} refers to the wavelength at which impurity photoresponse ceases. The difference in the response magnitudes of these two spectral regions corresponds to the high absorption of the lattice for photons in the intrinsic region, as compared to the weak absorption by low-density impurities in the extrinsic region. In order to improve the magnitude of the latter region, it is customary to house the detector in a small integrating chamber with a hole to admit the signal radiation. This causes the photons to make multiple passes through the detector, improving the probability of their absorption.

1. R. L. Petritz, *Proc. IRE* **47**, 1458 (1959).
2. W. Shockley, *Bell System Tech. J.* **28**, 435 (1949).
3. J. L. Moll, *Proc. IRE* **46**, 1076 (1958).
4. R. A. Smith, *Semiconductors*. New York: Cambridge Univ. Press, 1959.
5. G. Goudet and C. Meuleau, *Semiconductors*. London: MacDonald & Evans, 1957.
6. R. L. Cummerow, *Phys. Rev.* **95**, 16 (1954).
7. E. S. Rittner in *Photoconductivity Conference*. R. G. Breckenridge, B. R. Russell, and E. E. Hahn (eds.). New York: Wiley, 1956.
8. G. R. Pruett and R. L. Petritz, *Proc. IRE* **47**, 1524 (1959).
9. T. S. Moss, *Proc. Phys. Soc. (London)* **B66**, 999 (1953).
10. P. Aigrain and H. Bulliard, *Compt. rend.* **236**, 595 and 672 (1953).
11. Moss, Pincherle, and Woodward, *Proc. Phys. Soc. (London)* **B66**, 743 (1953).
12. S. W. Kurnick and R. N. Zitter, *J. Appl. Phys.* **27**, 278 (1956).
13. S. W. Kurnick and R. N. Zitter in *Photoconductivity Conference*. New York: Wiley, 1956.
14. L. Pincherle, *Photoconductivity Conference*. New York: Wiley, 1956.

15. O. Garreta and J. Grosvalet, *Progress in Semiconductors*. London: Heywood & Co., 1956, Vol. 1, p. 167.
16. W. van Roosbroeck, *Phys. Rev.* **101**, 1713 (1956).
17. R. N. Zitter, *Phys. Rev.* **112**, 852 (1958).
18. P. W. Kruse, *J. Appl. Phys.* **30**, 770 (1959).
19. M. W. Zemansky, *Heat and Thermodynamics*. New York: McGraw-Hill, 1943.
20. R. de Waard and E. M. Wormser, *Proc. IRE* **47**, 158 (1958).
21. R. de Waard and E. M. Wormser, Navord Report 5495 (April, 1958).
22. H. A. Zahl and M. J. E. Golay, *Rev. Sci. Instr.* **17**, 511 (1946).
23. M. J. E. Golay, *Rev. Sci. Instr.* **18**, 357 (1947).
24. H. Nyquist, *Phys. Rev.* **33**, 110 (1928).
25. J. B. Johnson, *Phys. Rev.* **32**, 97 (1928).
26. R. L. Petritz, *Phys. Rev.* **104**, 1508 (1956).
27. J. J. Brophy, *J. Appl. Phys.* **27**, 1383 (1957).
28. T. G. Maple, L. Bess, and H. A. Gebbie, *J. Appl. Phys.* **26**, 490 (1955).
29. R. L. Petritz, *Proc. IRE* **40**, 1440 (1952).
30. J. J. Brophy and N. Rostoker, *Phys. Rev.* **100**, 754 (1955).
31. J. J. Brophy, *Phys. Rev.* **106**, 675 (1957).
32. L. Bess, *J. Appl. Phys.* **26**, 1377 (1955).
33. A. U. MacRae and H. Levinstein, *Phys. Rev.* **119**, 62 (1960).
34. J. J. Brophy, *J. Appl. Phys.* **27**, 1383 (1956).
35. L. Bess, *Phys. Rev.* **103**, 72 (1956).
36. J. R. Morrison, *Phys. Rev.* **104**, 619 (1956).
37. K. M. van Vliet, *Proc. IRE* **46**, 1004 (1958).
38. A. van der Ziel, *Proc. IRE* **46**, 1019 (1958).
39. V. F. Weisskopf, National Defense Research Committee Report NDRC 14-133 [May 15, 1943 (unpublished)].
40. H. C. Torrey and C. A. Whitmer, *Crystal Rectifiers*. New York: McGraw-Hill, 1948, Chap. 6.
41. R. C. Tolman, *Principles of Statistical Mechanics*. Oxford: Clarendon Press, 1938, p. 512.
42. P. B. Fellgett, *J. Opt. Soc. Am.* **39**, 970 (1949).
43. R. A. Smith, F. E. Jones, and R. P. Chasmar, *The Detection and Measurement of Infrared Radiation*. Oxford: Clarendon Press, 1957.
44. R. Clark Jones, *Advances in Electronics*. New York: Academic Press, 1953, Vol. 5.
45. R. H. Bube, *Photoconductivity of Solids*. New York: Wiley, 1960.
46. Jones, Goodwin and Pullan, *Standard Procedure for Testing Infrared Detectors and for Describing their Performance*. Washington, D. C.: Office of the Director of Defense Research and Engineering, 12 September 1960.
47. H. Levinstein *et al.*, *Interim Report on Infrared Detectors*. Syracuse University under Air Force Contract AF 33(616)-3859 (September, 1958), p. 13.

CHAPTER 11

DETECTOR EVALUATION FROM
THEORETICAL CONSIDERATIONS

The signal and noise-voltage equations derived in Chapter 10 indicate that detector parameters such as size, time constant, and bandwidth of operation are important factors in evaluating a detector's capability. Detectors are made of many different materials; they also differ in sizes and time constants. The engineer is thus faced with the difficult problem of selecting the best one for his purpose. On the basis of the analysis of Chapter 10, he has the basic ingredients for such a selection. However, an examination of the signal and noise equations would involve him in a tedious nonprofitable task of juggling these equations to fit his immediate problem. What is needed is a simple number which provides a detector "rating" independent of the bothersome parameters, from which he can make a quick, proper detector selection. The purpose of this chapter is to describe and discuss the substantial effort that has been put forth to provide this "universal" number for rating detectors.

The treatment that follows extends the discussion of Chapter 8, and begins with a general analysis of NEP (Noise Equivalent Power). It then continues with detailed analysis of the photoconductive and thermocouple detectors in their various noise-limited conditions. These will serve as examples of treatments applicable to the quantum and thermal classes of detectors. Detector classification schemes based on NEP will be presented thereafter.

11.1 NEP (Noise Equivalent Power)

Consider an infrared detector exposed to some incident radiation, in a circuit which provides an electric signal voltage proportional to the radiant power. Assume also that the dominant electrical noise in the circuit is generated by the detector, *not* the preamplifier. Let the radiant power P be expressed as $H \cdot A$, where H is the irradiance and A is the area of the detector. The absorption of power P by the detector results in a signal voltage V_S in the circuit. When the power source is removed or masked and the detector allowed to see only the background, a noise voltage V_N is obtained. The predominant mechanism causing this noise might be internal to the detector, such as from Johnson, shot and/or lattice governed G-R noise sources. In the case of the best detectors, this noise might well be governed by the fluctuations in photon flux irradiating the detector, that is, the background noise limited condition. A simple proportionality can be set up, relating these voltage readings and the power P:

$$\frac{\text{NEP}}{V_N} = \frac{H \cdot A}{V_S} \tag{11-1}$$

Thus if Johnson noise is responsible for V_N, then NEP represents the amount of power that would have to fall onto the detector to generate an equivalent voltage V_N. This relationship is more usually observed in the form:

$$\text{NEP} = \frac{H \cdot A}{V_S / V_N} \tag{11-2}$$

Clearly, NEP is also the power exposure required by the detector to obtain a signal-to-noise voltage ratio of unity.

A relatively simple analysis can be first attempted for the purpose of providing some insight to the area dependence of NEP. Assume first a simple detector in a circuit, from which is obtained a signal voltage V_S and a noise voltage V_N. The noise voltage is assumed due to a uniform distribution of noise sources throughout the bulk of the detector. Consider two of these detectors placed adjacent to one another at their ends (end to end) and connected electrically in series. The total signal voltage is simply $V_{S1} + V_{S2}$, since the signals are coherent. The noise voltages add as their mean squares, since they are incoherent. The noise voltage of each unit is the rms value of the voltage fluctuation, or $V_N = \sqrt{\overline{v^2}}$ where $v = v(t) - v_{\text{Av}} v(t)$ is the instantaneous value of the noise voltage, and v_{Av} is the average value. The signal-to-noise ratio from the combined units is:

$$\frac{V_{ST}}{V_{NT}} = \frac{V_{S1} + V_{S2}}{(V_{N1}^2 + V_{N2}^2)^{1/2}} \tag{11-3}$$

If the two detectors are identical in area and thickness, $V_{S1} = V_{S2}$, and equal noise is generated from each of them. Then:

$$\frac{V_{ST}}{V_{NT}} = \frac{2 V_{S1}}{\sqrt{2} V_{N1}} = \sqrt{2} \frac{V_{S1}}{V_{N1}} \tag{11-4}$$

Suppose these two detectors are now placed side by side, and connected electrically in parallel. Since currents can be added in a straightforward manner when dealing with parallel circuits, consider the noise sources as from current generators. The total noise becomes (this is similar to the noise-voltage analysis):

$$I_{NT}^2 = I_{N1}^2 + I_{N2}^2 \qquad (11\text{-}5)$$

and for identical detectors:

$$I_{NT} = \sqrt{2I_{N1}^2} \qquad (11\text{-}6)$$

The signal current is now:

$$I_{ST} = I_{S1} + I_{S2} = 2I_{S1} \qquad (11\text{-}7)$$

The signal-to-noise current ratio becomes

$$\frac{I_{ST}}{I_{NT}} = \frac{2I_{S1}}{\sqrt{2}\,I_{N1}} = \sqrt{2}\,\frac{I_{S1}}{I_{N1}} \qquad (11\text{-}8)$$

The noise current can be expressed as a noise voltage by simply multiplying the total noise current by the effective resistance of the circuit. Therefore:

$$r_t = \frac{r_1 r_2}{r_1 + r_2} = \frac{r_1}{2} \text{ for } r_1 = r_2 \qquad (11\text{-}9)$$

and

$$V_{NT}^2 = I_{NT}^2 \cdot r_t^2 = \frac{I_{N1}^2 \cdot r_1^2}{2}$$

or

$$V_{NT} = \frac{1}{\sqrt{2}}\,I_{N1} r_1 \qquad (11\text{-}10)$$

The signal voltage is $V_{ST} = V_{S1} = V_{S2}$, since the circuit is now equivalent to two identical batteries placed in parallel.

$$\frac{V_{ST}}{V_{NT}} = \frac{I_{S1} \cdot r_1}{\frac{1}{\sqrt{2}}I_{N1} \cdot r_1} = \sqrt{2}\,\frac{V_{S1}}{V_{N1}} \qquad (11\text{-}11)$$

The analysis can readily be extended to three or more detector units. It is immediately apparent from the treatment with two units, however, that with either the series or parallel arrangement, the signal-to-noise ratio depends on the square root of the rotal detector area. This, then, indicates that the NEP of a detector should also depend on the square root of the area by insertion in Eq. (11-2).

11.1.1 *Analysis of NEP for the Photoconductive Detector*

A detailed analysis of the dependence of NEP on area, for the various noise-limited cases, can be developed starting with the definition of NEP, Eq. (11-2).

The procedure followed will be to substitute appropriate expressions for the signal and noise voltages in this equation, and generate an equation which delineates the geometry, time constant, and bandwidth dependence of NEP. The photoconductive detector will be the only type of photodetector treated here, since the procedure is straightforward and can be applied by the reader to any other detector types.

The factor for the incident power will be $H \cdot A$, where H is the irradiance, and the signal voltage is as given by Eq. 10-8. Therefore:

$$\text{NEP} = HA \frac{V_N}{I_{dc} \cdot (\rho l/dw) \cdot [\eta_S J_S \tau/nd \sqrt{1 + (\omega\tau)^2}]} \qquad (11\text{-}12)$$

11.1.1.1 *Johnson Noise.* In Section 10.3.1, the Johnson noise voltage was given by:

$$V_N = \sqrt{\overline{v^2}} = \sqrt{4kTr\,\Delta f}$$

Inserting Eq. (10-95) into Eq. (11-12) provides:

$$\text{NEP} = HA \frac{\sqrt{4kTr\,\Delta f}}{I_{dc} \cdot (\rho l/dw) \cdot [\eta_S J_S \tau/nd \sqrt{1 + (\omega\tau)^2}]} \qquad (11\text{-}13)$$

where $r = \rho l/dw$ and $I_{dc} = idw$. In the last term, i = current density $= \sigma E$, where E = electric field strength and $\sigma = 2ne\mu\,(\mu = \mu_n = \mu_p)$. This equation can be simplified to fundamental physical quantities by first rewriting σ in the form: [using Eqs. (10-11) and (10-16)]

$$\sigma = 2ne\,\frac{D}{kT/e} = \frac{2ne^2}{kT} \cdot \frac{L^2}{\tau} \qquad (11\text{-}14)$$

Simplifying so that all factors other than area, time constant, and bandwidth are lumped together, provides:

$$\text{NEP} = K_1 \frac{\sqrt{A \cdot \Delta f}}{\sqrt{\tau}} \cdot \sqrt{1 + (\omega\tau)^2} \qquad (11\text{-}15)$$

where

$$K_1 = \frac{kT\sqrt{2nd}}{e\eta_S J_S El} \cdot H$$

Thus the relationship between NEP, area, time constant, and bandwidth are clearly spelled out for the Johnson noise limited case by:

$$\text{NEP} \propto \sqrt{\frac{A \cdot \Delta f}{\tau}} \qquad (11\text{-}16)$$

Notice that the Johnson noise exists without current flow, while the photoconductive signal requires a bias current. Even though a basic difference exists between processes reponsible for signal and noise generation, a $\sqrt{A}$ dependence evolves compatible with our discussion of Section 11.1.

11.1.1.2 *Current, 1/f, Modulation, or Excess Noise.* In Section 10.3.2 this noise was described by the equation:

$$V_N = I_{dc} \cdot r \sqrt{C \Delta f / wdlf}$$

Inserting Eq. (10-97) in Eq. (11-12) provides:

$$\text{NEP} = HA \frac{I_{dc} \cdot r \sqrt{C \Delta f / wdlf}}{I_{dc} \cdot (\rho l / wd) \cdot [\eta_S J_S \, \tau / nd \sqrt{1 + (\omega \tau)^2}]} \qquad (11\text{-}17)$$

$$\text{NEP} = K_2 \sqrt{\frac{A \cdot \Delta f}{f}} \frac{\sqrt{1 + (\omega \tau)^2}}{\tau} \qquad (11\text{-}18)$$

where

$$K_2 = [(n \sqrt{cd})/(\eta_S \, J_S)] \, H \qquad (11\text{-}19)$$

In this instance, both the signal and noise are associated with bias currents. However, even though a complete understanding of the source of 1/f noise is not yet available, it is clear that for a uniform generation of noise throughout the bulk and/or surface of the detector, the NEP will depend upon the square root of the detector area. In addition, NEP will vary as $f^{-1/2}$.

11.1.1.3 *Generation-Recombination and Background Noise.* In Section 10.3.3, G-R noise was described by Eq. (10-98):

$$V_N = I_{dc} r \, (\sqrt{\overline{\Delta N^2}/N})$$

The signal-to-noise voltage ratios then become

$$\frac{V_S}{V_N} = \frac{I_{dc} \cdot r \cdot (\Delta N_S / N)}{I_{dc} \, r \, (\sqrt{\overline{\Delta N^2}_N / N})} = \frac{\Delta N_{sig}}{\sqrt{\overline{\Delta N^2}}_{noise}} \qquad (11\text{-}20)$$

where from Eq. (10-107):

$$\sqrt{\overline{\Delta N^2}} = 2 \sqrt{A \tau^2 \Delta f (\eta_B J_B + \eta_l J_l)/[1 + (\omega \tau)^2]}$$

The change in the number of carriers due to signal radiation is given by Eq. (10-7):

$$\Delta N_{sig} = \frac{A \eta_S J_S \tau}{\sqrt{1 + (\omega \tau)^2}}$$

Therefore

$$\frac{V_S}{V_N} = \frac{\eta_S J_S}{2 \sqrt{\eta_B J_B + \eta_l J_l}} \sqrt{\frac{A}{\Delta f}} \tag{11-21}$$

$$NEP = K_3 \sqrt{A \cdot \Delta f} \tag{11-22}$$

where

$$K_3 = 2H \sqrt{\eta_B J_B + \eta_l J_l} \Big/ \eta_S J_S \tag{11-23}$$

In this instance, as for current $(1/f)$ noise, the signal and noise are associated with bias current flow. Here, the square root areal dependence of NEP arises from the averaging process required in arriving at the value for the mean square fluctuation in carriers generated at random by the background photons. Notice that NEP in this case does not depend upon the time constant. This is due to the behavior of the detector now being controlled by the same processes for signal and noise. Both the quantities Δn_{sig} and $\sqrt{\overline{\Delta N^2}}_{noise}$ are linearly dependent on τ. Their ratio being independent of τ means that the detector will respond equally well in time to background photons and signal photons, for information not requiring a response time appreciably less than τ.

11.1.1.4 *Shot Noise.* In Section 10.3.4, the shot-noise contribution to photoconductive film noise was given by Eq. (10-104):

$$V_N = r \sqrt{\frac{2 e I_{dc} \Delta f}{n_l l}}$$

The noise equivalent power becomes, on substituting Eq. (10-104) into Eq. (11-12):

$$NEP = HA \frac{r \sqrt{2 e I_{dc} \Delta f / n_l l}}{I_{dc} r (\eta_S J_S \tau / nd \sqrt{1 + (\omega \tau)^2})} \tag{11-24}$$

Substituting as before in Eq. (11-14), to get:

$$I_{dc} = \sigma E w d = 2 n e \mu^* E w d \tag{11-25}$$

where μ^* is an average, reduced mobility for carriers in the film, and

$$\mu^* = (l^2 / kT) \cdot (e / \tau) \tag{11-26}$$

to obtain

$$NEP = K_4 \sqrt{A \Delta f / \tau} \cdot \sqrt{1 + (\omega \tau)^2} \tag{11-27}$$

where

$$K_4 = \sqrt{\frac{dnkT}{eEn_l} \cdot \frac{H}{\eta_S J_S l}} \qquad (11\text{-}28)$$

11.1.1.5 *Summation.*   In all four noise-limited conditions examined here, NEP is clearly dependent on the square root of the product of the bandwidth and the area of the detector. The time constant and frequency dependencies of shot-noise-limited and Johnson-noise-limited detectors are identical. This should be expected since both noise spectrums are essentially flat. The factor in the NEP expression denoting this identical condition is

$$\sqrt{[1 + (\omega\tau)^2]/\tau}$$

The case of $1/f$ noise provides a factor given by

$$\sqrt{[1 + (\omega\tau)^2]/f} \cdot (1/\tau)$$

while G-R noise leads to an expression independent of frequency and time constant. Finally the G-R, background noise-limited NEP does not contain any factors associated with a detector mechanism of operation. This should be expected since a detector measuring background noise is limited by that external noise, and thereby loses its identity. In other words, any number of different detectors operating with the same spectral characteristics could not be distinguished from one another in terms of NEP, if they were all limited by background noise. If the detectors are G-R phonon noise limited, then J_B in Eq. (11-23) must be smaller then J_l. In that event, charge carriers produced by the detector lattice dominate as the noise source, and the noise can be identified by its temperature dependence.

11.1.2 *Photovoltaic and PEM Detectors*

As noted above, detailed analysis of NEP for the photovoltaic and PEM detectors will not be carried out here. From the discussion of signal generation in Sections 10.1.2 and 10.1.3, together with the treatment of noise in Section 10.3, the interested reader can follow the same procedure used in 11.1.1 to obtain the NEP properties of these two detectors. However, some of this work has already been carried out, and will be summarized here.

Pruett and Petritz[1] derive the signal-to-noise ratio, and NEP for the back-biased photovoltaic detector. This detector is limited by shot noise,[2] and the NEP is given by:

$$\text{NEP} = HA\,[(\sqrt{\Delta f} \cdot \sqrt{N_{\text{noise}}})/e\eta A J_S] \qquad (11\text{-}29)$$

where the noise is given by:

$$N_N = \frac{\overline{i_n^2}}{\Delta f}$$

$$= 2e\left[I_{SC} + \frac{I_s}{\beta}\left(\exp\frac{ev}{\beta kT} + 1\right)\right] + 4kTG_{sh}$$

$$+ \left[\frac{k_1 G_{sh}^2 V^2 + k_2(I - G_{sh}V)^2 + k_3 I^2}{f}\right] \quad (11\text{-}30)$$

The signal-to-noise ratio is maximized by operating V slightly negative, but near $V = 0$. This permits practically the elimination of the $1/f$ noise term, and

$$I_{SC} \gg \frac{I_s}{\beta}\left[\exp\frac{eV}{\beta kT} + 1\right] \quad (11\text{-}31)$$

C. Hilsum and O. Simpson[3] have treated all three photodetectors in an extensive manner, examining particularly the dependence of their NEP's in the Johnson-noise-limited case. Some of their conclusions are as follows:

The PEM mode is favored for a semiconductor with high carrier mobility and short lifetime (e.g., InSb), while the PC mode is favored for a semiconductor of long lifetime and low density of carriers. This is apparent from the factor $\sqrt{n_i/\mu_n\mu_p\tau}$ which appears explicitly in the PEM formula, compared with n_i/τ in the PC formula. Reducing the crystal thickness below the diffusion length of the carriers results in no advantage for the PEM mode, but a proportionate advantage can be gained in the PC mode, provided that the surface recombination velocity is sufficiently low. The p-n junction is preferred for semiconductors with low carrier density and low mobility; the depth of the junction below the surface is not critical so long as it is less than the minority carrier diffusion length.

For values of μB small compared to 1, it is clear from the earlier discussion of the PEM signal, that the observation of high carrier mobility favoring a PEM detector is appropriate. However, some modification appears necessary for increasing values of μB, since the dependence of PEM signal on mobility changes. Values suggested by Kruse[4] for the InSb PEM detectors indicate detector operation is in a region where the PEM signal depends upon μX, for X less than 1.5. This causes NEP to depend inversely on μ raised to a power less than 1. It would also be useful to derive the expression for NEP in the other noise-limited cases.

In principle, it appears that the best detector obtainable should be the photovoltaic, G-R, background-noise-limited detector. This comes about because the other two detectors in this noise-limited condition have a G-R noise that depends upon fluctuations induced by both the generation and recombination processes. However, the photovoltaic detector does not suffer from this statistical fluctuation on recombination, since the process here is essentially a minority carrier moving back to its majority carrier status on crossing the barrier. Thus the background noise fluctuation observed for this detector is $1/\sqrt{2}$ less than for the photoconductive and PEM detectors.

11.1.3 *Analysis of NEP for the Thermocouple*

This section treats the derivation of NEP for the thermocouple, as an example of the general treatment for thermal detectors.

Following our treatment of the semiconducting photodetectors, we now define:

$$\text{NEP} = \frac{HA}{V_S/V_N} = \frac{V_N}{\gamma} \qquad (11\text{-}32)$$

where γ is the responsivity and V_N is the rms noise voltage. The responsivity of the thermocouple was derived in Section 10.2.1 to be:

$$\gamma = \frac{SR}{\sqrt{1 + (\omega\tau)^2}}$$

while the noise voltage is given by

$$V_N = \sqrt{4kT\Delta f(r + Z_D)}$$

where r_g is omitted since it is not intrinsic to the detector. Thus:

$$\text{NEP} = \frac{\sqrt{4kT\Delta f(r + Z_D)}}{SR} \cdot \sqrt{1 + (\omega\tau)^2} \qquad (11\text{-}33)$$

It is clear then, that the NEP contains two terms, one involving the $\sqrt{r}$ and the other the $\sqrt{Z_D}$. The first term gives the usual Johnson noise governed by the resistance r, while the second is unique to the thermocouple since

$$Z_D = \frac{R_D}{\sqrt{1 + (\omega\tau)^2}} = \frac{S^2RT}{\sqrt{1 + (\omega\tau)^2}} \qquad (11\text{-}34)$$

contains the thermoelectric power. The dominant source of the thermal resistance R determines the noise limiting condition. When R is primarily due to thermal conduction through the leads and the mounting, the noise remains of the Johnson noise type. However, when the detector is connected thermally to its surroundings primarily by radiation, R is the resistance to radiation and the detector is background-noise-limited. Let us now use these expressions to derive an expression for NEP when the thermocouple is limited by these two different noise limitations.

11.1.3.1 *Johnson Noise Limited*

$$NEP = \frac{\sqrt{4kTr\Delta f}}{SR} \cdot \sqrt{1 + (\omega\tau)^2} \qquad (11\text{-}35)$$

By the Wiedermann-Franz law:[5]

$$r = RT[L_1^{1/2} + L_2^{1/2}]^2 \qquad (11\text{-}36)$$

where R is the thermal resistance due to the two thermocouple wires, and L_1, L_2 are their lengths. Therefore:

$$NEP = \frac{(L_1^{1/2} + L_2^{1/2})\sqrt{1 + (\omega\tau)^2}}{S} \cdot \sqrt{\frac{4kT^2\Delta f}{R}} \qquad (11\text{-}37)$$

Multiply numerator and denominator by the square root of the heat capacity C,

$$C = C_P \cdot A \qquad (11\text{-}38)$$

where C_p is the heat capacity per unit area of the detector, to obtain:

$$NEP = \frac{(L_1^{1/2} + L_2^{1/2}) T\sqrt{4kC_p}}{S} \cdot \sqrt{\frac{\Delta f \cdot A}{\tau}} \qquad (11\text{-}39)$$

11.1.3.2 *Background Noise Limited*. For this case, from Eqs. (11-33) and (11-34), it follows that:

$$NEP = \frac{\sqrt{1 + (\omega\tau)^2}}{SR} \cdot \sqrt{\frac{S^2 RT}{1 + (\omega\tau)^2}} \cdot \sqrt{4kT\Delta f} \qquad (11\text{-}40)$$

where R is the resistance to thermal radiation

$$NEP = \sqrt{4kT^2\Delta f/R} \qquad (11\text{-}41)$$

The resistance to thermal radiation is given by

$$R = \frac{1}{4\sigma_T \varepsilon' A T^3} \qquad (11\text{-}42)$$

where ε' is the emissivity of the detector,
σ_T is the Stefan-Boltzmann constant.

$$NEP = \sqrt{16kT^5\sigma_T \varepsilon' A \Delta f} \qquad (11\text{-}43)$$

But, this is the rms value of the fluctuation in radiation power flow to a body of emissivity ε which is at the same temperature as its environment (the background).*

---

*For derivations of the expressions for resistance to thermal radiation and fluctuations in radiation power, see References 6 and 7.

Thus it is clear that NEP in the background-limited case is simply the expected rms fluctuation in radiation power. Parameters such as thermoelectric power and time constant do not appear in Eq. (11-43), since to do so would mean that they affect the background power fluctuation. These observations are of the same kind as made for the photoconductive detector in the background-limiting case. Finally, it should be noted here also that NEP depends on area and bandwidth according to:

$$\text{NEP} \propto \sqrt{A \cdot \Delta f}$$

In practice, all thermal detectors made to date are Johnson noise limited. Furthermore, trends to date toward thermal detectors of fast response are accomplished by an increased, controlled thermal leak through a detector's leads and mounting, and a smaller receiver heat capacity.[8,9] Thus Z_D is reduced in Eq. (11-33) compared to r, and as shown in Eq. (11-41), the NEP increases. Increased speed of response in this manner is not necessarily detrimental to NEP, however, since the Johnson noise contributed by the electrical resistance r may already be the governing noise factor. The importance and utility of thermal detectors is in their ability to respond to wavelengths out to 14 μ without cooling, and reaching the background-limited condition is not essential to numerous applications. Finally, it should be pointed out that the increased response time that must accompany an increased R to attain the background-limited condition can be compensated electronically for a wider frequency response and shorter effective operating response time. This matter is discussed in Section 11.2.3.

11.2 Detector Classification, Figures of Merit, and Methods of Rating

The NEP (noise equivalent power) is defined and analyzed for its areal and bandwidth dependence in Section 11.1. Detector classification schemes generally start with this NEP expression, and modify it in some way to obtain a convenient comparison of any detector to the best possible performance that a detector might offer. Optimum performance is usually judged with reference to the limiting background-radiation-noise condition. Detector rating is expressed then in terms of its spectral response and/or its response to a blackbody at some reference temperature, compared to the best possible values obtainable. In this section, the dependence of NEP on λ and T is discussed first, and the classifications suggested by various contributors to improve the rating method follows thereafter.

11.2.1 *Dependence of NEP on Wavelength and Background Temperature*

Consider the expression for NEP in the background-limited case, given by Eq. (11-23):

$$\text{NEP} = (2\sqrt{\eta_B}/\eta_S)\,(\sqrt{J_B}/J_S)\,H\sqrt{A \cdot \Delta f}$$

Assume for simplicity that the efficiency factors for background and signal are equal to unity. Then

$$\text{NEP} = 2 \left(\sqrt{\overline{J_B}} / J_S \right) H \sqrt{A \cdot \Delta f} \tag{11-44}$$

The irradiance H can be expressed in terms of the number of photons per unit (area $\cdot$ time) multiplied by appropriate photon energies and summed up. However, a particular area of interest here is the detector operating at the cutoff wavelength λ_c. Suppose then that J_s is restricted to a wavelength $J_{s\lambda_c}$, and that H is given by:

$$H = J_{s\lambda_c} \cdot (hc/\lambda_c) \tag{11-45}$$

then

$$\text{NEP} = (2 hc/\lambda_c) \sqrt{J_B A \cdot \Delta f} \tag{11-46}$$

A plot of NEP versus λ_c can be obtained by substituting different values of λ_c, and corresponding photon flux densities J_B taken over the wavelength $0 \longrightarrow \lambda_c$ for the black background of temperature T. Gelinas and Genoud[10] obtained Table 11-1, following this procedure, for a $300\,^\circ$K background, for a detector of unit area and unit bandwidth of operation.

A standard of reference in calibrating a detector is its detection ability in responding to a $500\,^\circ$ blackbody source against a room temperature background. Therefore, it would be useful to know the minimum amount of $500\,^\circ$K radiant power necessary to equal background fluctuations. This can be determined by rewriting the expression for NEP in the form

$$\text{NEP} = \frac{2HA}{J_s \sqrt{A}/\sqrt{\overline{J_B}}} \tag{11-47}$$

Table 11-1

Minimum Detectable Power for Ideal Quantum Detector, 1 cm² Area, 300°K Background, 2π Solid Angle (adapted from Reference 10)

λ_C Cutoff Wavelength (μ)	N_B photons per sec on 1-cm² area	$P_{B\,min}\,\lambda_C$ (watts)
1.0	6.6	(5×10^{-19}) [a]
2.0	4.2×10^{10}	2.0×10^{-14}
3.0	5.8×10^{13}	5.0×10^{-13}
4.0	1.9×10^{15}	2.2×10^{-12}
5.0	1.3×10^{16}	4.5×10^{-12}
6.0	4.9×10^{16}	7.3×10^{-12}
8.0	2.2×10^{17}	1.2×10^{-11}
10.0	5.0×10^{17}	1.4×10^{-11}
∞	4.15×10^{18}	3.9×10^{-11}
(Ideal thermal detector)		

[a] The expression for $P_{B\,min}$ breaks down for very small values of N_B. This number is included only to show the rapid variation of $P_{B\,min}$ between 1 and 2 μ.

for unit bandwidth and efficiency. Therefore

$$NEP = 2\sqrt{A}\,\eta\,(\sqrt{J_B}/J_s)$$

However,

$$J_B = \int_0^{\lambda_c} J_\lambda(T_B)\,d\lambda$$

$$J_s = \int_0^{\lambda_c} J_\lambda(500^\circ)\,d\lambda \tag{11-48}$$

for detectors whose cutoff wavelength is λ_c. Therefore,

$$NEP = 2\sqrt{A}\cdot\eta\cdot\frac{\sqrt{\int_0^{\lambda_c} J_\lambda(T_B)\,d\lambda}}{\int_0^{\lambda_c} J_\lambda(500^\circ)\,d\lambda} \tag{11-49}$$

where $J_\lambda(T)$ is the background photon density as a function of body temperature. Figure 11-1 shows the dependence of NEP for a 500°K source, for background temperatures ranging from 200°K to 500°K and for detectors of different cutoff wavelengths λ_c. It is from a report by Gelinas and Genoud[10] who also note the following:

> For a 300°K background there is a wide range of λ_c for which $P_{B\,min\,500}$° remains almost constant. In other words, for an ideal quantum detector looking at a 500°K blackbody against a 300°K background, it makes essentially no difference what cutoff wavelength is chosen (beyond 1 μ): the increased response to background by raising λ_c is almost exactly compensated by the increased signal. For blackbody radiation it can be shown in general that $P_{B\,min}$ is insensitive to λ_c for a target temperature approximately twice the background temperature.
>
> For background temperature less than 300°K (and a 500°K source), it is advantageous to use as short a cutoff wavelength as possible, while the opposite conclusion holds for background temperatures higher than 300°K.

11.2.2 *Jones System of Classification*

Jones[7,11] has contributed a substantial effort to the understanding and categorizing of infrared detectors. He suggested that the reciprocal of NEP, denoted as "detectivity," was a more suitable quantity for rating detectors. It represents primarily a psychological asset, in that larger detectivities, rather than smaller NEP's, represent better detectors. Jones considers "detectivity" particularly desirable because it also avoids usage of the word "sensitivity," which has a variety of meanings in technical language.

Jones observed that when data taken from thermal and photodetectors were examined, they could be distinguished or classified by the way in

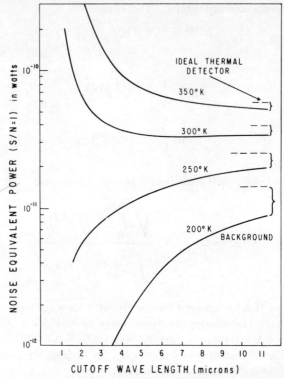

Fig. 11-1. NEP as a function of wavelength for different background temperatures *(by permission of R. W. Gelinas and R. H. Genoud, from Reference 10).*

which their detectivity is related to time constant and frequency response. He noted that their behavior, in one case, is like the detectivity obtained for an ideal thermal detector, while, in another, it is like that detained for an estimated best-obtainable thermal detector. Accordingly, two classes of detectors were set up, the first based on the detectivity obtained for the ideal detector (capable of seeing background thermal or photon noise), while the second was based on the best-obtainable heat detector from Havens' limit.

In establishing this system of classification, a reference condition of detector measurement is designated. It defines a reference or detective time constant and a bandwidth according to:

$$\tau = \frac{[D_1 (f_m)]^2}{4 \int_0^\infty [D_1 (f)]^2 df} \tag{11-50}$$

$$\Delta f = \int_0^\infty \left[\frac{D_1 (f)}{D_1 (fm)} \right]^2 df \tag{11-51}$$

and

$$\Delta f = (1/4\tau) \tag{11-52}$$

where $D_1(f_m)$ is the detectivity in a unit bandwidth for a modulation frequency that maximizes the detectivity. The motivation behind these reference conditions is to provide a measurement of the detectivity for the important special case where the bandwidth of the noise is the same as the bandwidth of the detector. The classifications then become:

Class I $$D = k_1 \sqrt{\tau/A} \tag{11-53}$$

Class II $$D = k_2 (\tau/\sqrt{A}) \tag{11-54}$$

Detectors limited by a flat noise spectrum, such as Johnson noise, have a detectivity in a unit bandwidth classified as:

Class Ia: $$D_1(f) = \frac{k_1}{2\sqrt{A}\sqrt{1 + (\omega\tau)^2}} \tag{11-55}$$

Class IIa: $$D_1(f) = \frac{k_2 \sqrt{\tau}}{2\sqrt{A}\sqrt{1 + (\omega\tau)^2}} \tag{11-56}$$

In the case of the $1/f$ noise-limited detector, Jones then found it necessary to redefine the reference time constant and bandwidth as:

$$\Delta f = 4f_m \tag{11-57}$$

$$\tau = \frac{1}{4}\tau_p \tag{11-58}$$

where τ_p is the detector time constant. The detectivity for a unit bandwidth has a maximum at the frequency f_m defined by:

$$f_m = (1/2\pi\tau_p) \tag{11-59}$$

Therefore:

$$\Delta f = (4/2\pi\tau_p) = (1/2\pi\tau) \tag{11-60}$$

From this it follows that:

Class Ib $$D_1(f) = \frac{2k_1 \sqrt{\pi}\sqrt{f\tau}}{\sqrt{A}\sqrt{1 + 16(\omega\tau)^2}} \tag{11-61}$$

Class IIb $$D_1(f) = \frac{2k_2 \sqrt{\pi}\sqrt{f\tau}}{\sqrt{A}\sqrt{1 + 16(\omega\tau)^2}} \tag{11-62}$$

In Section 11.1.1, analytical expressions were derived for NEP in the various noise-limited conditions. They can now be compared with Jones system of classification. In the analysis that follows, various constants (K_1, K_2, K_3, K_4) will appear and also k_1 equal to $1/K_1$, etc. These constants will not be equated to Jones constants k_1 and k_2, since our purpose here is to show only how the NEP relationships from Section 11.1.1 lead to Jones' system of classification.

A problem arises for the G-R noise limited case. Eq. (11-23) shows that the NEP for this noise is independent of frequency. Therefore, the detective bandwidth by the definition [Eq. (11-51)] above must be infinite, and the detective time constant equal to zero. To avoid this dilemma, and because the purpose here is only to derive expressions for detectivities from NEP's in forms suitable for comparison with the above expressions of Jones, the responsive time constant and bandwidth will be used here. These are defined as:

$$(\Delta f)_\gamma = \int_0^\infty \frac{[\gamma(f)]^2}{[\gamma_{max}]^2} \, df \tag{11-63}$$

$$\tau_\gamma = (1/4 \Delta f_\gamma) \tag{11-64}$$

11.2.2.1 *Johnson Noise Limited*. This detectivity is derived from Eq. (11-15):

$$D = \frac{1}{\text{NEP}} = \frac{1}{K_1} \frac{\sqrt{\tau}}{\sqrt{A \cdot \Delta f}} \cdot \frac{1}{\sqrt{1 + (\omega\tau)^2}} \tag{11-65}$$

in a unit bandwidth; therefore

$$D = k_1 \frac{\sqrt{\tau}}{\sqrt{A} \sqrt{1 + (\omega\tau)^2}} \tag{11-66}$$

which is defined as a class IIa detector. In the bandwidth $\Delta f = (1/4\tau)$, the detectivity becomes at zero frequency

$$D = k'_1 (\tau/\sqrt{A}) \tag{11-67}$$

which is the form of the class II detector.

11.2.2.2 *Excess(1/f) Noise Limited*. This detectivity is derived from Eq. (11-18):

$$D = \frac{1}{\text{NEP}} = \frac{1}{K_2} \frac{\tau_p}{\sqrt{1 + (\omega\tau_p)^2}} \sqrt{\frac{f}{A \cdot \Delta f}} \tag{11-68}$$

for a unit bandwidth,

$$D_1 = \frac{1}{K_2} \frac{\tau_p}{\sqrt{1 + (\omega\tau_p)^2}} \sqrt{f/A} \tag{11-69}$$

The constant τ_p is the detector responsive time constant. Jones defines a reference time constant $\tau = \tau_p/4$. Using this time constant, it follows that:

$$D_1 = k_2 \frac{\tau\sqrt{f}}{\sqrt{1 + 16\,(\omega\tau)^2}} \cdot \frac{1}{\sqrt{A}} \qquad (11\text{-}70)$$

which is the form of the class IIb detector.

11.2.2.3 *Generation-Recombination Noise Limited.* In this case, both signal and noise depend on the frequency in the same manner. Thus, the expression for NEP was found to be independent of the factor $\sqrt{1 + (\omega\tau)^2}$. The detectivity is derived from Eq. (11-22):

$$D = (1/K_3)\,(1/\sqrt{A\,\Delta f}) \qquad (11\text{-}71)$$

The detectivity in the reference bandwidth takes the form

$$D = k_3'\,\sqrt{\tau/A} \qquad (11\text{-}72)$$

which is a class I detector.

11.2.2.4 *Shot Noise Limited.* This detectivity is derived from Eq. (11-27):

$$D = \frac{1}{K_4} \cdot \frac{1}{\sqrt{1 + (\omega\tau)^2}} \cdot \sqrt{\frac{\tau}{A\,\Delta f}} \qquad (11\text{-}73)$$

Shot noise has a flat frequency spectrum, and provides a detectivity in a unit bandwidth similar to Johnson noise:

$$D_1 = [k_4/\sqrt{H(\omega\tau)^2}]\,\sqrt{\tau/A} \qquad (11\text{-}74)$$

and in the responsive bandwidth

$$D = [k_4'/\sqrt{1 + (\omega\tau)^2}]\,(\tau/\sqrt{A}) \qquad (11\text{-}75)$$

$$D = k_4'\,(\tau/\sqrt{A}) \qquad (11\text{-}76)$$

for zero frequency, which is the form of a class II detector.

11.2.2.5 *Figures of Merit.* By taking the ratio of the detectivity of class I detectors to that of the perfect thermal detector (limited by photon noise), Jones derives a figure of merit called M_1, expressed as:

$$M_1 = 2.76 \times 10^{-11} \times (D\sqrt{A}/\sqrt{\tau}) \qquad (11\text{-}77)$$

A figure of merit for the class II detector was derived using Havens' limit as the reference detector. Havens arrived at his estimate by treating such thermal detectors as heat engines, considering their operation from a theoretical analysis of the efficiency of such engines, and arriving at an ultimate limit of performance capability by including considerations of limiting noise, available materials, and techniques. On this basis, the class II figure of merit becomes:

$$M_2 = 3 \times 10^{-11} \, (D\sqrt{A}/\tau)$$

11.2.2.6 D-*Star* (D*). The expressions for detectivity, for the different limiting-noise types, always contain the factor $1/\sqrt{A \, \Delta f}$. Therefore, they are a function of detector size and the electrical bandwidth of operation. A more useful number is one that establishes the performance of the detector independent of these quantities. Jones suggested that the quantity $D*$, defined as:

$$D* = (\sqrt{A \cdot \Delta f}/\text{NEP}) = D\sqrt{A \cdot \Delta f} \qquad (11\text{-}78)$$

serves to characterize the detector in terms of the intrinsic properties of the material of which it is made.[12]

The wavelength dependence of $D*$ for the background-limited condition can be obtained by inserting the expression for NEP from Eq. (11-46) in $D*$ above, to obtain:

$$D* = \frac{\lambda_c}{2hc\sqrt{J_B}}$$

A sample calculation for the evaluation of $D*$ (obtained from an excellent report, see ref. 13) at 6 μ for a 6-μ cutoff detector is shown below:[13]

$$J_B = 4\pi c \int_0^{\varphi} \int_0^{\lambda_m} \frac{1}{\lambda^4} \frac{d\lambda}{\exp(hc/\lambda kT)^{-1}} \sin\varphi \cos\varphi \, d\varphi$$

$$= 2\pi c \sin^2\varphi \int_0^{\lambda_m} \frac{1}{\lambda^4} \frac{d\lambda}{\exp(hc/\lambda kT - 1)}$$

where J_B is expressed in photons/cm^2/sec, $\varphi = (\theta/2)$ is one-half the angular field of view, θ, and λ_m is the long wavelength threshold of the detector. The quantity after the integral sign may be determined from a radiation slide rule of the Lowan and Blanch tables.[14] For $\varphi = \pi/2$ (2π steradian field of view) and $\lambda_m = 6 \, \mu$, $J_B = 4.8 \times 10^{16}$ quanta/cm^2/sec, $(\lambda/hc) = (10^{20}/3.3)$ joules^{-1}. Thus, $D*$ at 6 μ is:

$$\frac{10^{20}}{2 \times 33 \times (4.8 \times 10^{16})^{1/2}} = 7 \times 10^{10} \frac{\text{cm}}{\text{watt} \cdot \text{sec}^{1/2}}$$

Figure 11-2 shows the variation of $D*$ at the spectral peak as a function of the long wavelength threshold for ideal photoconductive and photovoltaic detectors. In addition, this figure displays the capability of a wide variety of detectors. The data used to plot these curves was obtained from the open literature, unclassified Naval Ordnance Laboratory, Corona, California[15] and Syracuse University reports.[13]

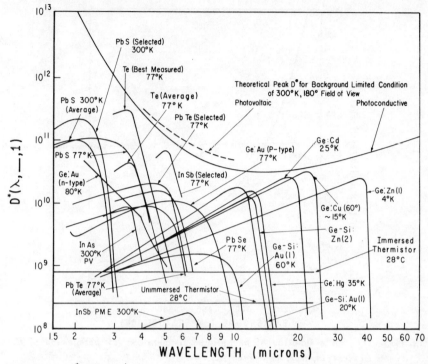

Fig. 11-2. D^* versus λ for various detectors, and the background-noise-limited condition.

D^* can be improved by reducing the magnitude of J_B. From Eq. (10-108), it is clear that this reduction can be accomplished by decreasing the temperature of the background radiation sources. This can be done by cooling the walls of the cell surrounding the detector, using a cooled filter to reduce the background radiation from a spectral region not present in the signal, and using the detector against a cooler background outside the cell. Figure 11-3 shows the variation of D^* at spectral peak as a function of background temperatures for three different values of detector cutoff. A further decrease in J_B can be achieved by reducing the angular field of view observed by the detector, as shown in Figure 11-4. Thus it appears well worthwhile to restrict the field of view of a detector to that value required for a particular application.

11.2.2.7 D-*Double Star* (D**). It is shown in Section 11.2.2.6 that D^* for the background-limited case is dependent on the angular field of view observed by the detector. Jones suggested that a quantity independent of this factor would be:[16]

$$D** = \left(\frac{\Omega}{\pi}\right)^{1/2} D* = \left(\frac{A\Omega\Delta f}{\pi}\right)^{1/2} D \qquad (11\text{-}79)$$

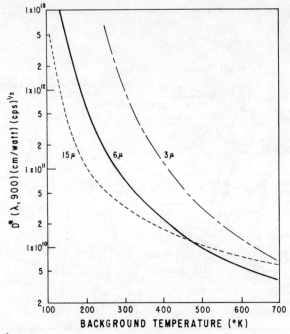

Fig. 11-3. $D^*_{\lambda_p}$ as a function of background temperature (*by permission of H. Levinstein, from Reference 13*).

where Ω is an effective weighted solid angle, referred to a solid angle of π steradians, that the detector element sees through the aperture in a cell's radiation shield. If the detector has circular symmetry, and the solid angle can be represented as a cone with the half-angle θ_0, then

$$\Omega = \pi \sin^2 \theta_0 \qquad (11\text{-}80)$$

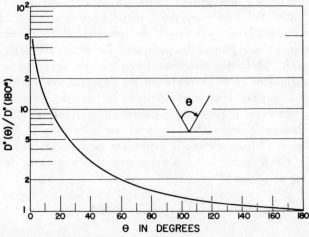

Fig. 11-4. D^* as a function of angular field of view (*by permission of H. Levinstein, from Reference 13*).

The effect of this concept is shown in Figure 11-5, where D^{**} is shown to be substantially independent of the angle.

11.2.2.8 *Discussion.*   The analysis carried out in Sections 11.2.2.1–11.2.2.5 indicates the following:

(1) Class I detectors are limited by background and G-R noise.

(2) Class II detectors are detectors limited by all other sources of noise.

(3) A class II detector can become a class I detector if its performance is improved to the point that background or G-R noise predominates over any other noise source. This can be done by cooling a detector. It appears that, when a detector becomes background limited, it loses its identity. Its NEP, as shown by Eq. (11-43) for thermal detectors, is the root-mean-square fluctuation in radiation power flow to the detector. Similarly, Eq. (11-46) for photodetectors shows the NEP is descriptive of the rms fluctuation in background photons striking the detector. Thus the performance of the detectors is completely described by the condition of the background. If a number of different detectors all having the same spectral response characteristics were background limited, they could not be identified individually on the basis of NEP, D, D^*, or a class I designation. This would be so even though they might be made of different materials and/or have different time constants.

(4) The significance of the Figures of Merit M_1 and M_2 is not clear, particularly in reference to Havens' limit. Since a detector can go from

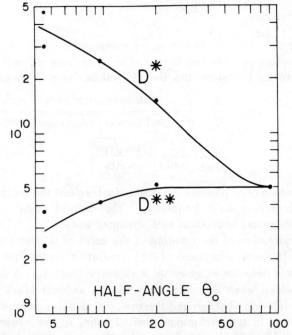

Fig. 11-5. D^{**} and D^* as a function of angular field of view (*by permission of R. C. Jones, from Reference 16*).

class II to class I, the reference might well be to the background limited condition in both cases.

(5) The units of $D*$ have received considerable attention and at one time were a matter of controversy. Jones'[11] original definition of $D*$ appeared in the form

$$D* = \sqrt{\frac{A}{1\,\text{cm}^2} \cdot \frac{\Delta f}{1\,\text{cps}} \cdot \frac{1}{\text{NEP}}}$$

Thus it appeared that the definition normalized $D*$ to a unit area and bandwidth, and that the unit of $D*$ was reciprocal watts. This unit seemed appropriate, since $D*$ was an intrinsic measure of a material's ability to detect radiation power. However, considerable opposition arose to the normalization procedure suggested by Jones, and the units ultimately accepted were those that appear in a straightforward examination of dimensions—that is, $\text{cm} \cdot (\text{cps})^{1/2} \cdot \text{watt}^{-1}$. These units might appear somewhat peculiar in that $D*$ is supposed to provide a measure of the intrinsic ability of a detector material to respond to radiation power, yet it contains the dimensions of size and frequency. Nevertheless, $D*$ appears to do its job, on the basis of data available to date. An explanation of this seeming contradiction appears to come from an examination of the equations derived earlier for NEP in the various noise limiting cases.

Consider the background limited case where

$$\text{NEP} = \frac{2\sqrt{J_B \eta_B}}{\eta_S J_S} \cdot H \cdot \sqrt{A \cdot \Delta f}$$

The factor $\sqrt{A \cdot \Delta f}$ cancels out in the computation of $D*$, so that the remaining factors provide the units. The quantities η_B and η_S are efficiency factors. Therefore, the dimensional analysis is simplified to:

$$D* = \frac{J_S}{\sqrt{J_B}} \cdot \frac{1}{H} = \frac{\#\,\text{Photons}_S/\text{cm}^2 \cdot \text{sec}}{\sqrt{\#\,\text{Photons}_B/\text{cm}^2 \cdot \text{sec}}} \cdot \frac{\text{cm}^2}{\text{watt}}$$

$$= \frac{\text{cm}}{\sqrt{\text{sec}}} \cdot \frac{1}{\text{watts}} = \frac{\text{cm}\sqrt{\text{cps}}}{\text{watts}}$$

since the numbers of photons are dimensionless and the reciprocal of time is equivalent here to a frequency. The derived units of $D*$ become $\text{cm}\,(\text{cps})^{1/2}/\text{watts}$, consistent with accepted usage.

An interpretation of the meaning of the units of $D*$ can now readily be put forth. In the measurement of NEP, radiation power from a blackbody illuminates a detector to generate a signal voltage V_S. A noise voltage V_N is obtained when the detector views an ambient black background. V_N may result from background fluctuations or noise sources internal to the detector. In the background limited case, it was shown above that $D*$ is dependent only on the factors J_S, J_B and H, while being explicitly independent of area and bandwidth. These are all factors in the measurement procedure, and the units of $D*$ can be attributed to J_S, J_B and H. Since these quantities represent the numbers of photons and watts per unit area, it is clear that the measurement is inherently normalized. Thus if one wishes to perform a series of measurements in which the bandwidth and/or the area were variables, the experiment would be carried on with constant J_S, J_B, and H. The evaluation of $D*$ in this situation is truly independent of detector area. It appears, therefore, that Jones' intuition and experience leading to his judgement of the significance of $D*$ were correct.

It is fruitful to examine the units of $D*$ in the Johnson and shot-noise-limited cases. The appropriate expressions can be obtained by inserting Eqs. (11-15) and (11-27) in (11-78) respectively. They are for: $D*$ limited by Johnson noise:

$$D* = \frac{\eta_S J_S \, eEL}{\sqrt{2nd} \, kTH} \cdot \sqrt{\frac{\tau}{1 + (\omega\tau)^2}}$$

$D*$ limited by shot noise:

$$D* = \sqrt{\frac{L^2 eEn_l}{ndkT}} \cdot \frac{\eta_S J_S}{H} \cdot \sqrt{\frac{\tau}{1 + (\omega\tau)^2}}$$

In the Johnson noise case, the quantities eEL and kT represent electrical and thermal energies, and have the same basic units. Let us separate out these factors in the dimensional analysis.

$$D* = \frac{eEL}{kT} \cdot \frac{1}{\sqrt{nd}} \cdot \frac{J_S}{H} \cdot \sqrt{\tau}$$

treating the case where $\omega\tau \ll 1$, and omitting all numerical factors. Substituting units provides:

$$D* = \frac{\text{Energy}_{elec}}{\text{Energy}_{therm}} \cdot \frac{1}{\sqrt{\frac{1}{\text{cm}^2}}} \cdot \frac{\# \text{ Photons/Area} \cdot \text{Time}}{\text{watts/Area}} \cdot \sqrt{\text{Time}}$$

$$= \frac{\text{Energy}_{elec}}{\text{Energy}_{therm}} \cdot \frac{\text{cm}}{\text{watts}} \cdot \frac{1}{\sqrt{\text{Time}}}$$

$$\therefore D* = \frac{\text{cm}\sqrt{\text{cps}}}{\text{watts}}$$

In the case of shot noise, the quantity $n_l \cdot L$ is unitless, eEL is an electrical energy, and $D*$ can be expressed dimensionally as

$$D* = \frac{\text{Energy}_{elec}}{\text{Energy}_{therm}} \cdot \text{cm} \cdot \frac{\# \text{ Photons/Area} \cdot \text{Time}}{\# \text{ watts/Area}} \cdot \sqrt{\text{Time}}$$

for the case of $\omega\tau \ll 1$. On simplifying:

$$D^* = \frac{\text{Energy}_{elec}}{\text{Energy}_{therm}} \cdot \frac{\text{cm}}{\text{watts}} \cdot \frac{1}{\sqrt{\text{Time}}}$$

$$D^* = \frac{\text{cm}\sqrt{\text{cps}}}{\text{watts}}$$

It is clear that units are consistently maintained for D^* in the different noise-limited cases. An interesting feature of this examination reveals that the ratio of an electrical energy to a thermal energy appears as a factor for the Johnson-noise-limited case, and the square root of this quantity appears in the shot-noise case. This is consistent with different mechanisms responsible for the two cases. In both cases, an increasing bias voltage and a decreasing temperature should result in increasing D^*. The density of carriers n is also dependent on T, and decreases with reduced temperature. However, reduced T can also affect the magnitude of the energy gap, changing the cut-off wavelength, and affects the time constant τ as well. These apparently are the factors that are adjustable. In particular, when seeking the optimum bias for a photoconductive detector, it may well be a matter of raising the bias until an increased temperature from Joule heating results. Further biasing could cause adverse temperature effects and, therefore, a reduced D^*.

(6) In a recent statistical analysis of the NEP's reported on lead compound film detectors, Limperis and Wolfe[17] reported that these excess-noise-limited detectors follow a $(A)^{1/2}$ dependence, confirming the treatment of Section 11.1.1.2. Until about 1959, data did not clearly indicate a consistent geometry dependence for NEP. There were two factors which prevented obtaining consistent data:

(a) Limiting detector noise sources were not uniformly distributed through the detector. That is, most of the noise was generated at the electrodes, around the detector periphery, localized regions on the crystal's surface, and similarly within the bulk. Detector technology has now reached the stage where uniform sources of noise from the crystal's surface and bulk are becoming the dominant factors.

(b) The photoresponse was generally nonuniform across a detector surface. The film detectors were particularly difficult to deal with in this regard, as shown in Figure 12-16. Therefore, an effective detector area has to be defined, which Jones suggested as:

$$A_e = \frac{\displaystyle\iint_a \gamma(x,y)\,dxdy}{\gamma_{max}}$$

where $\gamma(x,y)$ is the local responsivity of a detector at position x,y on the surface, γ_{max} is the maximum value of $\gamma(x,y)$ obtained on scanning a small light spot over the surface.

It appears that detector technology has improved to the point where uniformity of noise generation and response is sufficiently advanced to provide reliable data for analysis.

11.2.3 Petritz System of Classification

11.2.3.1 *Information Capacity and Efficiency.*   Efforts to establish performance capability have concentrated on NEP and its meaning in terms of a reference number such as $D*$.   Petritz suggested that to properly select or evaluate a detector, additional information is required. In particular, it is important to know not only an rms quantity such as NEP, but in addition the rate at which the detector is able to collect and provide information, and how efficiently it is able to convert absorbed signal photons to "bits" of information.   Petritz applied "information theory" to establish a complete system that would describe a detector, and provide a systematic approach to the selection of an optimum detector for a given application.   The treatment is somewhat detailed, and can only be summarized here.   The interested reader is referred to two publications which apply,[18,19] and from which the following material is drawn.

The basic equation of information theory states that the maximum attainable information capacity or rate C of a channel of infinitesimal bandwidth d_f is given by:[20,21]

$$C(df) = df \log_2 [1 + (V_S/V_N)^2] \, (\text{bits/sec}) \qquad (11\text{-}81)$$

while the capacity for a finite bandwidth $\Delta f = f_2 - f_1$ is

$$C(\Delta f) = \int_{f_1}^{f_2} \log_2 \left[1 + \left(\frac{V_S}{V_N}\right)^2\right] df$$

The unit of information, 1 bit, is the information gained in a measurement where there are two equally probable results.   Thus 1 bit of information is obtained when a particular value is measured.   For the case where the signal-to-noise ratio is independent of frequency (as for G-R noise), the information capacity is given by

$$C(\Delta f) = \Delta f \log_2 [1 + (V_S/V_N)^2] \qquad (11\text{-}83)$$

The dependence of $C(\Delta f)$ on V_S/V_N is shown in Figure 11-6.   Notice that when the signal to noise ratio is unity,

$$C_N = \Delta f \qquad (11\text{-}84)$$

or the number of bits of information per second is equal to the bandwidth. For the case:

$$\Delta f = (1/\tau)$$

the reciprocal of the time constant is also the information capacity.   The information efficiency is defined as:

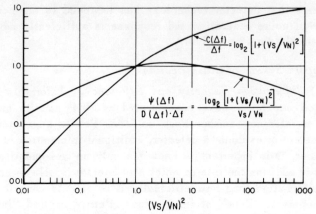

Fig. 11-6. Information capacity and information efficiency as a function signal to noise ratio (*by permission of R. L. Petritz, from Reference 18*).

$$\psi = \frac{C \,(\text{bits/sec})}{P \,(\text{watts})} = \frac{C}{P} \frac{\text{bits}}{\text{joule}} \tag{11-85}$$

or expressed in quanta:

$$\psi = \frac{C}{P/h\nu} \frac{\text{bits}}{\text{quanta}}$$

where P is the power flow to the detector.

The dependence of ψ on the signal-to-noise ratio for the narrowband condition is obtained from Eq. (11-81) and the definition of NEP:

$$\psi = \frac{\log_2 [1 + (V_S/V_N)^2] \Delta f}{(V_S/V_N)\,\text{NEP}}$$

$$= \frac{\log_2 [1 + (V_S/V_N)^2] \cdot D \cdot \Delta f}{V_S/V_N}$$

where D is independent of the signal to noise ratio. Figure 11-6 shows a plot of $\psi/D\Delta f$ versus V_S/V_N. A maximum appears at a ratio of signal to noise of unity, indicating that the detector is achieving an optimum number of bits of information per incident photon. This simple treatment provides a meaning for information capacity and efficiency. Petritz then goes on to systematically examine these quantities plus signal, noise, NEP, and detectivity for the Johnson, excess, and G-R noise-limiting cases, and for the general bandwidth case.

The result of this analysis provides a series of normalized expressions and curves suitable for evaluating NEP, C_N and ψ_N (subscript N refers to the case where $V_S/V_N = 1$), when experimental data for the detector's noise spectrum, signal spectrum, and responsivity are provided. In addition, it was found that a detector generally achieves an optimum information efficiency in or near the reference condition $\Delta f = 1/4\tau$ (where τ is the responsive time constant rather than the reference time constant of Jones); that it is generally costly in NEP, C_N, and ψ_N to use $\Delta f \gg 1/4\tau$; and finally that NEP is improved at the expense of C_N and ψ_N when $\Delta f \ll 1/4\tau$.

In conclusion, information efficiency was shown to be a measure of the performance of a detector in that it expresses how efficiently a cell converts radiation energy into bits of information. Furthermore, it expresses how NEP and information rates are exchangeable. It can be used to compare cells under the condition of equal information rates, under the condition of maximum information efficiencies, and under arbitrary conditions. Petritz recommends therefore that information efficiency be considered as a figure of merit for radiation detectors.

11.2.3.2 *Frequency Compensation*. From the remarks made above in Section 11.2.3.1 regarding the relationship between Δf and τ, it is clear that an exact relationship between Δf and τ is not sacred. If one needed improved NEP, and information efficiency or capacity were not important factors, a reduced bandwidth of operation could be used, at the expense of increased measuring time, to obtain a desired result. Ultimate performance along these lines would be obtained using a synchronous detector technique, where $\Delta f \ll \Delta f_\tau$, and signals well below noise levels become detectable. Very little has been said up to this point, however, about the possibility of using a bandwidth greater than that suggested by $1/4\tau$. It is clear from the subsections of 11.1 that the responsivity in our general, simple case decreases as $[1 + (\omega\tau)^2]^{-1/2}$ and that the noise may fall off in the same manner (G-R) as $1/f$ (excess), or be essentially flat (Johnson). It will be worth while to determine whether there is anything to be gained by an extended bandwidth operation for these limiting cases, where the signal-to-noise ratio is greater than unity. We shall consider here a G-R noise-limited condition, referring the reader to Petritz for a detailed treatment of all cases.[18] In this particular case, any frequency-compensation techniques must boost the detector's signal and noise the same extent. Therefore, any compensation that applies effectively must relate to the flat Johnson and shot noises of the preamplifier system, as an effective limiting condition. In the analysis that follows, the responsivity will have the frequency spectrum associated with a simple exponential type of photodecay, and the limiting noise will be treated as flat and associated with the preamplifier.

Consider Figure 11-7, where we are interested first in responsivity curves B and D. These two different responsivities are related to detector time constants τ_1 and τ_3 by

$$\gamma_1 = \frac{\beta_S \tau_1}{\sqrt{1 + (\omega\tau_1)^2}}$$

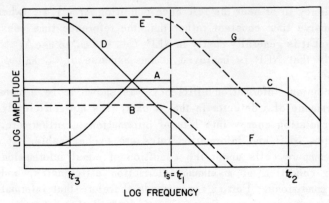

Fig. 11-7. Frequency compensation (*by permission of R. L. Petritz, from Reference 18*).

$$\gamma_3 = \frac{\beta_S \tau_3}{\sqrt{1 + (\omega\tau_3)^2}}$$

where β_S is a constant relating signal volts to watts independent of frequency and time constant. Finally there is also a flat noise spectrum V_N given by F. Thus for detector 1, the detectivity is given by

$$D_1 = \frac{\gamma_1}{V_N} = \frac{\beta_S \tau_1}{V_N} \cdot \frac{1}{\sqrt{1 + (\omega\tau_1)^2}}$$

Let us see if it is possible to apply frequency compensation to detector 3, so that its performance at extended frequency can be made comparable or better than detector 1. Consider a compensation system that has a frequency response

$$\gamma_f = \left[\frac{1 + (\omega\tau_3)^2}{1 + (\omega\tau_1)^2}\right]^{1/2}$$

The compensated response of detector 3 is

$$\gamma_{3C} = \gamma_3 \gamma_f = \frac{\beta_S \tau_3}{\sqrt{1 + (\omega\tau_1)^2}}$$

which extends the frequency response curve out to f_{τ_1} as shown by E. The flat noise F spectrum is also modified by compensation to:

$$V_{NC} = V_N \left[\frac{1 + (\omega\tau_3)^2}{1 + (\omega\tau_1)^2}\right]^{1/2}$$

as described by curve G. The new detectivity of detector 3 is:

$$\frac{\gamma_{3C}}{V_{NC}} = \frac{\beta_S \tau_3}{\sqrt{1 + (\omega\tau_3)^2}}$$

which is the same as for the uncompensated detector. Comparing this with detector 1,

$$\frac{\gamma_{3C}/V_N}{\gamma_1/V_N} = \frac{\gamma_3}{\gamma_1} = \frac{\tau_3}{\tau_1}\frac{\sqrt{1+(\omega\tau_1)^2}}{\sqrt{1+(\omega\tau_3)^2}} \geqslant 1$$

for all frequencies. Thus the compensated slow detector has as good or better responsivity as has the fast uncompensated detector! This results, basically, from the dependence of responsivity on lifetime. Thus, in this G-R case, compensation is profitable.

1. G. R. Pruett and R. L. Petritz, *Proc. IRE* **47**, 1524 (1958).
2. A. van der Ziel, *Proc. IRE* **46**, 1019 (1958).
3. C. Hilsum and O. Simpson, *Proc. Inst. Elec. Engrs.* (*London*) **106**B, Suppl. 1, No. 15, 398 (1959).
4. P. W. Kruse, *J. Appl. Phys.* **30**, 770 (1959).
5. R. C. Jones, *J. Opt. Soc. Am.* **39**, 344 (1949).
6. Smith, Jones, and Chasmar, *The Detection and Measurement of Infrared Radiation.* Oxford: Clarendon Press, 1957, pp. 23 and 204.
7. R. Clark Jones, *Advances in Electronics.* New York: Academic Press, 1953, Vol. 5, p. 18.
8. R. L. Petritz, *Proc. IRE* **47**, 1465 (1958).
9. R. deWaard and E. M. Wormser, *Proc. IRE* **47**, 158 (1958).
10. R. W. Gelinas and R. H. Genoud, Report of the Rand Corp., Santa Monica, California, P-1697 (1959), p. 8.
11. R. C. Jones, *Proc. IRE* **47**, 1495 (1958).
12. R. C. Jones, *Proc. IRIS* **2**, 9 (1957).
13. P. Bratt, W. Engeler, H. Levenstein, A. MacRae, and J. Pehek, *Germanium and Indium Antimonide Infrared Detectors.* Syracuse University under WADD contract No. AF 33(616)-3859 (February 1960).
14. A. N. Lowan and G. Blanch, *J. Opt. Soc. Am.* **30**, 70 (1940).
15. R. F. Potter, J. M. Pernett, and A. B. Naugle, *Proc. IRE* **47**, 1503 (1959).
16. R. C. Jones, *Proc. IRIS* **5**, No. 4, 35 (1960).
17. T. Limperis and W. Wolfe, *Proc. IRIS* **5**, No. 4, 141 (1960); also presented to the Optical Society of America, March 2–5, 1961.
18. R. L. Petritz, *Proc. IRIS* **2**, No. 1, 18 (1957).
19. R. L. Petritz, *Photoconductivity Conference.* New York: Wiley, 1956, p. 49.
20. D. A. Bell, *Information Theory.* London: Pitman and Sons, 1956, Second Edition.
21. Leon Brillouin, *Science and Information Theory.* New York: Academic Press, 1956.

CHAPTER 12

TEST PROCEDURES

The purpose of this chapter is to describe the experimental test program required to provide the necessary descriptive and evaluatory information for proper detector usage. The information provided is extensive. It is the responsibility of the engineer to properly interpret and to use as much of this information as is required for the design of his infrared system. Most of the experimental detail supplied here is descriptive of the facilities and procedures established at the Naval Ordnance Laboratory, Corona, California,[1] and Syracuse University.[2] These facilities have been sponsored by the Armed Services to provide up-to-date quantitative measurements on all types and kinds of photodetectors, with the philosophy that experimental procedures undertaken, and data provided, be in the spirit of a standards laboratory. The experimental information required is as follows:

(1) Optimum bias in the case of a photoconductive type detector.
(2) Noise spectrum.
(3) Response to a blackbody, usually set at $500\,^{\circ}$ K.
(4) Spectral dependence in terms of
    (*a*) Relative response.
    (*b*) Absolute response.
(5) Time constant or frequency response.
(6) Sensitivity contour.

From these data are evaluated various figures of merit, as listed in Table 12-1.

12.1 Determination of NEP

The circuitry used for measurement of signal response to a blackbody, noise, and determination of optimum bias is shown in block form in Figure 12-1. The important components of this circuitry are the infrared source, the preamplifier, and a wideband harmonic analyzer. The source is a blackbody emitter, with precision temperature controls. A standard condition used today in test procedures is to make measurements with a

Table 12-1

Figures of Merit

(from Reference 1)

Figure of Merit	Definition	Units
NEI	$NEI = \dfrac{HV_N}{V_S}$	Noise Equivalent Input in watts/cm^2
$NEP = P_n$	$NEP = \dfrac{HV_N A}{V_S}$	Noise Equivalent Power in watts
Jones' S	$S = \dfrac{NEP}{A^{1/2}}\left(\dfrac{f}{\Delta f}\right)^{1/2}$	Jones' S in watts/cm
D^*	$D^* = \dfrac{\sqrt{A \cdot \Delta f}}{NEP}$	The detectivity normalized to unit area and unit bandwidth in cm/watt
S_1	$S_1 = \dfrac{V_S}{HE}\dfrac{(r_c + r_L)^2}{4 r_c r_L}$	Specific sensitivity in cm^2/watt

blackbody set at a temperature of 500°K. The source is mechanically modulated by a disc-type chopper. Generally, this chopper is arranged with two speeds to provide radiation modulated at 90 cps and 900 cps. This chopped radiation causes a similarly modulated electrical signal to be generated in the detector system, amplified and measured with the harmonic wave analyzer. The wave analyzer is used also to determine the noise level by obtaining a reading when the detector is shielded from the chopped radiation.

The signal and noise for a photoconductive detector is determined as a function of bias voltage. The bias current is varied, with signal and noise voltage determined for different values of the current. For most detec-

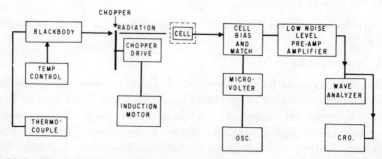

Fig. 12-1. Block diagram of system to measure detector NEP (*by permission of H. Levinstein, from Reference 9*).

tors, chopping frequency here is not significant in that optimum bias does not change appreciably with modulating frequency. Figure 12-2 shows a typical bias graph with plots of signal and noise versus bias current. This graph is typical of those supplied by the Naval Ordnance Laboratory using the radiation at 1.1μ from a helium source for the signal measurement. The optimal bias point is determined from this graph and used in all subsequent measurements. Typical circuitry of the cell bias and match box shown in Figure 12-1 is drawn schematically in Figure 12-3.

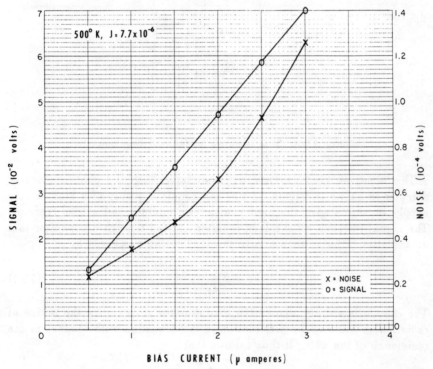

Fig. 12-2. **Determination of optimum bias** (*by permission of W. L. Eisenman and R. F. Potter, NOL, Corona, California, from NOLC Report 525, and the Philco Corporation*).

Two sets of input leads are shown from the detector to the match box, corresponding to the need for bias current with a photoconductive detector, and to the noncurrent-carrying photovoltaic and PEM detectors. Photovoltaic and PEM-type cells are usually tested by connecting them to the preamplifier through a transformer. This is because they have been low impedance devices. In particular, indium antimonide and indium arsenide are typical of such detectors. It is desirable to use a transformer whose impedance can be varied. This is important to insure that the equivalent noise input resistance of the preamplifier be transformed to an impedance lower than the impedance of the detector being tested.

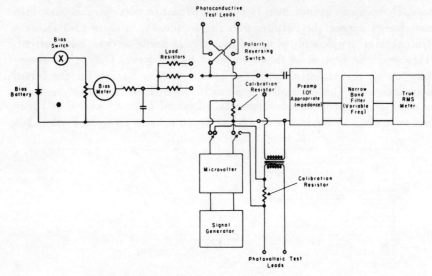

Fig. 12-3. Test circuitry for infrared detectors.

The simplest kind of circuitry associated with the photoconductive detector is shown in Figure 12-4(a) and consists simply of a bias battery supply in series with the photoconductive detector and a load resistor. The signal is taken off the load resistor and fed through a capacitor to a preamplifier. The voltage across the load resistor is given by

$$V_L = V \frac{r_L}{r_L + r_C} \tag{12-1}$$

The change in voltage across the load resistor produced by the action of radiation is attained by differentiating this equation with respect to the resistance of the cell. It then follows that

$$V_s = V \frac{r_L \, r_C}{r_L + r_C} \cdot \frac{\Delta r_C}{r_C} \tag{12-2}$$

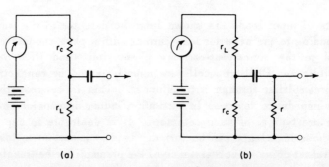

(a)   (b)

Fig. 12-4. Photoconductive detector circuits.

The signal voltage V_s is symmetrical with respect to the load resistor and the cell or detector resistance, so that the same signal voltage could have been picked off of the photoconductor or the load resistor. When the load resistance is much larger than the detector resistance, a constant bias current condition prevails. Maximum signal voltage is obtained when the load resistance equals the detector resistance, while extended frequency response is obtained for small values of load resistance. This latter requirement usually appears when dealing with high resistance fast detectors. In this situation capacitive effects become important, and in order to match the response time capability of the detector, it is necessary to use a small load resistor, resulting in reduced signal amplitude but flat frequency response over a wider frequency range.

A modification of this simple circuit is shown in Figure 12-4(b). It involves placing a dc load resistor in series with the detector and an ac load resistor across the detector through a coupling capacitor. The output is fed to the preamplifier from the ac load resistor. The effect of this type of circuitry is to permit varying the load resistor to the preamplifier without influencing the biasing current of the photoconductor detector. This is important in attaining the optimal bias current. One would like to retain this condition and yet have the flexibility for varying the load resistor to the preamplifier for an independent control on frequency response.

In making any noise-limited measurements, it is important that the preamplifier noise be less than the detector noise. There are two types of noise to consider with respect to the preamplifier: (1) an effective series noise; (2) an effective parallel noise.

The series noise is experimentally determined by shorting the input to the preamplifier and noting the signal voltage at its output. The parallel noise is determined by opening the circuit input and recording the noise level. Then, starting with large resistances, place a sequence of resistances of decreasing value across the input to the preamplifier and note the output noise. These resistances are reduced to a point where a change in the noise output from the open circuit condition of the preamp is recorded. Detector resistance is then maintained below this value. The resistance of the detector must provide a noise greater than the preamplifier noise and this condition is equivalent to the resistance of the detector, being larger than the series resistance of the preamplifier, but less than the shunt resistance. This condition is a sensible one. If two resistors are placed in series, the effective noise power is the sum of the two contributed by each of the resistors. If one is much larger than the other, then its noise predominates. When two resistors are placed in parallel, the effective resistance is that of the smaller resistance, and, correspondingly, the dominant noise is that which is associated with the smaller resistor. Therefore, the shunt resistances that may be incorporated in the preamplifier input, together with any other shunt resistance across the detector, must always be larger than the detector resistance. This requirement becomes difficult when one is forced to deal with very high impedance detectors, usually significantly higher than 15 or 20 megohms. Otherwise, the problem of shunt noise is not serious, and one usually finds that the series noise requires the most caution.

The primary purpose in measuring signal and noise voltages with the equipment of Figure 12-1 is to determine the photodetector noise equivalent power. This can now be done since the power density of the radiation from the blackbody that falls on the detector is known. This value can be calculated, starting with the Stefan-Boltzmann law given by (see Chapter 1):

$$W = \varepsilon \sigma_s (T^4 - T_0^4) \tag{12-3}$$

where W = radiant emittance, or radiant power per unit area emitted from a surface, T and T_0 are the absolute temperatures of the radiating body and background, respectively, ε is the emissivity, and σ_S is the Stefan-Boltzmann constant. The power density H from a source of radiance N at a distance X to the detector is the detector irradiance:

$$H = N \frac{A_s}{X^2} = \frac{W}{\pi} \cdot \frac{A_s}{X^2} \tag{12/4}$$

where A_s is the source area, N is the radiant flux emitted by the source per unit area, per unit solid angle, and is equal to W/π. For a circular source aperture of diameter D_s, the power density is

$$H = \frac{W}{\pi} \cdot \frac{\pi D_s^2}{4 X^2} = \frac{W}{\pi} \cdot \frac{A_s}{X^2} \tag{12-5}$$

and therefore NEP is given by

$$NEP = \frac{H \cdot A_d}{V_s / V_N} = \frac{W}{4} \left(\frac{D_s}{X} \right)^2 \cdot \frac{V_N}{V_s} A_d \tag{12-6}$$

The gain of the circuitry used to determine NEP is checked with an oscillator and a microvolter connected to the input of the preamplifier. The noise bandwidth of the system is determined by measuring the Johnson noise generated in a wire-wound resistance as

$$\Delta f = \overline{e^2} / 4 k T r \tag{12-7}$$

where k is the Boltzmann constant, T is the absolute temperature, and r is the resistance. The signal-to-noise ratio of a detector at a given bias current is generally independent of the load resistance. However, as shown by Eq. (12-2), the signal voltage, and correspondingly the noise voltage, are a function of the load resistor. Since different applications may require different load resistors, a listing of detector signal and noise measurements must include the value of the load resistance used in making the measurements.

12.2 Time Constant

A knowledge of a detector's speed of response is of great importance to the system designer. In conjunction with noise spectra, it tells him at what frequencies he may operate the detector and still retain sufficient signal for his purposes. He may also then select the frequency which will optimize the signal-to-noise ratio for his system's performance. Speed of response information is usually provided in one of two forms. They are (1), a plot of response versus frequency from which a detector time constant can be estimated and (2), the photodecay characteristic after removal of a photoexcitation source. Information of type (1) is generally obtained by amplitude modulation of radiation from an infrared source irradiating the detector, and varying the frequency of modulation, while type (2) is obtained by observing the signal wave shape of the photodetector response to periodic pulses of light. Systems for making measurements to provide the two types of information are described below.

12.2.1 Frequency Response*

This measurement is usually made with a metallic disc light chopper. The disc is ringed with slits spaced symmetrically, so that the separation distance between slits equals a slit's width.

The modulation frequency is given by the spinning rate of the disc multiplied by the number of slits in the disc. The higher the frequency of modulation required, the higher the spinning rate, and/or the greater the number of slits cut in the disc. Increasing the number of slits results in slits of decreasing width (for any one size disc), until eventually an optical system is required to image down the infrared source onto the slit. The radiation passing through the slits is then focused onto the detector. For low-frequency operation, sinusoidal modulation can be obtained by proper selection of the chopper opening.[3]

The frequency response determined at Corona[1] uses a variable-speed chopper, giving a frequency range of 100 to 40,000 cps. Radiation from a Nernst glower is sinusoidally modulated by the chopper, and is usually filtered by a selenium-coated germanium window. The signal from the detector is measured by putting the output of a cathode follower and a preamplifier into the y-axis input of an oscilloscope. An incandescent tungsten source is simultaneously modulated by the chopper, and activates a photomultiplier whose signal is fed into a preamplifier and a tachometer; the latter's output is proportional to frequency and is put on

---

*See also Section 10.4.2

the x-axis of the oscilloscope. The oscilloscope display is photographed as the chopper slows down from its maximum speed. Syracuse University, using a wheel cut with 1400 circular holes spinning at a rate of 10,000 rpm, obtains a maximum chopping frequency of 240,000 cps. This equipment uses a glow bar as the light source and an As_2S_3 (arsenic trisulfide) lens to focus the source onto the slit. For photodetectors whose response can be described by

$$v_S = \frac{v_0}{\sqrt{1 + (\omega\tau)^2}}$$ (12-8)

this high-frequency chopping rate permits an evaluation of time constants as short as 0.5 μsec. Typical frequency-response data reported from NOL, Corona, is shown in Figure 12-5.

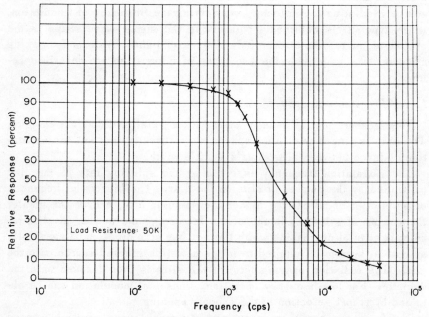

Fig. 12-5. Detector frequency response (*by permission of W. L. Eisenman and R. F. Potter, NOL, Corona, California, from NOLC Report 525, and the Philco Corporation*).

12.2.2 Pulse Response*

Another approach to the measurement of speed of response of the detector is a direct measurement of the decay or rise characteristics of the detector. For detectors with slow response and high sensitivity, it is fairly easy to design a mechanical light chopper with sufficient speed

*See also Section 10.4.1.

so that the dynamic characteristics measured belong to the photodetector, and not to the chopper. However, when one is forced to deal with photo-detectors whose response times are less than a microsecond, and where the signal is noise limited, then it becomes increasingly difficult to make this measurement using normal procedures. To measure the decay or rise characteristics of the detector requires a light source whose rise or fall time is approximately 1/10 the time that is to be measured. Optical spinning mirror systems can provide such rapid rise and fall light pulse time. A rather simple arrangement is shown in Figure 12-6. A collimated

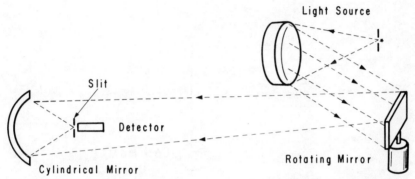

Fig. 12–6. Simple spinning mirror for periodic light pulse generation.

beam of light is deflected by a rotating mirror. A distance X away from the mirror is placed a decollimating mirror which focuses the infrared radiation on the detector. The rise time of the light pulse is the time it takes the leading edge of the pulse to fill the decollimating mirror, and the fall time is the time required for the trailing edge of the light beam to move off of that same mirror. The velocity with which the light ray moves across this mirror is given by the distance between the spinning mirror and the decollimator, multiplied by the angular velocity of the spinning mirror. The rise time and decay time, assuming a symmetrical light pulse are both then equal, and equal to the width of the decollimator divided by the velocity. Obviously, by making X sufficiently large, the rise and fall times can be made shorter, but generally at the expense of decreasing intensity at the detector. The energy may be increased by the use of a cylindrical mirror which compresses without affecting its width. Light pulses with rise and decay times of the order of 50 mμsec have been generated with this technique, using a mirror spinning at 10,000 rpm.

Another useful spinning mirror technique is that described by Garbuny et al.[4] The method consists of surrounding a rotating multisided mirror by a set of stationary mirrors (see Figure 12-7). This assembly is so adjusted that the collimated light from the source is repeatedly reflected between the central and the stationary mirrors. Each face of the mirror

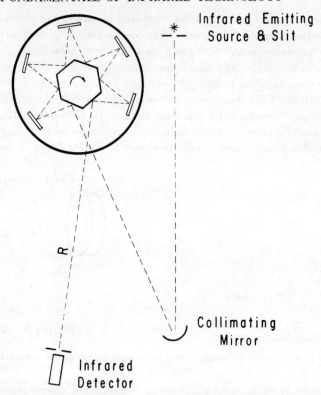

Fig. 12-7. Spinning mirror system for periodic light pulse generation in the mμsec time domain (*adapted from Reference 4*).

rotating with angular velocity ω adds 2ω to the rotational speed of the emerging light beam. If D is the width of a slit in the image plane, and is less than the width of the light beam δ, the rise time and the fall time of the pulse are given by

$$\tau_r = \frac{D}{2N\omega X} \qquad (12\text{-}9)$$

and the flat part of the pulse,

$$\tau_d = [(\delta - 2D)/2N\omega X] \qquad (12\text{-}10)$$

where N is the number of faces on the rotating mirror and X its distance from the image.   By using a multisided spinning mirror to obtain high tangential velocities, it is possible to substantially reduce the radial distance from the spinning mirror to the detector over that required in a construction like Figure 12-6. Using mirror optics for collimating the light source permits any infrared emitter to be used. With a 0.5 mm detector, a spinning mirror rotation rate of 10,000 rpm, $X = 1$ meter, and $N = 6$, rise times of 30 mμsec are readily available. Using a turbine-drive motor system to spin the mirror, rotating speeds as high as 3000 rps can be obtained, so that pulse rise and decay time of less than a millimicrosecond become readily possible.

Often, in pursuing a research and development program on detectors, it is necessary to observe in detail the wave shape of the photoresponse to a light pulse. These observations often have to be made in the noise-limited condition. Examples of such cases are: (1) the examination of fractional microsecond signals from high-impedance generators such as gold-doped germanium; the measurement technique here requires the ac loading of the detector [see Figure 12-4(b)] with a low enough resistance to provide flat frequency response over the spectrum of interest; (2) the examination of fractional microsecond signals from low-impedance generators such as the indium antimonide (InSb) detector; this measurement is difficult because the noise level of a wideband preamplifier is higher than that of the detector; (3) the reproduction of low-level signals caused by low-level radiation sources. This is the case for wavelength dependent measurements. A device has been developed which makes measurement in these cases readily possible, and with signal-to-noise ratios less than 1.

The device applies a sampling technique and integration (or averaging) to the direct measurement of the shape of periodic noise-limited waveforms. This may be compared to the usual coherent detector which can be described with reference to Figure 12-8. The signal wave shape is

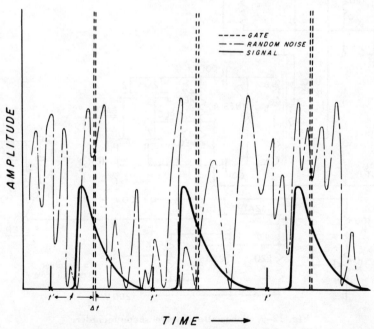

Fig. 12-8. Signal, noise, and gate relationship in wave shape recorder.

periodic, triggered in the same manner that would be required for good high speed oscillographic reproduction, while the noise is random in nature. The interval Δt represents an (on time) of an electronic switch, during which the signal and noise voltage is fed directly into an integrator. By sampling successive intervals and averaging, it is possible to reduce the noise-voltage fluctuation observed at the integrator output without affecting the signal level. Quantitatively, the noise-voltage fluctuations are reduced by $1/\sqrt{N}$, where N is the number of observations made during an average measurement. The signal-to-noise voltage ratio is then improved by the square root of N. If Δt is made small compared to the signal transient time, and is slowly and uniformly retarded in time with respect to signal onset, an accurate chart record of the signal wave shape may be produced.[5]

The circuit for the device is shown in Figure 12-9, and is similar to the box car circuit used in radar. Its components include a driven block-

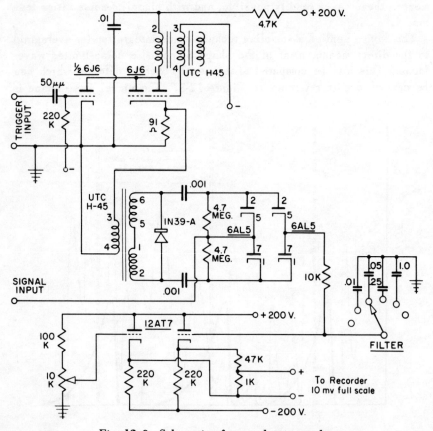

Fig. 12-9. Schematic of wave shape recorder.

ing oscillator activated by positive trigger pulses, an electronic switch, an integrator, a cathode follower, and a recorder. The driven blocking oscillator provides a pulse to close the electronic switch. The switch connects the input of the integrator to the signal plus noise voltage occurring during Δt. During the (off time), the capacitor of the integrator will maintain its potential until the next (on time), when a new signal plus noise level is sampled. To avoid signal attenuation, the output of the integrator is connected to a cathode follower, and no continuous dc is allowed to flow. Since the purpose is to permit operation with signal-to-noise ratios less than unity, long integration times are required which are compatible with chart recorders.

A block diagram of a complete experimental arrangement for photon-excited signals is shown in Figure 12-10. It is necessary that the signal

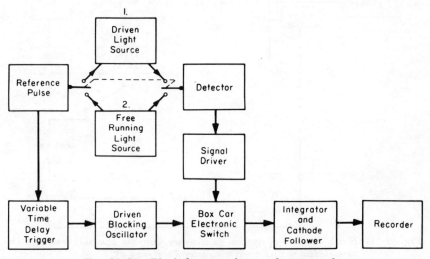

Fig. 12–10. Block diagram of wave shape recorder.

of interest and the switch (on time) be made to accurately follow some time reference. Two systems are shown which meet this requirement. The first system is used when the light sources are available that are capable of being driven by an electrical signal such as a CRO lamp or electro-optic shutters. The sequence of events can then be demonstrated from a noise-free reference pulse provided by a stable oscillator.

The second system is used when mechanical light modulators such as spinning mirrors and rotating choppers are necessary. Now the reference pulse cannot be supplied by an external source, but must be generated by the modulator itself. This can be done by causing a light source to excite a fast photodetector such as a photomultiplier prior to excitation of the photodetector of interest. In both systems, if a variable delay is provided with respect to the reference, the electronic switch (on time) may be slowly and uniformly retarded in time and a chart recording of the complete voltage waveform will be produced. Using the Garbuny spinning mirror, noise has been reduced by a factor of 300, with 50 mμsec light pulses.[5]

12.3 Spectral Response*

Measurements of the wavelength dependence of infrared photodetectors are generally made with an experimental setup such as is illustrated in Figure 12-11. The measurement is made with a measured energy irradiation

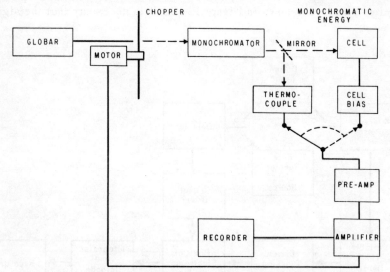

Fig. 12-11. Block diagram of system to measure detector spectral response (*by permission of H. Levinstein, from Reference 9*).

at the detector by monitoring the output from the exit slit of the monochrometer with a thermocouple, throughout the spectral range of measurement. This may seem like a strange procedure considering that the photodetectors described here are photon counters rather than energy detectors. However, to make the measurement at measured photon densities requires a reference photodetector flat in response over an extended infrared wavelength region. Such detectors are not yet available. Thermocouples, however, are flat over the wavelength region of interest here, and, therefore, are readily applicable to this kind of measurement. The result of this procedure is to obtain wavelength-dependent curves that are sawtoothed in appearance rather than flat topped. This is expected,

_____
*See also Section 10.5.

as explained in Section 10.5. Two monochrometers are in normal use at Corona: one, a Leiss double monochrometer, has CaF_2 prisms, giving a range from 0.6 to 8 μ, the other, a Perkin-Elmer model 98, has NaCl prisms, giving a range from 2 to 15 μ.

The energy flux from the exit slit is measured at each wavelength with a thermopile or thermocouple. As the wavelength is changed, the energy falling on the thermocouple is raised or lowered to a convenient value by opening or closing the entrance slit of the monochrometer, with the middle and exit slits usually remaining fixed. Once this level is set, the energy flux is allowed to fall onto the detector, and the response is then obtained. A typical relative response curve from Corona is shown in Figure 12-12. Generally, the chopping rate of the light input to the monochrometer is 10 to 13 cps, compatible with the response characteristics of the thermocouple. However, since

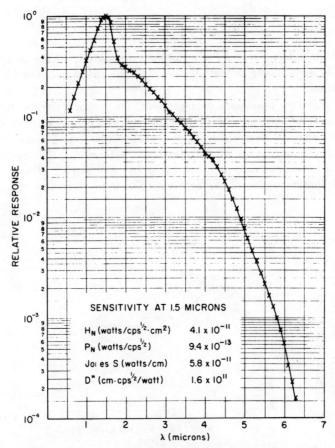

Fig. 12-12. Detector relative spectral response (*by permission of W. L. Eisenman and R. F. Potter, NOL, Corona, California, from NOLC Report 525, and the Philco Corporation*).

most photodetectors show considerable improvement of NEP at higher chopping rates, it is advantageous when possible to modulate the spectral radiation at frequencies of about a few hundred cps. At Syracuse, the chopper is operated at 208 cps, and the detector signal is measured by feeding it through a filter of 30-cps bandwidth tuned to 208 cps, a preamplifier, and a vacuum-tube voltmeter. At the low chopping frequency, the detector signal is fed directly into the amplifying system of the monochrometer.

Along with the measured relative spectral response curve, it is important that the detector user be provided with an absolute calibration sufficiently universal that the spectral dependencies of figures of merit such as NEI, NEP, D^*, can be readily derived. The information available from the measurements of NEP and relative spectral response, and the theoretical law for blackbody spectral radiation distribution, is sufficient to provide the absolute calibration.

The NEP is defined by

$$NEP = (P/V_s/V_N) = (V_N/\gamma_T) \qquad (12\text{-}11)$$

where $P = H \cdot A$, $\gamma_T = (V_s/P)$, γ_T is the responsivity of the detector to a blackbody usually set at $500°\,K$, and P is the radiation power falling on the detector.

Since this is a blackbody measurement, the responsivity is determined in an absolute manner, and represents an average value taken over the spectral range of sensitivity of the photocector. In Figure 12-13 the averaged absolute value of the responsivity is shown (C) together with the blackbody spectral radiation curve (A) and a plot of the relative spectral photoresponse of the detector (B). It is clear that one can pro-

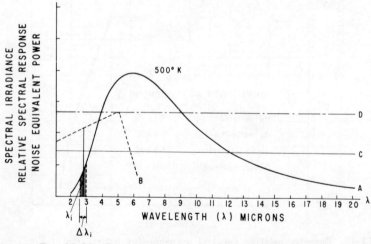

Fig. 12-13. Determination of absolute spectral response.

vide an absolute scale corresponding to curve C, but it still has to be determined where curve B should be placed with respect to this scale. When curve B is properly placed on the scale corresponding to an absolute calibration, the product

$$\sum_{i=0}^{\infty} \gamma_{a,\lambda_i} \cdot \Delta P_{\Delta \lambda_i}$$

where γ_{a,λ_i} is the absolute response at wavelength, $\Delta P_{\Delta \lambda_i}$ is the power in the bandwidth $\Delta \lambda$ centered at λ_i, summed over the wavelength of detector spectral sensitivity, equals the signal voltage obtained in the NEP measurement, and therefore also the averaged absolute responsivity curve C.

The quantity needed for calibration is the absolute value of the spectral response determined at the "peak" of curve B. To arrive at this value, assume that another (unknown) photodetector response curve (D) is flat (a black detector), and passes through the peak of our photodetector curve B. The ratio of the signal voltages generated by these two different detectors is given by:

$$\xi = \frac{V_r}{V_{\text{Blackbody}}} = \frac{\displaystyle\sum_{i=0}^{\infty} \gamma_{r,\lambda_i} \cdot P_{\lambda_i} \cdot \Delta \lambda_i}{\displaystyle\sum_{i=0}^{\infty} \gamma_{\text{Blackbody},\lambda_i} P_{\lambda_i} \cdot \Delta \lambda_i} =$$

$$\frac{\displaystyle\sum_{i=0}^{\infty} \gamma_{r,\lambda_i} P_{\lambda_i} \Delta \lambda_i}{\gamma_{\text{Blackbody},\lambda_i} \displaystyle\sum_{i=0}^{\infty} P_{\lambda_i} \Delta \lambda_i} \qquad (12\text{-}12)$$

If one normalizes, taking $\gamma_{\text{Blackbody},\lambda_i} = 1$

$$\xi = \frac{\displaystyle\sum_{i=0}^{\infty} \gamma_{r,\lambda_i} P_{\lambda_i} \Delta \lambda_i}{\displaystyle\sum_{i=0}^{\infty} P_{\lambda_i} \cdot \Delta \lambda_i} \qquad (12\text{-}13)$$

The denominator is simply the blackbody radiant power falling on the black photodetector of unit response, while the numerator provides a smaller number representing the signal voltage derived from our photo-detector. Obviously, the numerator is smaller than the denominator, and ξ represents an effectiveness factor indicating how close the average response of B comes to that of the black detector D.

The absolute value of the averaged spectral response C, as noted earlier, is a quantity obtained in the NEP measurement. Therefore an absolute determination of the peak spectral response can now be obtained by dividing the responsivity value from the NEP measurement by the effectiveness factor. Similarly, this procedure provides an absolute spectral dependence for the other figures of merit. To calculate the effectiveness factor, the expression for ξ is simplified to:

$$\xi = \frac{\sum_{i=0}^{\infty} \gamma_{r,\lambda_i} H_{\lambda_i} \Delta\lambda_i}{\sum_{i=0}^{\infty} H_{\lambda_i} \Delta\lambda_i} \qquad (12\text{-}14)$$

where $P_\lambda = H_\lambda \cdot A$ and H_λ is the radiant power per unit wavelength at the wavelength λ, for the blackbody used in the measurement (here taken at $500\,^\circ K$). However, a correction to the expression for γ must be considered. In practice the experiment performed to determine NEP involves using chopped radiation from a $500\,^\circ K$ blackbody source. However, the chopper generally is a black mechanical spinning disc whose temperature is about $300\,^\circ K$ (room temperature). Therefore the ac signal response is actually the result of the detector looking alternately at $500\,^\circ K$ and $300\,^\circ K$ sources, and not simply at a $500\,^\circ K$ source against a background of absolute zero. The detector is then actually sensitive to the shaded portion of the radiant power, shown in Figure 12-14. The effectiveness factor should then more properly be expressed as:

$$\xi = \frac{\sum_{i=0}^{\infty} (H_{\lambda_i}^{500^\circ} - H_{\lambda_i}^{300^\circ}) \gamma_{r,\lambda_i} \Delta\lambda_i}{\sum_{i=0}^{\infty} H_{\lambda_i}^{500^\circ} \Delta\lambda_i - \sum_{i=0}^{\infty} H_{\lambda_i}^{300^\circ} \Delta\lambda_i} \qquad (12\text{-}15)$$

The denominator is determined from the Stefan-Boltzmann law [see Eq. (12-3)]

$$W = \sigma_s (T^4 - T_0^4)$$

where σ_s is the Stefan-Boltzmann constant, T and T_0 are $500\,^\circ K$ and $300\,^\circ K$, respectively. The quantity H is therefore the power exposure re-

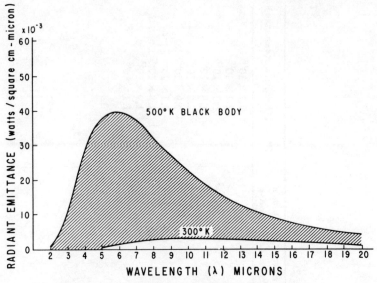

Fig. 12-14. Blackbody spectral radiant emittance.

sponsible for the detector signal response, and is a constant. The "power fraction" given by:

$$F_{\lambda_i} = \frac{\left(H_{\lambda_i}^{500°} - H_{\lambda_i}^{300°}\right)\Delta\lambda_i}{H} \qquad (12\text{-}16)$$

where $H_{\lambda_i}^{500°}\Delta\lambda_i$ is the radiant power within the bandwidth $\Delta\lambda_i$ at the center wavelength λ_i, can now be used in the determination of ξ, since

$$\xi = \sum_{i=0}^{\infty} F_{\lambda_i} \cdot \gamma_{r,\lambda_i}$$

The power fraction may be calculated at different wavelengths, either by the use of a radiation slide rule or the tables of A. N. Lowan and G. Blanch.[6] A table can then be prepared to evaluate ξ, as shown by Table 12-2.[2]

Once the effectiveness factor is calculated, the peak value of NEP or D^* can readily be computed since:

$$\text{NEP}_{\lambda,\text{peak}} = \text{NEP}_{\text{Blackbody}} \cdot \xi$$

or

$$D^*_{\lambda,\text{peak}} = \frac{D^*\left(500°_{\text{Blackbody}}\right)}{\xi}$$

as shown in Table 12-2.

Table 12-2
Evaluation of ξ (from Reference 2)

Wavelength Interval (μ)	Energy Fraction (500°K Blackbody)	Relative Response (Midinterval)	Energy Fraction × Relative Response [a]	D* = K (Relative Response)
1–1.5	7×10^{-6}	20.		0.7×10^{10}
1.5–2.0	3.7×10^{-4}	32		1.1×10^{10}
2.0–2.5	0.0032	44	0.1	1.5×10^{10}
2.5–3.0	0.012	55	.7	1.9×10^{10}
3.0–3.5	0.024	66	1.6	2.3×10^{10}
3.5–4.0	0.038	84	3.2	2.9×10^{10}
4.0–4.5	0.050	90	4.5	3.1×10^{10}
4.5–5.0	0.058	80	4.6	2.8×10^{10}
5.0–5.5	0.062	55	3.4	1.9×10^{10}
5.5–6.0	0.063	30	1.9	1.1×10^{10}
6.0–6.5	0.061			
6.5–7.0	0.058			
7.0–7.5	0.054			
7.5–8.0	0.050			
8.0–8.5	0.045			
8.5–9.0	0.041			
9.0–9.5	0.037			
9.5–10.0	0.033			

10.0–10.5	0.029
10.5–11.0	0.027
11–12	0.045
12–13	0.035
13–14	0.029
14–15	0.022
15–16	0.019
16–17	0.015
17–18	0.013
18–19	0.011
19–20	0.0084
20–22	0.015
22–24	0.0097
24–26	0.0072
26–28	0.0058
28–30	0.0029

[a] ξ Sum: 20.0.

$D^*(500^\circ\text{K}, 900 \text{ cps}) = 7 + 10^9$ cm $\text{cps}^{1/2}$ watt^{-1}

$$D^*(500^\circ\text{K}, 900 \text{ cps})$$

$$\text{Cell Response} = \frac{D^*(500^\circ\text{K}, 900 \text{ cps})}{\text{Factor } (K)} = \frac{7 \times 10^9}{\Sigma (\text{Energy Fraction} \times \text{Relative Response})} = \frac{7 \times 10^9}{20} = 3.5 \times 10^8$$

12.4 Noise Spectrum

The noise-voltage spectrum is obtained with the system described in Section 12.1. However, the light source is removed and the noise voltage is obtained by simply reading the voltage at the wave analyzer. A typical plot of noise spectrum is shown in Figure 12-15.

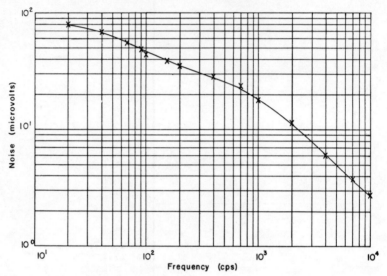

Fig. 12-15. Detector noise spectrum (*by permission of W. L. Eisenman and R. F. Potter, NOL, Corona, California, from NOLC Report 525, and the Philco Corporation*).

12.5 Sensitivity Contours

If a microscopic ray of light is projected onto the surface of a photo-detector, and the photoresponse recorded as a function of the ray's position, it is found that the photoresponse generally changes with the ray's position. The surface of the detector is thus rarely uniform in its photoresponse. The film detectors (lead compound family) are the worst offenders in this regard. If a graph of photoresponse versus light-ray position is made, and points of equal photoresponse are linked together, the resultant plot provides a "sensitivity contour," illustrated by Figure 12-16.

At Corona, the experimental arrangement to obtain sensitivity contours uses a microtable which allows the cell to be moved a small measured amount. The table is linked through a system of gears to a plotting table which gives up to a 36/1 increase in the scale. The exciting radiation is from an incandescent tungsten bulb chopped at 90 cps, and is passed in reverse through a microscope such that a spot 0.066 mm in diameter is focused onto the detector. As the detector is moved beneath this radiation, the relative response at 10 per cent intervals is noted on

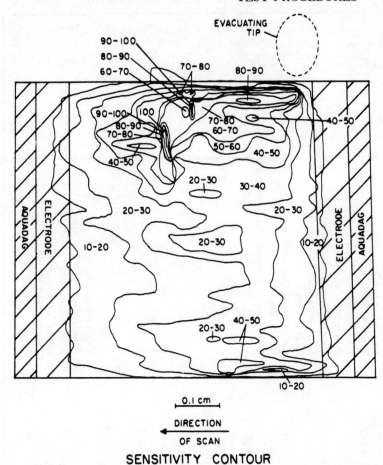

SENSITIVITY CONTOUR

Fig. 12-16. Detector sensitivity contour (*by permission of W. L. Eisenman and R. F. Potter, NOL, Corona, California, from NOLC Report 525, anonymous film detector*).

the plotting table. Lines connecting equal points of sensitivity are then drawn to obtain a plot such as Figure 12-16. This light-probe technique is also important for its utility in fundamental research programs on detector materials, where it is used in studies of diffusion length, time constant, and mobility.[7]

Contours of the sensitive area of a photodetector are of principal concern when the optical system associated with the detector does not utilize the full area. Also, they are important in determining an averaged evaluation of the surface area for substitution in the expression for D^*.

12.6 General Comments

A summation of data necessary to evaluate a detector is shown in Figure 12-17, which consists of a typical data sheet from an NOLC re-

CONDITIONS OF MEASUREMENT

Chopping frequency (cps)	90
Bandwidth (cps)	5
Humidity (%)	23.5
Cell temperature (°C)	−195
Dark resistance (ohms)	5.2×10^6
Dynamic resistance (ohms)	.....
Load resistance (ohms)	5.5×10^6
Transformer	.....
Cell current (μ amps)	1.5
Cell noise (μ volts)	47
Blackbody flux density (μ watts/cm², rms)	7.7

CELL DESCRIPTION

Type: Ge (AuSb doped)	
Angular field of view: approx. 110°	
Window: sapphire	
Method of preparation: crystal	
Area (cm²): 2.25×10^{-2}	

PHILCO CORP., CELL NO. 1207

CELL SENSITIVITY

500° K blackbody response

H_N(watts/cps$^{1/2}$ · cm²)	
(500, 90, 1)	4.5×10^{-9}
(500, , 1)	.....
P_N(watts/cps$^{1/2}$)	
(500, 90, 1)	1.0×10^{-10}
(500, , 1)	.....
Jones S (watts/cm)	
(500, 90, 1)	6.5×10^{-9}
(500, , 1)	.....
D^* (cm · cps$^{1/2}$/watt)	
(500, 90, 1)	1.5×10^9
(500, , 1)	.....
Spectral peak (μ)	1.5

Response at spectral peak

H_N(watts/cps$^{1/2}$ · cm²)	
(λ, 90, 1)	4.1×10^{-11}
(λ, , 1)	.....
P_N(watts/cps$^{1/2}$)	
(λ, 90, 1)	9.4×10^{-13}
(λ, , 1)	.....
Jones S (watts/cm)	
(λ, 90, 1)	5.8×10^{-11}
(λ, , 1)	.....
D^* (cm · cps$^{1/2}$/watt)	
(λ, 90, 1)	1.6×10^{11}
(λ, , 1)	.....
Effective time constant (μ sec)	8.1×10^1

DATA SHEET NO. 675

Fig. 12-17. Detector data sheet (*by permission of W. L. Eisenman and R. F. Potter, NOL, Corona, California, from NOLC Report 525, and the Philco Corporation*).

port. Notice that the data for blackbody and spectral response are followed by sets of three numbers in parentheses. These numbers represent quantities which have become essentially standards for rating infrared detectors. The notation $D*(500,90,1)$ under blackbody response means that the test blackbody was operated at $500°K$, the radiation from the blackbody was amplitude modulated at a frequency of 90 cps, and the bandwidth of the evaluation was normalized to 1 cps. For $D*(\lambda,90,1)$ under spectral response, λ refers to the wavelength at which detector response is a maximum, while the other numbers mean the same as above. The quantities H_N and P_N refer to detector noise equivalent irradiance and NEP, respectively.

A quantity denoted as Jones' S appears in the table, and merits discussion. The term was suggested by R. C. Jones early in the development of infrared photoconducting detectors.[8] Referring to Eq. (11-68), separating out the factors of frequency, bandwidth, and area, it follows that the detectivity in the excess-noise-limited case is proportional to the square root of the frequency, and inversely proportional to the square root of the product of area and bandwidth. It follows that the quantity defined as:

$$\text{Jones' } S = (\sqrt{f}/D*)$$

is a quantity independent of the frequency of a measurement, and, therefore, useful for evaluating intrinsic detectivity. The development of infrared detectors, however, has advanced to a state where $1/f$ noise limitations have been reduced to the point where this concept is no longer useful. It is incorrectly used when applied to any of the other types of noise limitations. Jones has recommended that Jones' S be discontinued as a means of rating detectors. This probably will happen in the near future.

Finally, as a generally useful report, which covers much of infrared detector technology, see Reference 9.

1. R. F. Potter, J. M. Pernett, and A. B. Naugle, *Proc. IRE* **47**, 1503 (1959).
2. P. Bratt, W. Engeler, H. Levenstein, A. MacRae, and J. Pehek, *Final Report on Ge and InSb Infrared Detectors*, Syracuse University under Air Force WADD Contract No. AF 33 (616)-3859 (February 1960).
3. R. B. McQuistan, *J. Opt. Soc. Am.* **48**, 63 (1958).
4. M. Garbuny, T. P. Vogl, and J. R. Hansen, *Rev. Sci. Instr.* **28**, 826 (1957).
5. S. Nudelman and J. T. Hickmott, *Bull. Am. Phys. Soc.* **4**, 153 (1959).
6. A. N. Lowan and G. Blanch, *J. Opt. Soc. Am.* **30**, (1940).
7. K. Loric-Horovitz, V. A. Johnson, and L. Marton (eds.), *Methods of Experimental Physics*. New York: Academic Press, 1959, Vol. 6B, p. 352.
8. R. C. Jones, *Rev. Sci. Instr.* **24**, 1035 (1953).
9. W. J. Beyen, P. R. Bratt, H. W. Davis, L. F. Johnson, H. Levinstein, and A. V. MacRae, *Final Report on Germanium and Lead Telluride Detectors*. Syracuse University, under Air Force WADC Contract AF 33(616) 2221 (February, 1957).

CHAPTER 13

TYPES OF EQUIPMENT; DESIGN PROCEDURES

13.1 Introduction (Difference between Civil and Military Applications)

Infrared devices find applications in many fields, the most important being science, industry, and military operations. Since the design and application of infrared devices for most civil applications has been well described in available texts[1] (see Reference 1 for an extensive bibliography) and reference books, the present chapter will be concerned principally with devices for military applications. These have been called "military" only as a convenience in designating a class of devices and techniques having certain features in common. They are equally applicable to many nonmilitary problems, and although they are not yet much used in those areas, it is expected that they will be in the near future.

For the most part, there is a marked difference between civil and military devices both in function and in design. Most industrial and scientific applications involve quantitative measurements of the radiation from, or transmission through, some source for the purpose of making inferences concerning the physical state of the source, e.g., its temperature or its chemical constituents. The source is usually at the disposal and under the direct control of the operator who is at liberty to position it with respect to the instrument. Competing signals can, to a large extent, be eliminated, and the instrument output usually consists of a meter indication or a graph. In most military sensory device applications, on the other hand, the devices are required to make comparative measurements for the purpose of establishing the existence of certain possible types of sources, indicating the source position, and possibly identifying it in a gross sense—e.g., with respect to vehicle type rather than identifying its chemical constituents. In the latter type of application, the source is almost never known before the fact to exist; the operator has no control over source position, but must determine it. Competing signals are almost always present, so that a vital function of the instrument is to discriminate between the source of interest and all other signals. The output required of the usual military device includes indication of source existence, positional information, and possibly pictorial representations of source and surroundings.

The functions performed by military infrared sensory devices are search, detection, acquisition, tracking, and identification. Search is the process of examining a region for items of interest. Detection is the process of deciding that some part of the region being searched contains something of interest without, however, necessarily providing any information regarding what that something is. In contrast to detection, identification is the process of making some judgments concerning the nature of a detected object. Acquisition is applicable when tracking is to be started. It consists of establishing a relationship between an item of interest and a tracking operator or device, so that after acquisition the tracking mechanism may, without further aid, follow the item. Tracking is the process of following, automatically or manually, an item of interest.

A second class of military device having a function and structure different from most devices for civil applications is composed of infrared communications devices. Their function is the transmission and reception of information by means of modulated infrared radiation.

Quantitative measurements of the type employed in civil applications are sometimes made for military purposes, but are usually in support of the design and employment of a military sensory device having the functions outlined above.

Military infrared devices can be conveniently categorized into the following types: communications devices; active devices of all sorts; passive tracking, and fire-control devices; and passive surveillance sensors. Brief descriptions of these categories will be given, followed by a discussion of device design procedures.

13.2 Types of Devices

13.2.1 Communication Devices

Communication devices consisting of modulated sources, such as cesium vapor lamps with visible output suppressed by filter, and optical receiving units are useful in certain military activities. Pulse-code modulation, voice-amplitude modulation, teletype, and facsimile are all employed. Security and immunity to jamming are relatively high in comparison with many other communications methods. These advantages stem from the fact that the beamwidths can be made quite narrow, requiring the receiver to be in the beam to detect any signal at all; the surface range is limited to line of sight; and slant range is limited by atmospheric absorbtion and scattering. A further advantage is that infrared devices, in general, can be made smaller and lighter than their electronic counterparts. The most serious disadvantage of infrared radiation for communications is its inability to penetrate clouds, dense fog, and heavy rain. Except in the case of light haze, which infrared radiation penetrates better than visible radiation, infrared penetrates poor weather perhaps only 15 per cent better than does visible radiation. For those reasons, except in weatherless environments, infrared is restricted to short-range, good weather applications. There is also at present some difficulty in constructing sources with the desired power output. That problem, however, is expected to yield to further research (see section 13.4).

13.2.2 *Active Sensory Devices*

All active infrared sensory devices have been lumped into a single category because active methods fail to take advantage of some of the unique features of the infrared spectrum, and for that reason have tended to be replaced by passive methods. The fact that all objects at normal temperatures radiate with peak efficiency in the infrared part of the spectrum makes passive surveillance possible. Passive surveillance through an absorbing medium suffers only from the losses along a single path. An active process involves a triple energy loss; one in the path between source and target, a second in reflection losses, and a third in the path between the target and the receiver.

The sniperscope is a fairly representative active device; it consists of a combined source and image-forming receiver for attachment to a rifle and gives the user a certain nighttime advantage over an adversary unequipped with infrared equipment. However, an adversary with only a receiver—a much simpler equipment—can detect the sniperscope source at greater ranges than he can be detected by the sniperscope operator, due to inverse range squared and atmospheric losses. Furthermore, employment of a visible searchlight by an adversary not only nullifies any sniperscope advantage but also leaves the operator impeded with a useless piece of equipment of not inconsiderable weight and bulk. Nevertheless, the sniperscope does have some utility in certain restricted surprise situations.

Another type of active application is the use of an infrared searchlight with some percentage of the user troops equipped with image-forming receivers. This technique may be used for such applications as night driving. As with the sniperscope, however, the sources are susceptible to detection and counteraction, and any advantages can be nullified by enemy use of visible searchlights.

The use of active infrared in surveillance applications as compared to other active techniques such as radar appears to have some slight advantage in relative security, and a clear advantage in finer resolution.

These are, however, obtained by sacrificing all-weather capability. Furthermore, active techniques fail to capitalize on the principal unique aspect of infrared, i.e., the self-radiation of all material substances is usually greatest in the infrared region and is large enough that it can be used directly not only for observation, but to furnish information regarding target temperatures which are an indication of activity.

13.2.3 *Passive Tracking and Fire Control*

Certain types of military targets contain power sources, and, therefore, generate significantly more heat than their surroundings. These consist principally of vehicles—ground, sea, and airborne. Infrared devices are used in weapon aiming and homing operations against those targets. Typical applications are: (1) use as an auxiliary to radar target trackers which are associated with conventional artillery to provide finer angular coordinate information about a target than radar, (2) use as the primary information source in guided air-to-air missiles employed against aircraft targets, providing target-angle and angular-rate information to the missile guidance computer; and (3) use as an automatic means of stellar navigation, tracking continuously two or more stars, and providing a navigation computer with their angular coordinates with respect to the detecting device.

All of these devices possess certain common characteristics, and they are therefore placed in the same category, tracking and fire control; none of them is necessarily an image-forming device, since their function is to continue automatically pointing toward a single target, which usually subtends a very small angle at the tracking device, and which radiates significantly more energy per unit area than do its surroundings. The requirement that the equipment remain pointed at a single target necessitates that it have the ability to sense the target location when it is within the device's field of view, and also requires that there be a mechanism for turning the device so as to keep the target within the field of view. The normal information output of this class of device consists of target azimuth, elevation angles, and angular rates all measured with respect to some predetermined coordinate system which frequently takes the form of a gyro-stabilized platform.

13.2.4 *Passive Surveillance Sensors*

The function of a so-called surveillance sensor is distinct from that of a tracker in that, rather than being required to indicate the position of a single target over an extended period of time, the surveillance sensor must examine periodically a relatively large volume to determine the existence of items of interest; but it must not be operated so as to produce very detailed information from some part of the volume of space at the expense of reduced or no information from the remainder of the volume.   Such devices are frequently employed to find the targets to which tracking devices are subsequently assigned.

Surveillance sensors of the simplest class are called intrusion detectors, and function much like the common photoelectric burglar alarm or door opener with the difference that the burglar acts as the radiation source rather than a beam interrupter.   A typical such device may be placed at the side of a highway and have a fan-shaped fixed field of view, with its wide dimension vertical, extending across the highway. The electrical signal due to background radiation, which changes relatively slowly, can be effectively suppressed by electrical filtering so that only rapidly changing signals trigger the device.   More sophisticated models can indicate the direction in which an object crosses the field of view.   A similar function is performed in aircraft.   Since in that application the volume of interest is larger, the device usually must be scanned, making it more complex.   There is some possibility that in the near future such infrared devices will be employed by the civil airlines for collision avoidance.

One of the more sophisticated and potentially most useful surveillance sensors is the airborne ground scanner.   These devices produce a pictorial type of record showing both natural terrain features and human artifacts.   Among the more important reasons that the use of infrared techniques is profitable in this application are the following:

1. With infrared devices, information can be obtained concerning certain target characteristics, namely, temperature and emissivity, which cannot be obtained by any other remote sensing means.   Thus, no matter what other sensory means are employed simultaneously, an infrared device will contribute new, unique information.   Furthermore, temperature is one of the more reliable indicators of human activity.

2. The use of infrared devices permits penetration and detection of ordinary visual camouflage.

3. With the exception of visible light techniques, the use of infrared techniques gives better resolution than any other means.   This is shown by the Rayleigh resolution criterion

$$\alpha = 1.22 \, (\lambda/D)$$

where α is the minimum resolution angle, λ is the wavelength of the radiation employed, and D is the diameter of the collecting aperture of the optical device.   In the infrared region λ is sufficiently small that less than one-milliradian resolutions are easily obtainable with aperture diameter of about one foot.   This not only results in information of high resolution but makes the devices extremely difficult to countermeasure. Radar, for instance, can be noise-jammed due to finite antenna-pattern side lobes, but since infrared devices have virtually no side lobes, they cannot be noise-jammed, although they can be decoyed.

4. The use of infrared devices permits passive night and day surveillance. When the device is located on an aerial platform, this is useful not so much because of reduced vulnerability (the carrying vehicle is usually easily detectable), but because the enemy is denied information regarding the frequency employed to observe him, or even the knowledge that he is being observed. This information denial prevents him from making best use of even the decoy-type countermeasure. When the device is located on the ground, vulnerability *is* reduced because the device itself, being lodged in a complex background, is not easily detectable.

5. Infrared devices are sensitive to many of the types of terrain feature displayed on ordinary maps. This coupled with the fact that infrared air-to-ground scanner output can be conveniently presented in map-type format, results in ease of correlation between infrared strip maps and conventional maps.

6. Since elevated temperature is a good indication of human activity and, therefore, items of interest, the use of infrared makes it possible to examine large areas for items of interest without the necessity for detailed human examination of all parts of the area. Hence infrared would appear to be useful in conjunction with photography. The infrared results would indicate subareas of interest, obviating the need for detailed examination of the entire area, and photography would furnish added detail in the selected subareas.

The design and performance of an airborne ground scanner is analyzed in some detail in Chapter 14. Reference to a specific type of instrument facilitates the discussion and causes little loss in generality since most of the features present in all infrared devices appear in that type of device.

13.3 Design Procedures

13.3.1 *Form of the Problem*

Problems requiring the design of an infrared sensory device usually have a characteristic form. Although the specific purpose or function of the device may vary from case to case, the factors given as requirements are usually the same. Those factors most often specified to some extent in advance are:

1. The function the device is to perform.
2. The volume of space to be covered by the sensory device.
3. The time intervals in which sensing over the volume must be accomplished.
4. The resolution desired.
5. The range between device and target.
6. The type of target to be sensed.

7. The type of sources emitting competing radiation, i.e., background clutter.
8. The altitude of operation for device and targets.
9. The desired form of the device output.
10. Practical limitations on size, weight, complexity, reliability, etc.

Starting with the above types of information in more or less detail, it is desirable to have an organized design procedure to follow. There is, unfortunately, no universally satisfactory design procedure which can be specified in detail. One scheme which has been used with some success will be described. Although it may require modifications for each specific design problem, it should be useful as a general guide.

The design process can be broken into the following four major steps;

1. Selection of gross type of implementation.
2. System sensitivity analysis.
3. Scanning and/or tracking analysis.
4. Output analysis.

It will not be possible to describe all of these processes with the same degree of precision. Some are amenable to an analytic approach, and others are not.

13.3.2 *Gross Type of Implementation*

Given the function and types of requirements listed above, a useful first design step is to reduce the number of possible gross types of implementation to a single or a few types which appear to be worth more detailed consideration. This step is very likely the one least susceptible to detailed organization and the use of analytic methods. Thus it is here that most reliance must be placed on the experience, judgment, and inventiveness of the designer. There are, however, a few semiorganized techniques which are helpful.

A "brainstorming" technique is useful to effect that reduction in number of possibilities, and yet keep to a minimum the chance of failing to consider some type particularly adapted to the application at hand. This consists in first constructing a list of all possible types of implementation which might serve, and then eliminating from the list those types having some obvious shortcomings. Such a list may be compiled by first drawing on the experience of the designer; second, reviewing the literature dealing with similar applications; third, designing new arrangements of subassembles from several existing types of device, and fourth, *ad hoc* inventing of new device concepts. At this stage the weeding out must be accomplished by application of stated requirements of the type described above. All the devices listed are presumed to perform the required function to some degree, so that factor will not help in the elimination. The search volume, time, and resolution requirements individually may rule out some devices, and joint consideration of those factors establishes a required system information rate which may eliminate other items from the list, usually because of detector time constant limitations. The target-device range, the spectral distributions of target and clutter radiation, together with a knowledge of atmospheric transmission, will possibly imply a preference for operation in some spectral region which may eliminate some devices from the list. Of the practical requirements, usually only size and weight are often the cause of rejection at this stage of the design. Other factors such as reliability can frequently be strongly influenced by minor design changes. Size may preclude the use of long-focal-length systems, and weight may dictate some maximum diameter for the optics.

By means of the above "brainstorming" and rejection processes, it will usually be possible to arrive at a single or, at most, a few types of implementation which seem worthy of more refined consideration.

13.3.3 *System Sensitivity*

A logical next step in the design process is analysis of system sensitivity for the surviving possible types of implementation. This step is perhaps the most susceptible of any to the use of a unified analytical approach.

An infrared device is fundamentally an information-handling and -processing system. As such, its operation is conveniently visualized by using the well-known process of tracing the sequence of events as a piece of information is introduced into and passes through the device. In this application, the process corresponds to tracing the history of some small amount of radiant power as it leaves the radiating source, travels to the infrared device, and is converted into an electrical signal which is then transformed in various ways by the device until the results are finally displayed to either a human operator or some automatic actuating device. A generalized diagram depicting that series of events is shown in Figure 13-1. The diagram serves as a mnemonic device to call to mind all the processes which must be taken into account in the analysis, and the order in which they occur.

Target radiation, after being emitted, travels some distance through an absorbing atmosphere in order to reach the infrared device. In so doing, it suffers attenuations of several different types. There is first the geometrical ("inverse-square" law) reduction in radiation density dependent on the distance between target and infrared device. Second, there will be absorption by the atmospheric constituents; and finally there will be some power which does not reach the infrared device because of scattering by atmospheric particles. The radiation which does reach the infrared device will be accompanied by and mixed with radia-

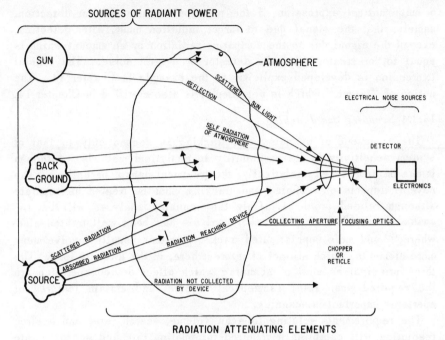

Fig. 13-1. Generalized diagram of infrared processes.

tion from background objects in the vicinity of the target, by radiation emitted by the atmosphere itself and, during daylight, by scattered and reflected radiation from the sun. (Direct radiation from the sun is not considered since, under those circumstances, the device will usually be saturated and insensitive to all other likely signals.) Some fraction of the total target and competing radiation will enter the optical system of the infrared device where it may suffer still further attenuation due to the imperfect transmitting and reflecting properties of the optical components. In the optical system the radiation may be modulated by a chopper or reticle. The results of such chopping may be quite complex, especially when the target signal itself varies with time. Finally, the radiation will fall on the detector where it is usually converted into an electrical signal. A further effective attenuation occurs during that process since the detector will usually not be sensitive to all the wavelengths present, nor will all photons be absorbed.

The nature of the emission, attenuation, and detection processes involved are discussed individually in considerable detail in the earlier chapters. Fortunately the processes are for the most part independent of each other so their combined effects can be expressed mathematically as a linear product of the functions describing the individual processes. The analytical expression for system sensitivity is obtained by writing a mathematical expression of the principal requirement for detection, namely, that the signal due to target radiation must, after detection, exceed the signal due to the competing radiation by an amount which is equal to, or greater than, the detector or system noise. The general expression is developed explicitly in the example in Chapter 14. The notion of "target," which is not simple, is also clarified in Chapter 14.

13.3.4 *Scanning and Tracking*

The treatment of scanning and tracking is second only to that of system sensitivity in its amenability to analytical methods. Although it can be approached analytically, the treatment cannot be unified. The several aspects of scanning and tracking must be treated as separate although related problems. Only the scanning analyses will be discussed here. The simple tracker analysis has been well treated elsewhere,[2] and more sophisticated tracker problems usually involve many more elements, which are not of interest here, in the tracking loop. The three principal aspects of scanning which affect device operation are the required scan rate, geometrical effects, and certain features of apertures important in scanning.

The requirements relating to scan volume, search rate, and desired resolution will establish a required information rate and scanning rate for the device. The information rate required will establish the system bandwidth and constrain the type and number of detectors employed, principally by requiring a definite range of detector time constant. The scan rate will impose certain restrictions on the type and size of scanning elements because of strength limitations as well as permissible distortions in the optical elements. Information and scan-rate treatments may be done analytically.

Geometrical effects will influence device resolution. The resolution of optical devices is most conveniently described by specifying their angular resolution. However, the characteristic of most interest to the user of a sensory device is the linear resolution at the target range. Unlike angular resolution, which is constant for a given device, linear resolution will vary with target-device range and a number of other factors. Linear resolution and its variation are subject to analysis, and it is important that the designer and user understand their behavior.

The influence of a stationary aperture on radiation passing through it is relatively straightforward. When the aperture is scanned, however, so that its projected field of view passes over a complex background containing targets, certain features of the aperture and the target-background complex interact in a way that exerts a strong influence on the resulting varying signal. The aperture size, shape, transmission, and scan rate, and their relation to target-background geometry and radiance, will act to influence the resolution and bandpass of the device. The analysis of these interactions bears certain similarities to the methods employed in electrical circuit analysis, and frequently makes it desirable to describe targets and backgrounds in terms of spatial power spectra. A brief introduction to those methods of analysis is given in Chapter 14.

13.3.5 *Output Analysis*

The final design stage is concerned with the analysis of the infrared device outputs. In the previous design steps, it has been possible and desirable to treat the infrared device as an entity in itself. In treating the device outputs, however, it will be necessary to consider the infrared device as a subsystem or component of some larger-scale system having a function of broader scope to perform. The larger-scale system will impose certain requirements on the infrared subsystem, particularly on the nature and form of the subsystem outputs, and may furnish certain inputs to the infrared device; e.g., in the case of an infrared single-target tracking device, the larger-scale system would provide the target-acquisition information. Discussion of the design of large-scale systems is outside the scope of this volume; for an introduction to that subject the reader is referred to Reference 3. The present discussion will be confined to certain specific features of the infrared device output as influenced by the operator or device to which the outputs are provided. The principal factor influencing the form of the outputs will be whether they will be used by an automatic device of some sort or by a human operator.

When the function of an infrared device is the detection of targets smaller than the device resolution, or single-target tracking, or multiple-target tracking while scanning, an automatic device can generally use the infrared device outputs as well as or better than a human operator. In that case the analysis is amenable to analytical methods involving the usual relations among signal-to-noise ratio, detection probability, and false alarm rates. The analysis will provide functions relating device parameters, usually threshold levels, to detection probability and false alarm rates, but will not give direct information regarding specific "best" device operating conditions. The latter decision will require additional information regarding the "value" of a correct detection versus the "cost" of a false alarm. Given the latter information, which must usually be furnished by the device user, device operating conditions may be optimized for specific applications by the methods of operations analysis.[4]

When the output of an infrared device is to be employed directly by a human operator, it will usually be profitable to present the output in a pictorial or maplike form so that the operator can exercise the human capability for shape or pattern recognition, a function that cannot be performed with any great success by present-day devices. The nature of the operator-display interaction cannot be treated analytically, and, at the present state of the art of human factors as applied to pictorial displays, only very rough guidance is available regarding display design. When the pictorial display is formed by a scanning operation, exactly the same scanning aperture effects occur as were described above and the methods of analysis are similar.

13.4 Conclusion (State of the Art)

A design procedure for infrared sensory devices has been briefly sketched. Chapter 14 contains an example of the application of that procedure to the design and performance analysis of a specific device in order to amplify and make more concrete the design process. The results of earlier chapters on components and processes are integrated into the example. The techniques of large-scale system design, human factors, and operations analysis, although they must be employed in any real device design, will not be discussed further; each constitutes an entire field of specialization.

The infrared devices discussed in this chapter are representative of the current state of the art. The field of applied infrared is, however, in a stage of rapid development so it is expected that in the very near future many new devices, applications, and techniques will make their appearance. Much of the infrared art involves phenomena falling within the provinces of quantum and information theories, and both of those fields have only recently reached the state of development where their influence is being felt in practical applications. A case in point is the fact that, as this volume was being written, the first optical and infrared lasers were operated successfully. The laser provides, for the first time, a source of coherent infrared and optical radiation, opening up many new possibilities in the area of active infrared and optical devices. Concurrently, with the appearance of new technical capabilities, there is arising a whole series of new problems suitable for the application of infrared and optical techniques. The problems of surveillance, navigation, and communication is space, as well as many problems of instrumentation and control in industrial automation, are providing many new areas in which the application of infrared and optical techniques appears profitable.

1. Henry L. Hackforth, *Infrared Radiation.* New York: McGraw-Hill, 1960.
2. Arthur S. Locke, *Guidance, Principles of Guided Missile Design.* Princeton: D. Van Nostrand, 1958.
3. Harry H. Goode and Robert E. Machol, *System Design, Control System Engineering.* New York: McGraw-Hill, 1957.
4. C. West Churchman, Russell L. Ackoff, and E. Leonard Arnoff, *Introduction to Operations Research.* New York: Wiley, 1957.

CHAPTER 14

EQUIPMENT DESIGN

14.1 Introduction

The foregoing chapters treat infrared phenomena, measurements, components, and design procedures. In this chapter the results of the previous chapters are brought together and applied to the design and performance analysis of a specific infrared sensory device, an infrared air-to-ground strip-mapping scanner. The presentation follows the general design procedure of the last chapter.

14.2 Methods of Implementation

14.2.1 *Requirements*

The function of an airborne ground mapper is to examine a large area of the ground for terrain features and military targets. Since one of the most important classes of targets consists of military vehicles, the resolution of the instrument must be relatively fine, especially if information regarding vehicle type is to be obtained. In cases where vehicles are of interest, the sensor vehicle is likely to be flying at altitudes of about 1,000 ft. In cases where large industrial complexes are of interest, the vehicle may be flying at altitudes of about 100,000 ft. In both applications angular resolutions in the neighborhood of 1 mrad seem to be indicated. In the low-altitude applications particularly, the requirement for examining a large area necessitates a large total field of view and high speed of operation. In flights over enemy-held terrain, vulnerability is reduced by high speeds and by minimizing the number of passes required to cover a given area. Ease of interpretation indicates the desirability of a pictorial type of presentation of the information. With information in that form, use can be made of conventional photointerpretation techniques, and correlation with conventional terrain maps is facilitated. The pictorial representation in itself requires that the scan pattern be relatively simple. Thus, it is desirable that such a mapper have high resolution, high speed of operation, wide field of view, pictorial-type presentation of the information, and a simple scan pattern.

It is possible to implement such a mapper in a number of ways. Several of the more important are described below. They are the use of direct-image-forming detectors, image-plane scanning, pushbroom scanning, and object-plane scanning.

14.2.2 Direct Image-Forming Devices

There is a class of infrared detectors typified by the evaporograph which are virtually complete sensors in themselves without the need for auxiliary equipment. In one operation they form a complete image of an extended area, and hence require no scanning. They are not complex in construction, and are very fast in *effective* scanning speed, being equivalent to a very large number of small field of view detectors operated in parallel. The pictorial presentation of information given by these devices can be viewed directly or photographed. Using them is very simple, quite similar to the use of ordinary telescopes and cameras. They have two strong advantages; their mechanical simplicity, and their relatively high speed in obtaining information from a large area. Their angular resolution capabilities are satisfactory. These striking advantages are, however, outweighed by certain disadvantages at the present stage of development. Although their effective speed in obtaining information from a large area is quite good compared to a scanned detector with a small field of view, the speed at which the image is formed is so slow as to be a handicap. Being thermal rather than quantum detectors, their response times tend to be rather slow. The image is formed sufficiently slow that their use from a moving platform is impracticable. Furthermore, utilization of their image-forming capability requires good-quality, wide-field optical systems in the infrared region, and these are not readily available at present. With mirrors, wide fields cannot be had without sacrifice of resolution and, at the edges of the field, reduction in effective collecting aperture. Also, when the ground is viewed from an airborne platform, aperture reduction at the edges of the field of view can be least afforded, since there the range to the ground is longest, so the power reaching the aperture is smallest. In the visible part of the spectrum wide field can be obtained with refractive optics, but the present state of the art in the infrared lags behind the visible. There is a relative dearth of satisfactory optical materials in the infrared. So in general, present-day infrared devices of all types tend to use reflective optics.

There is a second type of image-forming detector which, however, must be scanned; that is the photothermionic image-converter tube. The detector does not have to be scanned over object space; it forms an image of a large area directly. The image itself is not visible, so it must be scanned by an electron beam, in order that the information may be presented to an operator. The electronic scanning does not suffer from the speed and mechanical problems of ordinary scanning methods. This type of detector, however, does require high-quality, wide-field optics.

Because of the difficulties mentioned above, neither type of direct image-forming detector finds much use, at present, in air-to-ground mapping.

14.2.3 *The Pushbroom Technique*

The ground can be mapped from a moving airborne platform in which the only scanning motion is the vehicle motion. A linear array consisting of a large number of detectors, each having an instantaneous field of view equal to the desired resolution and the number of elements determined by the desired width of the map, is positioned so as to receive energy from a very long, narrow strip of ground at right angles to the vehicle flight path. As the vehicle moves forward, information will be received from a series of such strips each contiguous to its neighbors. The scanning operation is similar to moving a rake with very closely spaced teeth along the ground. The advantages of this method are that no scanning device is required, and that the effective scanning rate, in terms of area examined per unit time, is much greater than is possible with a scanned single-element detector. There are, however, two major disadvantages. First, each detector of the array must have a separate preamplifier. Then, either all the remaining electronics must be replicated or a sequencing switch provided. Second, with a single optical system the wide-field high-quality problem must be faced; or, with individual optical systems for each element of the array, the price of complexity and reduced areas of the individual apertures must be paid. In addition, it is necessary to match the responses of the information channels, either by matching the array elements, or by adjusting the preamplifiers. These factors make the pushbroom technique somewhat undesirable for the mapping operation.

14.2.4 *Image-Plane Scanning*

A third alternative is to form an image of a part of the ground, which changes as the vehicle moves, and scan the image with a single detector. Since the image rather than object space is scanned, there is no necessity for moving the collecting aperture. The scanning parts can be made quite small, and thus withstand the required high speeds without distortion. The primary difficulty with this method is the familiar requirement for wide-field high-quality optics. Thus, the image-plane scanner is seldom used for the mapping application.

14.2.5 *Object-Plane Scanning*

Finally, there is the technique which is currently preferred: an object-plane scanner using a single-element detector or a short linear array of relatively few elements. Such a device usually has a very narrow (1 to 10 mrad^2) instantaneous field of view which is scanned at right angles to the flight line of the carrying vehicle. For a single sweep this causes an area on the ground to be scanned which is very narrow in the direction of vehicle travel, and extends from directly below the vehicle out to both sides a considerable distance. Such a single sweep is usually called a "line" of scan. The motion of the vehicle is such that successive lines are contiguous. The resulting information is usually placed line by line on photographic film in approximately the same way that it was scanned. The result is a pictorial type of presentation in which the discrete line characteristic of the information has been suppressed just as is the case with television images. In contrast to television, however, the infrared picture is scanned only once and the single raster is effectively endless, hence the term "strip map" for the end result. In appearance the strip maps are remarkably like somewhat low-resolution photographs of the conventional type.

Scanning of the object plane requires motion of the collecting aperture, which is difficult since the aperture must be relatively large, about 6 inches in diameter. However, to date, attempts to move large apertures rapidly have been more successful than attempts to solve the problems inherent in some of the other scanning methods. Therefore, object-plane scanning is currently the preferred method.

Methods for analysis of the performance of the air-to-ground strip-map scanner using object-plane scanning are considered below in some detail.

14.3 System Sensitivity (Object-Plane Scanner)

14.3.1 *Introduction (Mapping versus Target Detection)*

An airborne strip mapper is used for two purposes which, for lack of more suitable terminology, will be called mapping and target finding. The two applications impose somewhat different requirements on the scanner.

In the mapping application the desired information resides principally in the pictorial aspects of the presented information, i.e., in the shapes of objects in the map. Shape information will be available only for objects which are considerably larger than the instantaneous field of view of the scanner. Objects of interest in this category include terrain features, roads, large man-made structures such as factories, and industrial complexes.

For certain purposes those objects will be targets, but the term "target finding" will be reserved for targets of size small enough that no shape information is available.

It will be assumed that shape information is contained principally in the contrast between adjacent spots in a picture; the spots being of a size corresponding to the instantaneous field of view of the scanner. Thus, for a mapping scanner, "temperature sensitivity" is the principal quantity of importance.

The term temperature sensitivity is usually expressed with reference to a blackbody so that, in applications, cognizance must be taken of the fact that real bodies are not black, but have emissivities less than one.

In the target-finding application, no shape information being available, the required information resides principally in the amplitude of the signal from each area equivalent to the instantaneous field of view, or equivalently in the brightness of corresponding spots in the pictorial information display. This means, that to be categorized as a target an object must radiate an amount of power which is different from its surroundings by an amount which is greater than the average fluctuations in power from the background. Thus, for target-finding the most important factor is not a feature of the scanning device at all, but the ratio of target power to average variation of background power.

The mapping case may be most conveniently treated as a target-finding case in which there is a uniform background with no variations, radiating a power equal to the average power radiated by the actual background of interest. Under those circumstances, system noise will set the limiting sensitivity.

This section covers the mapping application treated as a uniform-background target-finding case, and the true target-finding application.

14.3.2 *The Mapping Application*

14.3.2.1 *Method of Analysis.* As remarked earlier, an infrared scanner is basically an information-handling device and is conveniently analyzed by following the natural sequence of events as a piece of information travels from its source to the device, and through the device to the user display. That method is followed here by discussing the radiating sources and transmission effects, the scanner optical system, and the infrared detector, in that order. Finally, the individual effects are expressed in a single equation giving system sensitivity. Scanning effects and display problems are treated in later sections.

14.3.2.2 *Sources and Transmission Effects.* The sources of radiation are terrain, bodies of water, vegetation, and man-made objects of all types. None of these radiates precisely as an ideal blackbody. However, the radiation of all those sources regarded as blackbody radiation can be modified by an emissivity function $\varepsilon(\lambda)$, where λ is wavelength. The spectral emittance of a blackbody at a temperature of $T°$ Kelvin is by the Planck law

$$ W_\lambda = \frac{C_1 \lambda^{-5}}{e^{C_2/\lambda T} - 1} $$

watts per square centimeter per micron at wavelength λ, where λ = wavelength in microns, $C_1 = 3.74 \times 10^4$, $C_2 = 1.43880 \times 10^4$.

The radiation from a flat surface is not distributed with equal intensity in all directions. Also, in traveling from the source to the scanner the radiation is attenuated by the atmosphere, and the radiation density decreases with the range between source and scanner. The power which finally reaches the scanner is not all equally useful since any real detector is not necessarily equally sensitive at all wavelengths. In order to obtain a measure of the useful radiation arriving at the scanner, all those factors must be taken into consideration.

True blackbody radiation from a flat surface obeys the Lambert cosine distribution law.* Although real sources of interest are not true blackbodies, most of them are close enough to being so that it is customary to assume that the Lambert law applies. By the Lambert law the radiation intensity (power per unit solid angle) in the direction of the normal to the radiating surface is just $1/\pi$ times the total power radiated by the surface. The effect of observing the surface from some nonnormal direction may be taken into account by using the area of the projection of the target onto a plane normal to the line of observation. See (5-48).

The atmosphere, principally water vapor and carbon dioxide, absorbs strongly in some wavelength regions. This effect will be represented by a transmittance $\tau_A(\lambda, r)$ which is a function of wavelength and range between source and scanner. The geometrical dilution of power density with range need not be considered explicitly at this time if we compute the power or flux density per unit solid angle. That effect will be taken account of when we consider the collecting aperture and the angle it subtends from the target. The spectral transmittance of the optical system is a function of wavelength only, and will be designated by $\tau_O(\lambda)$.

Except for the thermal type such as bolometers, detectors are not usually equally sensitive to radiation of all wavelengths. This effect may be accounted for by employing a factor $\Gamma(\lambda)$, representing the relative spectral responsivity of the detector.

---

*There is also a Lambert law dealing with absorption, stating that equally thick layers of the same absorbing material will always absorb the same fraction of incident radiation.

Combining all these factors, and assuming the scanner views the source from a normal direction, the total useful radiation reaching the vicinity of the scanner collecting aperture from a source of area A may be expressed as

$$\frac{A}{\pi} \int_0^\infty \frac{C_1 \lambda^{-5}}{e^{C_2/\lambda T} - 1} \, \varepsilon(\lambda) \, \tau_A(\lambda, r) \, \tau_O(\lambda) \, \Gamma(\lambda) \, d\lambda = \frac{A}{\pi} H(T, r) \quad (14\text{-}1)$$

in watts per unit solid angle. H is the irradiance of a hemispherical surface of radius r centered at the source and due to unit source area; and the expression for H takes account of the various attenuations suffered by the radiation in traveling from the source to the surface. The units of H are watts per unit source area. The source is assumed to be Lambertian and to radiate all its energy into a hemisphere.

There is also arriving in the vicinity of the scanner's collecting aperture some competing radiation which is usually neglected. That radiation results from direct emission by the atmosphere itself. By Kirchhoff's law, a nonblackbody will radiate well in just those spectral regions where it absorbs well. Thus, it may be desirable to filter out radiation in those regions where the atmosphere absorbs. That effect will not be considered explicitly here. Scattering losses also occur, but are inevitably included in any measured transmission curve.

It is not sufficient to consider only the total power from the source. The scanner must be able to distinguish the difference in power from the source of interest and from a uniform background at some temperature T_0. Assuming a source of interest which completely fills the field of view of the scanner, the change in power as the scanner looks first at the source of interest and then at the background is

$$\frac{A}{\pi} \Delta H = \frac{A}{\pi} [H(T_1, \varepsilon_1, r) - H(T_0, \varepsilon_0, r)] = P \quad (14\text{-}2)$$

watts per unit solid angle. This, then, is the power the scanner has to work with.

14.3.2.3 *The Optical System.* The scanner's optical system can be treated in terms of an equivalent simple lens focusing power on the detector. The influence of the optical system is felt principally in the fact that it determines the actual amount of usable power falling on the detector. The actual diameter, D, of the collecting aperture is usually not fully utilized because of some obscuration and optical losses. This is an effective attenuation independent of wavelength that is not accounted for in the spectral transmissivity term. It may be taken account of by assigning an efficiency factor l which, when multiplied by D, gives an effective lossless circular aperture of area $lD^2\pi/4$. The effective solid angle from which the scanner collects source radiation is then $lD^2\pi/4r^2$. This may be expressed in alternative forms by defining

$$F \equiv \text{focal length of the optics}$$

$$S \equiv \text{length of the side of a square detector}$$

$$\ell \equiv F/D$$

The angular instantaneous field of view σ of the optical system is then given by

$$\sigma = S/F$$

and D may be expressed as

$$D = S/\sigma \ell$$

Using those relations, the total useful power focused on the detector may be written as

$$\frac{A}{\pi} l \Delta H \frac{D^2 \pi}{4 r^2} = A l \Delta H \frac{S^2}{4 r^2 \sigma^2 \ell^2} \tag{14-3}$$

Note that the cell is presumed to be cooled, so far all practical purposes all that power is utilized.

14.3.2.4 *Detector Sensitivity.* It is quite feasible to build a scanner so that the only significant source of noise is detector noise. The information available on detectors and detector materials normally takes the form of NEP (noise equivalent power) as a function of frequency and $D*$ for specific detectors. The NEP is characteristic of the specific detector measured. The $D*$, while derived for specific detectors, tends more than NEP to be representative of the material in general since it is normalized to unit area. Its use in designing a scanner is, however, restricted by the fact that it is computed for a single or a narrow band of frequencies, and is not independent of frequency changes.

NEP and $D*$ are connected by the relation $\text{NEP}_M = \sqrt{a} \sqrt{\Delta f}/D*$, where NEP_M is the NEP over only the band of frequencies Δf centered around the frequency for which $D*$ applies, and $a = S^2$ is the detector area. That relation may be used to obtain the type of information of most interest in scanner design.

In general the desired detector size (assumed square in shape) will be known prior to detector selection. Normally, information on detectors of just that size may not be readily available. However, it may be obtained from the relation above. Taking the primed quantities to represent known data on cells of the desired material, but not necessarily the proper size and shape, and the unprimed quantities as the desired quantities, the following ratio holds:

$$\frac{\text{NEP}_M}{\text{NEP}'_M} = \frac{\sqrt{a} \sqrt{\Delta f} D*'}{\sqrt{a'} \sqrt{\Delta f'} D*}$$

Usually Δf is some standard bandwidth such as 1 cycle. Assume $\Delta f = \Delta f'$. Then $D* = D*'$, since neither depends on area. Canceling and rearranging:

$$\text{NEP}_M = \sqrt{a/a'}\ \text{NEP}'_M \qquad (14\text{-}4)$$

Now this relation is true at all frequencies, so the subscripts confining the relation to a single frequency may be dropped, resulting in an ex-expression for NEP as a function of frequency in terms of known quantities.

The quantity, then, which restricts the sensitivity of the scanner is just the integral

$$\int_{f_1}^{f_2} \text{NEP}\ df = \frac{S}{S'} \int_{f_1}^{f_2} \text{NEP}'\ df \qquad (14\text{-}5)$$

where f_1 and f_2 define the frequency band in which the scanner will operate. The integration bounds f_1 and f_2 will be established by scanning requirements to be discussed in Section 14.4.2. If the noise frequency spectrum is expressible analytically, the integral may be evaluated analytically.

It has been assumed that the frequency-response capability of the detector has not been exceeded. It will be part of the objective of the scanning analysis later to ensure that that condition is satisfied.

14.3.2.5 *System Sensitivity*. It is now possible to formulate an expression for system sensitivity based on the above factors, providing a detectability criterion is chosen. The usual detectability criterion is that the difference signal between the source of interest and the uniform background must exceed the detector noise (in a detector-limited system) by a factor of k. A k value of 5 gives a high probability of detection. The detectability criterion is expressed as

$$A\left[H(T_1, \varepsilon_1, r) - H(T_0, \varepsilon_0, r)\right] \frac{lD^2}{4r^2} \geq k \int_{f_1}^{f_2} \text{NEP}\ df \qquad (14\text{-}6)$$

or, rearranging,

$$A\,\Delta H \geq \frac{4r^2 k S}{lD^2 S'} \int_{f_1}^{f_2} \text{NEP}'\ df \qquad (14\text{-}7)$$

assuming both known and desired detector to be square. Since for this case $A/r^2 = \sigma^2$ we may transpose, and using the relation

$$D = S/\sigma f$$

rewrite as

$$\Delta H \geq \frac{4 k f^2}{lSS'} \int_{f_1}^{f_2} \text{NEP}'\ df \qquad (14\text{-}8)$$

Other rearrangements are possible and useful depending on the specific constraints of the design problem.

In making actual computations, approximations are usually made to make the labor manageable. In (14-8) the only part of the right member which is laborious is the integral. It is usually done graphically or by quantizing the NEP' function in discrete manageable intervals. The left member is quite laborious since its full expansion is

$$\Delta H = \int_0^\infty \left(\frac{C_1 \lambda^{-5}}{e^{C_2/2T_1} - 1} \varepsilon_1(\lambda) - \frac{C_1 \lambda^{-5}}{e^{C_2/\lambda T_0} - 1} \varepsilon_0(\lambda) \right) \tau_A(\lambda, r) \tau_0(\lambda) \Gamma(\lambda) d\lambda$$

The Planck's law expressions, while analytic, are at best difficult to compute. The usual procedure is to use a special radiation slide rule[1] to get specific values. None of the factors $\varepsilon(\lambda)$, $\tau_A(\lambda, r)$, $\tau_0(\lambda)$, and $\Gamma(\lambda)$ is expressible analytically. In "hand" computations they are usually quantized in manageable intervals. It is profitable to use analog or digital computers if the equipment is available, and if many such computations must be made. With analog computers the very wide range of values encountered requires either some loss of accuracy, or doing the problem in parts so that scale factors may be adjusted to maintain accuracy for the extreme values.

14.3.3 *The Target-Detection Application*

In the target-detection application it is necessary to be able to make the decision that a source is a target and not a piece of background. The target in this case is sufficiently small that no shape information is available. Two cases arise, one in which the target fills the scanner's instantaneous field of view, and the other where the target is smaller than the instantaneous field of view.

For the target filling the field of view, consider a target at temperature T and a background varying between T_0 and T_1. The target will be assumed warmer than the background, since that is usually the case in practice. With the exception of a few changes in sign, the method is identical for targets colder than the background.

Since almost any scanner can detect some variations in terrain, scanner temperature sensitivity is in no sense a limiting factor in this application. The useful detectability criterion is that the difference between the target signal and the signal from the highest background temperature* must exceed the difference in signals from backgrounds of extreme tem-

---

*To be completely rigorous, the discussion should be in terms of the type of background radiating the greatest power per unit area, since the emissivity may be as important as temperature in influencing the magnitude of the radiated power.

peratures by some factor k. If high false alarm rates are tolerable, fractional values of k are permissible. The criterion is expressed as

$$\sigma^2 r^2 \frac{1}{\pi}[H(T, \varepsilon, r) - H(T_1, \varepsilon_1, r)] \geq k \frac{\sigma^2 r^2}{\pi}[H(T_1, \varepsilon_1, r) - H(T_0, \varepsilon_0, r)] \quad (14\text{-}9)$$

so

$$H(T, \varepsilon, r) \geq (k + 1) H(T_1, \varepsilon_1, r) - k H(T_0, \varepsilon_0, r) \quad (14\text{-}10)$$

where $T_1 > T_0$. Note that this is a description of what targets are detectable against a given background and not, properly speaking, a statement about a scanner at all.

In the case of a target not filling the instantaneous field of view, the so-called "target signal" is a composite made up of the sum of true target signal plus some background signal. For a target of area A the effective target signal is

$$\frac{A}{\pi} H(T, \varepsilon, r) + \frac{\sigma^2 r^2 - A}{\pi} H(T_0, \varepsilon_0, r) \quad (14\text{-}11)$$

taking the worst case, i.e., background at temperature T_0. Then, employing the same criterion as above the expression is

$$\left[\frac{A}{\pi} H(T, \varepsilon, r) + \frac{\sigma^2 r^2 - A}{\pi} H(T_0, \varepsilon_0, r) \right] - \frac{\sigma^2 r^2}{\pi} H(T_1, \varepsilon_1, r) \geq$$
$$\frac{k\sigma^2 r^2}{\pi} \left[H(T_1, \varepsilon_1, r) - H(T_0, \varepsilon_0, r) \right]$$

or

$$A H(T, \varepsilon, r) \geq \sigma^2 r^2 (k + 1) H(T_1, \varepsilon_1, r) -$$
$$- [\sigma^2 r^2 (k + 1) - A] H(T_0, \varepsilon_0, r) \quad (14\text{-}12)$$

14.3.4 *Digression on Range Computation*

Under certain circumstances it is desirable to compute the maximum range at which an infrared device will perform its function. This is seldom a simple computation to make. To illustrate the nature of the difficulties, two cases will be considered: the familiar mapping and the target detection cases.

For the case of an air- or spaceborne sensory device for mapping the surface of the earth we have Eq. (14-7):

$$A \Delta H \geq \frac{4 r^2 k S}{l D^2 S^1} \int_{f_1}^{f_2} NEP' \, df$$

In this case the equipment is noise limited and the radiating sources all lie at substantially the same range. Solving for r gives the inequality,

$$r \leq \sqrt{\frac{A \Delta H}{(4kS/lD^2 S') \int_{f_1}^{f_2} \text{NEP}' \, df}} \tag{14-13}$$

This equation cannot be used directly because

$$\Delta H = \int_0^\infty \left(\frac{C_1 \lambda^{-5}}{e^{C_2/\lambda T_1} - 1} \varepsilon_1(\lambda) - \frac{C_1 \lambda^{-5}}{e^{C_2/\lambda T_0} - 1} \varepsilon_0(\lambda) \right) \tau_A(\lambda, r) \tau_0(\lambda) \Gamma(\lambda) \, d\lambda$$

is a function of r by virtue of the term $\tau_A(\lambda, r)$. For devices operated at relatively low altitudes, i.e., within the atmosphere, it is necessary to make some simplifying assumptions regarding $\tau_A(\lambda, r)$ which will permit a separation of the type $\tau_A(\lambda, r) = \tau_A'(\lambda) \tau''(r)$. Then an explicit solution for r may be obtained. In the case where the infrared device is above the atmosphere, τ_A will not depend on r, and Eq. (14-13) may be solved directly.

With respect to the target-detection application, the cases of most interest are ground-to-air and air-to-air operation, and the targets are usually smaller than the field of view of the device. The applicable equation is (14-12):

$$AH(T, \varepsilon, r) \geq \sigma^2 r^2 (k + 1) H(T_1, \varepsilon_1, r) - [\sigma^2 r^2 (k + 1) - A] H(T_0, \varepsilon_0, r)$$

Solving for range gives

$$r \leq \sqrt{\frac{A [H(T, \varepsilon, r) - H(T_0, \varepsilon_0, r)]}{\sigma^2 (k + 1) [H(T_1, \varepsilon_1, r) - H(T_0, \varepsilon_0, r)]}} \tag{14-14}$$

In this case the system is background- rather than noise-limited. The same difficulty is apparent here, namely, the functions H are dependent on r through the term $\tau_A(\lambda, r)$.

In the ground-to-air and air-to-air applications the background sources will be distributed at many different ranges. Sky background consisting principally of clouds will be randomly distributed in size, shape, range, and radiance. Even ground background, since it will seldom be observed from a normal direction, will exist at a variety of different ranges. For that reason the nature of the background signal is not expected to be a strong function of device–target range. As a result, in those applications serious ʻerror is not likely to result from the assumption that $H(T_0, \varepsilon_0)$ and $H(T_1, \varepsilon_1)$ are substantially independent of r. Then the range equation simplifies to

$$r \leq \sqrt{\frac{A [H(T, \varepsilon, r) - H(T_0, \varepsilon_0)]}{\sigma^2 (k + 1) [H(T_1, \varepsilon_1) - H(T_0, \varepsilon_0)]}} \tag{14-15}$$

leaving $H(T, \varepsilon, r)$ as the only term on the right involving r. As was the case in the mapping application, some assumption permitting separation of Eq. (14-15) into separate wavelength and range-dependent parts is required to permit a solution explicit in r.   For very high altitude and space applications τ_A will be essentially constant with respect to both λ and r.

14.4 System Scanning

14.4.1 A Representative Implementation

A typical scanning mechanization is shown in Figure 14-1.   Scanning at right angles to the vehicle flight path is accomplished by means of an n-sided prism.   Each face of the prism is inclined at $45°$ to the prism axis, and the prism rotates about its own axis, which is positioned along the vehicle flight path. A typical ray from the ground is directed by the prism to a paraboloidal collector focused on the detector. Usually a folding flat mirror is employed to get the detector back out of the radiation path between the prism and the collector. The major source of obscuration is the folding flat mirror and its supporting spider.

A simplified sketch of the scan geometry is shown in Figure 14-2. The principle important parameters are:

v = vehicle speed
σ = instantaneous angular field of view
β = total angle of scan
r = distance from scanner to ground element
within the instantaneous field of view.

Directly under the aircraft r becomes h, the vehicle altitude. The sketch illustrates the case of a single-element detector. The only change when using a linear detector array of p elements is that p adjacent lines will be swept out simultaneously. In either case it is usually assumed that, for points directly under the vehicle, the scanned strips, or lines, are contiguous without overlapping. This implies that at distances out to the side of the

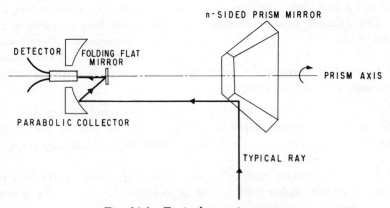

Fig. 14-1. Typical scanning system.

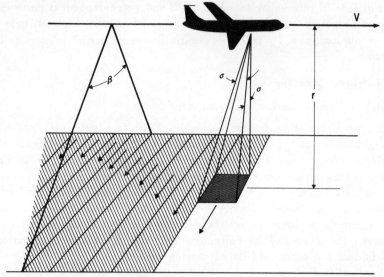

Fig. 14-2. Simplified scanning geometry (*from Proc. IRE, September 1959*).

vehicle flight path there will be overlapping, the consequences of which will be investigated later.

Since prisms are normally made with an integral number of faces, β is related to n by $\beta = 360/n$ in degrees where n is an integer. Hence, arbitrary values of β are not possible without implementing for the next larger "permitted" value, and discarding information from the extremities of the scan.

14.4.2 *Scan Rate Requirements and Consequences*

The two principal requirements which the scanner must meet are that:

a. The instantaneous field of view must dwell on each patch of terrain or target for a time not less than $g\tau$, where τ is the detector time constant and g is a dimensionless numerical factor usually equal to 1 or 2.

b. The scanner must be operated at such a rate that no parts of the ground within the strip to be scanned remain unscanned. Overlapping scan lines may be permitted for some applications since the redundancy may be used to improve the information. Normally, however, scanners are designed for minimum overlap.

If these conditions are met directly under the vehicle, they will certainly be met for ground points to the side of the vehicle because of the spread of the instantaneous field of view with range. Thus only the case of $r = h$ will be considered.

If the prism rotation rate is s, the number of elements scanned per second is $2\pi s/\sigma$, and the dwell time on a single element is the inverse

$\sigma/2\pi s$. Condition (a) is then expressed by:

$$(\sigma/2\pi s) \geq g\tau \qquad\qquad (14\text{-}16)$$

In the direction of vehicle travel, the width of the strip scanned by each detector element is σh for points directly under the aircraft. For a linear detector array of p elements, an n-faced prism, and a prism rotation rate of s, the width of the strip scanned each second is $\sigma hpns$. This must be greater than or equal to the vehicle rate of travel v. So condition (b) is expressed as:

$$\sigma hpns \geq v \qquad\qquad (14\text{-}17)$$

Rearranging these two expressions gives:

$$s \leq (\sigma/2\pi g\tau) \qquad\qquad (14\text{-}18)$$

$$s \geq (v/hpn\sigma)$$

All quantities are positive which facilitates the manipulation of inequalities. It is clear that s has an upper limit set basically by the detector time constant τ, and a lower limit set by the requirement that no ground be unscanned, i.e., basically by the ratio v/h.

For detectors with very short time constants the upper bound on s may be fixed by another factor at a value lower than the one set by τ. That other factor is the maximum prism rotation rate set by mechanical considerations such as strength of materials, vibrations, and allowable distortions. That type of constraint is not expressible analytically in any simple fashion.

Eliminating s from the above inequalities, we obtain a constraint on σ:

$$\sigma \geq + \sqrt{(2\pi g/np)\,(v/h)}\,\tau \qquad\qquad (14\text{-}19)$$

Unlike s, σ is constrained only by a lower limit. The constraint is imposed by the joint action of v/h and τ.

Under the limiting condition of minimum overlap, the inequalities become equalities, and somewhat symmetric independent expressions for s and σ may be obtained:

$$\begin{aligned} s &= + \sqrt{(1/2\pi \, gnp)\,(v/h)\,(1/\tau)} \\ \sigma &= + \sqrt{(2\pi g/np)\,(v/h)}\,\tau \end{aligned} \qquad\qquad (14\text{-}20)$$

The individual terms in these expressions warrant some discussion. The designer usually will have little or no control over v, h, τ, and g. The first two are usually set by considerations relative to vehicle operation. The properties of detector materials determine τ, and these are not subject to change. Some small choice is available by selecting different detector materials at the possible expense of having to accept a nonoptimum spectral region of operation. The amount of signal degradation which is tolerable determines g, which frequently cannot be less than 2. The only free variables are n, p and, to a lesser extent, σ in that it is constrained by a least but not a greatest value. Usually, in practice it is desirable to make β large, and thus n small to minimize the amount of time spent over enemy-held terrain. Also, σ is usually required to be quite small to give as much detail as possible. To minimize both σ and r, the designer has only p at his complete disposal. Thus, the factor p occupies a central position in scanner design.

At this point, it is possible to establish the integration limits f_1 and f_2, left undetermined from Section 14.3.2.4 in the expression for detector noise [Eq. (14-15)]. Assuming that the frequency response of the detector is not limiting, the upper frequency limit f_2 is set by the number of resolution elements scanned per second. Thus:

$$f_2 = bs\,(2\pi/\sigma) \tag{14-21}$$

where b is a constant, s is the prism rotation rate in revolutions per second, and $2\pi/\sigma$ is the number of resolution elements per revolution. One common method of selecting b is to assume that, for good square wave response, the frequency response must be 10 times the square-wave fundamental. Then $b = 10$.

The lower frequency limit f_1 is set by the prism rotation rate. The detector and electronics must be able to sustain a signal for one line of sweep. Such a signal could arise when scanning a large uniform body of water. Thus,

$$f_1 = dns \tag{14-22}$$

where d is a constant, n is the number of faces on the prism, and s is the prism rotation rate in revolutions per second. By the same type of reasoning as used for selecting b, a common value for d would be 1/10.

Two types of reconnaissance missions appear to permit reasonable safety to the aircraft. These are very low, fast flight, or very high, very fast flight. The first, a low-altitude high-speed reconnaissance system, is represented by the following parameters: $g = 2$, $n = 2$, $v = 1000$ ft/sec, $h = 1000$ ft, and $\tau = 10^{-5}$ sec; then $s = 63$ $(1/\sqrt{\ }$ rps, $\sigma = 7.8 \times 10^{-3}$ $(1/\sqrt{p})$ rad. If $p = 1$, the simplest configuration to implement, then $s = 3780$ rpm, and $\sigma = 7.8$ mrad.

An s of 3780 is reasonable, since apertures commonly used in such devices are about 6 inches in diameter, and such mirrors can be rotated at rates up to 6000 rpm without undue difficulty in holding distortion within optical limits, i.e., to the order of 25 μ.

A σ minimum of 7.8 mrad is larger than is desirable, since optical components can be made with resolution better than 1 mrad. If, in an attempt to improve σ without p increasing, the fastest detector readily available is selected, i.e., $\tau = 10^{-6}$ sec, then $s = 12,000$ rpm and $\sigma =$

2.5 mrad. This has still fallen short of the desired instantaneous field of 1 mrad, and the rotation rate is becoming a serious problem. Thus, decreasing detector time constant cannot greatly improve the performance of single-element detector scanners operating with large β.

.If, on the other hand, p is increased to achieve a σ no greater than 1 mrad, p must be at least 9, and in this case $s = 4000$ rpm and $\sigma = 0.8$ mrad for $\tau = 10^{-6}$ sec. Both of these are achievable values. Note again that further decreasing τ would result in unrealistic values for s.

The second example concerns itself with very high altitude reconnaissance. At present, it is not unreasonable to think of flight altitudes of 100,000 ft, an increase by a factor of 100 over the 1000-ft altitude considered in the above example. An increase in v by the same factor does not seem possible at present. Considerations relative to propulsion units and aerodynamics seem to restrict v to about 3000 to 5000 ft/sec. In addition, if these limitations are neglected there is another limit on v of approximately 25,000 to 30,000 ft/sec, speeds quite close to escape velocity. Thus, very high and very fast operation must result in a reduction of the ratio v/h. But due to the manner in which v/h enters the expressions for s and σ, this results in values for these quantities which are relatively easy to obtain. Thus, the low and fast operation considered in the example is the most difficult of achievement in terms of scanner use. So, the example is a worst case and any other method of operation is bound to be easier in terms of scanner implementation.

There is one exception to the last statement. If it is desired to maintain, at very high altitudes, the same linear resolution on the ground that is obtainable at low altitudes, a difficulty arises. At an altitude of 1000 ft an angular resolution of 1 mrad implies a linear ground resolution of 1 ft; at an altitude of 100,000 ft a ground resolution of 1 ft implies an angular resolution of 10^{-2} mrad. But the Rayleigh criterion states that, for a circular aperture of diameter d, the best obtainable resolution at a wavelength λ is given by $\sigma = (1.22\lambda/d)$. At a wavelength of $10\,\mu$, a desired σ of 10^{-2} mrad requires a circular aperture of 12 cm, or about a 4-in. diameter. This aperture lies within the range of those which can be ·employed in airborne vehicles. However, the Rayleigh criterion is an idealized limit assuming a perfect optical system. In practice, such performance cannot be realized. Thus, at very high altitudes linear ground resolution may have to be sacrificed because of fundamental physical limitations.

14.4.3 *Scanning Geometry*

There are two features of the operation of the scanner described above which must be considered in connection with ground resolution. First, although the angular resolution is constant, the linear resolution on the ground is not; it becomes progressively larger as the optical axis of the scanner is inclined at larger angles from the vertical, and it does not change isotropically. Second, when a linear detector array is employed, the projection of the instantaneous field of view of the array on the ground rotates as the scan angle increases. These effects are discussed below; the mechanism of resolution change in direction of aircraft travel as a function of angle of view, away from the vertical is sketched in Figure 14-3.

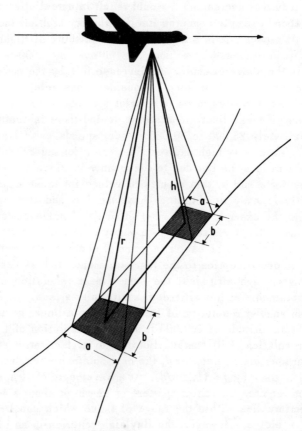

Fig. 14-3. Ground-resolution variation (*from Proc. IRE, September 1959*).

In Figure 14-3 and what follows, a flat-earth approximation is assumed. The angle away from vertical is designated by θ, r is the range from the scanner to the earth at any instant, and a is the length of the instantaneous field of view in the direction of aircraft travel. It can be seen from the figure that $a = \sigma r$, and $r = h \sec \theta$, so that

$$a = \lambda h \sec \theta \qquad (14\text{-}23)$$

To obtain an expression for the change in the other dimension of the instantaneous field of view as a function of θ, refer to Figure 14-4. From this figure:

$$S_2 = h \tan(\theta + \phi) = h \frac{\tan \phi + \tan \theta}{1 - \tan \phi \tan \theta}$$

$$S_1 = h \tan(\theta - \phi) = h \frac{\tan \theta - \tan \phi}{1 + \tan \theta \tan \phi}$$

But $\tan \phi \approx \phi$ for small ϕ; therefore,

$$S_2 \approx h \frac{\phi + \tan \phi}{1 - \phi \tan \theta}$$

$$S_1 \approx h \frac{\tan \theta - \phi}{1 + \phi \tan \theta}$$

$$b = S_2 - S_1 \approx 2h\phi \frac{1 + \tan^2 \theta}{1 - \phi^2 \tan^2 \theta}$$

For values of θ not more than $85°$, $\tan \theta$ is not much larger than 10. Since ϕ is about 10^{-3} rad, $\phi^2 \tan^2 \theta$ can be ignored. Thus,

$$b \approx h\sigma(1 + \tan^2 \theta) = h\sigma \sec^2 \theta \qquad (14\text{-}24)$$

We therefore have the results that the field of view changes as the $\sigma h \sec \theta$ in one direction and $\sigma h \sec^2 \theta$ in the other.

It is also true that, when a linear detector array is used with a rotating prism scanner of the type discussed here (i.e., with prism faces inclined at $45°$ to the axis of prism rotation), the projection of the elements of

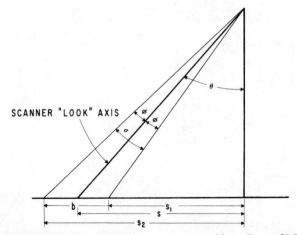

SCANNER "LOOK" AXIS

Fig. 14-4. Geometry of ground-resolution variation (*from Proc. IRE, September 1959*).

the linear array upon a flat earth rotates as the projection moves laterally to the aircraft flight path. The angle of rotation of the projected array elements is very nearly equal to the angle θ away from the vertical through which the element prism face has rotated.

14.4.4 *Aperture Effects in Scanning*

14.4.4.1 *Qualitative Treatment.* In any scanning device having a finite viewing aperture, the aperture geometry and the nature of the scanned signal interact to limit the scanning process. It is desirable that the equipment designer understand the nature of that interaction in order to minimize the undesirable effects on the scanning process, and, in special circumstances, take advantage of the effect. In the special case of searching for small bright targets in a cluttered background, the effect can be used to advantage, as described in Appendix A. The nature of the aperture-signal interaction will be described first qualitatively and then analytically.

The mechanism of aperture-signal interaction may be qualitatively illustrated by considering a small number of idealized signals. The signals to be considered are illustrated in Figure 14-5. Consider the same

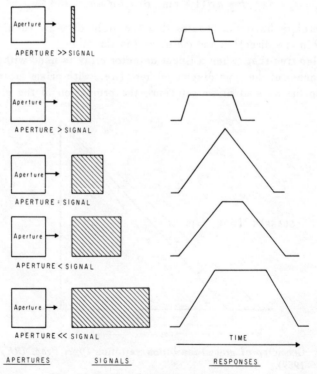

Fig. 14-5. Signal-aperture interaction.

aperture passing in turn over each of the five signals. The response curves are plots of relative power passing through the aperture as a function of time. The process may be considered to occur in either object space or image space. In the former case, the examples would represent the motion of the projection of an aperture over a real target signal. In the latter case, the examples would represent the motion of a real aperture over a target signal image. Assume the targets to be radiating energy and surrounded by a nonradiating environment.

In all cases, when the aperture moves at the rate of one length unit per second, the total length of the response will be equal to the width of the signal plus the width of the aperture.

In the case where aperture is wider than the signal, the response is very nearly a square wave with slightly canted skirts. As the signal length is increased, both the height and length of the response increase, the sloping skirts occupying more and more of the total response length. Finally, when aperture equals signal, the response has become triangular of length equal to twice the aperture length. Up to this point, the response amplitude has been determined by the signal area assuming that all signals radiate the same amount per unit area. As the signal length increases beyond the point at which it equals the aperture width, the response amplitude does not change but the response length does. In this region, the response amplitude is established by the aperture area.

From the foregoing, the following types of conclusions can be drawn. If an aperture is being scanned in search of a small bright target, and if target existence is to be inferred from response amplitude, there is no loss in making the aperture smaller until it matches the size of the target. Beyond that point, further reduction in aperture size will cause a reduction of response amplitude. This assumes that no time integration of the response is employed, which is, in general, true in current devices. If the target lies in a background of objects of larger size, the optimum aperture size is the one just equaling the target size, for at that point no target response amplitude has as yet been sacrificed, but the response amplitudes of background objects larger than the target have been reduced. In general, it can be said that the technique of matching the aperture size to that of the target will permit some enhancement of signal contrast between a target and background objects of larger size and lesser brightness.

14.4.4.2 *Analytic Treatment*. A more refined method of describing aperture-signal interaction is available. It has the advantage of being analytic, and suggests the possibility of other methods of discrimination.

The analytic method is essentially identical with certain techniques employed in electrical circuit theory. An electrical signal is frequently described as a function of amplitude and time. By Fourier methods, the same electrical signal may be given an equivalent description in terms of amplitude and frequency (i.e., cycles per unit time) or, at the sacrifice of phase information, in terms of power and frequency. A static space signal may be expressed as a function of amplitude and a space parameter, usually length. That formulation is identical with the expression of electrical signals, save that length plays the role occupied by time in the electrical case. Likewise, the space signal case is amenable to an equivalent description obtained by Fourier methods. In that case, the space signal is described in terms of amplitude and space frequencies or, with sacrifice of phase information, in terms of power and space frequencies. A space frequency differs from a time frequency only in that it is a measure of cycles, or waves, per unit length rather than per unit time. Here again the only difference from the electrical case is that length replaces time as a parameter.

To analyze aperture-signal interaction, consider an idealized space signal composed of a single space frequency. Such a signal is sketched in Figure 14-6. The amplitude of the space signal is given by

$$A = S \text{ in } 2\pi k x + 1 \tag{14-25}$$

where k is the number of cycles per unit length. Consider the cross-hatched area to be radiating uniformly and the unhatched area not radiat-

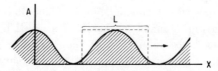

Fig. 14-6. Aperture-scanning sinusoidal signal.

ing. If an aperture of length L is scanned along that signal, the response R, or the amount of radiation passing through the aperture when its center is at x, is given by

$$R = \int_{x-(L/2)}^{x+(L/2)} [\sin 2\pi k \, \xi + 1] \, d\xi$$

$$= \left[-\frac{1}{2\pi k} \cos 2\pi k \, \xi + \xi \right]_{x-(L/2)}^{x+(L/2)} \tag{14-26}$$

$$= -\frac{1}{2\pi k} \left[\cos \left(2\pi kx + 2\pi k \frac{L}{2} \right) - \cos \left(2\pi kx - 2\pi k \frac{L}{2} \right) + L \right]$$

Using the cosine addition law, this becomes

$$R = (\sin \pi k L / \pi k) \, S \text{ in } 2\pi k x + L \tag{14-27}$$

As the aperture moves, the term L remains constant while the trigonometric term varies. Since most scanning infrared equipments make use of the varying component only, the term L will not be discussed further.

For a given k and L, the alternating component of R will be sinusoidal. If k is held fixed and larger L are considered, i.e., if the effect of larger apertures is considered, it is obvious that for some L, no ac will be generated. That will occur when the product kL is an integer making sin $\pi kL = 0$. In other words, for fixed k, changing the size of L will cause a periodic variation in R due to the term sin πkL.

Of more interest is the effect of changing k while holding L fixed. The effect on the term sin $2\pi kx$ is merely to change the frequency. The effect on the term sin $\pi kL/\pi k$ is, first, to shift the points at which zeros occur, and second, to decrease the size of the term as k grows larger since

$$\lim_{k \to \infty} \frac{\sin \pi kL}{\pi k} = 0.$$

A sketch of this behavior is shown in Figure 14-7. This curve is characteristic of those encountered in electrical filter theory. Hence, it is said that "space filtering" occurs.

It is because of the above method of analysis that efforts have been made to describe targets and backgrounds in terms of their space-frequency distributions in space. The resemblance of the aperture-signal interaction to electrical filter theory suggests using aperture characteristics to suppress unwanted signals, thus increasing target-background contrast.

14.4.5 *Digression on Choppers, Reticles, and Wiener Spectra*

14.4.5.1 *Introduction.* In infrared applications it is frequently useful to periodically interrupt the radiation at some point in the optical path within a device. The technique is not often employed in mapping devices but is, in many cases, very important in measuring and tracking devices. Choppers and reticles are, in general, employed for the following purposes:

1. To permit the detector and associated electronics to operate in some well-defined frequency band.

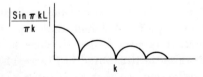

Fig. 14-7. Square aperture filter function.

2. To provide a means of rapid and frequent instrument calibration.

3. To provide target positional information.

4. To provide optimal use of contrast between targets and backgrounds.

The ability of a reticle to make use of target-background contrast depends, to a large extent, on the scanning aperture-signal interaction discussed in Section 14.4.4. As remarked there, the analytical treatment is facilitated if the signal or scene to be scanned is described in terms of a space-frequency power distribution or Wiener spectrum. Therefore, a discussion of Wiener spectra is included as part of the description of reticles used for discrimination.

Section 14.4.5 treats the simple chopper, the tracking reticle, and the discrimination reticle, in that order.

14.4.5.2 *The Simple Chopper.* The sources observed by many infrared tracking and measuring devices, such as radiometers and spectrometers, frequently do not fluctuate at rapid rates. Under those circumstances, the electrical signal from the infrared detector will be steady or fluctuating at very low frequencies. Since electronic circuits of high gain and stability are more easily constructed at somewhat higher frequencies where tuned circuit techniques can be employed, the radiation entering such infrared devices is often chopped, or interrupted, at an appropriate rate before falling on the infrared detector. For mechanical reasons the chopper most often takes the form of a slotted circular disc rotated about its axis of symmetry; a typical chopper is sketched in Figure 14-8. An additional reason for chopping the radiation is that some detectors generate more noise at very low electrical frequencies than they do at somewhat higher frequencies. Therefore, provided that the detector frequency response is not exceeded, chopping may result in increased signal-to-noise ratio.

When an infrared device is employed to make quantitative measurements of radiation, the questions of calibration and stability become crucial. In practice, stability is more easily obtained in quasi-blackbody calibration sources than it is in the electronic circuitry associated with the infrared device. Therefore, it is desirable to calibrate the device repeatedly at periods short with respect to the drift rate of the device electronics. For measurements of reasonable precision, that means recalibration at intervals of every few seconds. The most practical means of achieving such high calibration rates is to cause the instrument to view alternately the source of interest and the calibration source, and to measure the difference signal. Although that can be accomplished by nodding the instrument, it is most frequently done by means of a simple chopper, one form of which is illustrated in Figure 14-9. The chopper in this case is highly reflecting, so that as it rotates, the detector is exposed alternately to the target source and the calibration source. The

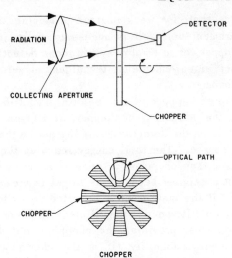

RADIATION

DETECTOR

COLLECTING APERTURE

CHOPPER

OPTICAL PATH

CHOPPER

CHOPPER
FRONT VIEW

Fig. 14-8. Simple chopper.

rate of rotation of the reflecting chopper will place the detector output
signal in the desired frequency band.

The simple reflecting chopper is also useful in instruments designed
for the detection or measurement of targets of small dimensions having
low contrast with their surroundings. In that application the reflecting
chopper may be employed to cause the instrument to view alternately, at
a rapid rate, the target and an equal-sized sector of its surround. Here
again, the effects of instrument fluctuations are to some extent canceled
by measuring or detecting the difference signal.

The simple slotted disc type of chopper is usually made with equal
numbers of transparent and opaque sectors of equal size, and the chopper
is usually not placed in an image plane. Under these circumstances the
power reaching the detector may be reduced by as much as 50 per cent,
depending on the angle of convergence of the rays, as compared to a
similar system without a chopper because of obscuration in the optical

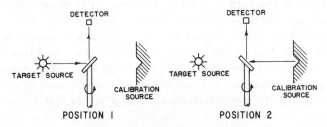

DETECTOR

DETECTOR

TARGET SOURCE

CALIBRATION
SOURCE

TARGET SOURCE

CALIBRATION
SOURCE

POSITION I

POSITION 2

Fig. 14-9. Reflecting chopper.

path. This means that, for weak sources producing signals not much greater than instrument noise, it is necessary either to forego the advantages of a chopper, or to employ synchronous detection, signal integration, and other signal-enhancing techniques developed by spectroscopists and astronomers.

The simple silvered chopper is also seldom placed in an image plane. However, unlike the slotted-disc chopper, it causes no reduction in radiant power falling on the detector during the period that the instrument views the target source. The total energy reaching the detector in any time interval longer than one chop is reduced as compared to a similar instrument without a chopper because the target is viewed only intermittently. Therefore, if the instrument is operated so as to measure power level, there will be no difference in the efficiencies of comparable chopped and unchopped systems, providing the chopping rate does not exceed the detector's frequency capability. If, on the other hand, the instrument is operated so as to measure total target energy falling on the detector by some form of integration over a time longer than a single chop, the chopped system will be less efficient than a comparable unchopped system.

14.4.5.3 *The Tracking Reticle.* An infrared target-tracking device will normally have an instantaneous field of view (i.e., collect radiation from an area) somewhat larger than the target being tracked. It is essential to the tracking operation that the device be able to sense the position of the target within the instantaneous field of view. Among the several methods of sensing target location is the use of a tracking reticle which is a chopper designed to give positional information. In general, tracking reticles are similar to the simple chopper in that they consist of a disc having alternate transparent and opaque sectors, the disc being rotated about its axis of symmetry. Unlike the simple chopper, the tracking reticle must be located in an image plane since it operates on a target image. The tracking reticle is capable of generating two positional coordinates of a target image: radial distance of target image from reticle axis of rotation, and an angular coordinate giving the position of the target image with respect to some fixed reference line in the reticle plane passing through the reticle axis of rotation. The former may be converted into the angle between the optical axis of the device and the line of sight between target and tracker. The latter indicates directly the angular direction of the target in a plane polar coordinate system centered on the tracker's optical axis and lying in a plane perpendicular to that axis. Those two coordinates provide sufficient information to permit the tracker to reorient itself so that it points directly toward the target.

There are many reticle patterns which will provide tracking information. One of the simplest is a disc having a single slot, illustrated in Figure

14-10.   The presence of a target image in the reticle plane will result in a detector response consisting of a sequence of essentially square pulses if the target image is very small. If the sides of the transparent strip of the reticle are parallel, the time duration of each square pulse will be a measure of the distance of the target image from the reticle axis.   If a reference signal is generated each time the reticle returns to some specific position, the relative phases of the target and reference pulses will be a measure of the angle between the reference line and a line from the reticle axis through the target image.   The number of different reticle patterns capable of generating target positional information about the target is limited only by the designer's imagination.   For instance, the angular displacement of the target image from the reference line may be obtained from a reticle having many transparent slots of

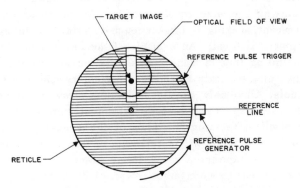

Fig. 14-10. Simple tracking reticle.

monotonically decreasing width and spacing around the disc. The target pulse width, spacing, and repetition rate would then vary cyclically, so that type of reticle is termed frequency modulated.

Since it must lie in an image plane, and providing the chopping rate does not exceed the detector's frequency-response capability, the tracking reticle will cause no reduction in target power reaching the detector. as compared to a similar system without a reticle, during those periods when the transparent sector is over the target image.

14.4.5.4 *The Discrimination Reticle.* An essential conclusion of Section 14.4.4 is that, for targets surrounded by background sources of larger sizes, a scanning aperture just matching the target in size will provide maximum target-background signal contrast. There are important applications where, due to other considerations, the aperture must be made considerably larger than the target image, resulting in loss of target-background signal contrast. Under those circumstances, a discrimination reticle may permit recovery of some of the contrast lost because of the necessity of using a scanning aperture of larger than optimum size. It should be emphasized that no reticle will provide more contrast than is available from an aperture matched to the target.

An example of an application requiring a larger-than-optimum scanning aperture is a device for detecting small, rapidly moving targets. Such a device might be employed for aircraft collision avoidance. The requirement is to scan some relatively large volume repeatedly at a high rate since the targets will be moving rapidly. The time in which one scan over the entire volume must be made can easily be so short that, if the scanning aperture were matched in size to the targets, the information rate would exceed the frequency-response capability of the infrared detector. Under those circumstances two solutions are possible: the use of a number of identical scanning units each with aperture matched to target size and capable of covering some subvolume in the required time; or relaxing the size requirement on the scanning aperture of a single instrument, making it large enough to bring the information rate down to a practical level. An example of the former appears in Section 14.4.2, illustrating that in many cases it is not necessary to duplicate entire equipments, but only to replicate detectors and associated electronic channels. Obviously, the linear-detector-array technique described there can be extended to two-dimensional detector arrays if useful. The second possibility, relaxing the size of the scanning aperture or instantaneous field of view, will entail loss of target-background contrast because the larger aperture, in an image plane, will admit additional background power but no more target power. A discrimination reticle may permit recovery of some of the lost contrast. Thus, the role of the discrimination reticle is apparent; it may, in certain applications, provide a means of avoiding the complexity of multiple channels without suffering the loss of an impractical amount of target contrast.

The action of a discrimination reticle is based on the aperture effects discussed in Section 14.4.4. Consider the example sketched in Figure 14-11. The viewing circle must be scanned at a rate greater than is permissible with instantaneous field of view matched to target image. Chopping with a reticle of many fine spokes permits sampling power from all parts of the image in the time taken to rotate one spoke width. Each spoke constitutes a narrow scanning aperture which discriminates against objects wider than the spoke, by the mechanism of Section 14.4.4. It is apparent that the spoke widths should match the size of the target image. Inspection of the sketch indicates the reasons that a reticle is unlikely to recover all of the contrast which could have been obtained by scanning with a small aperture matched to target image. First, although one dimension of a reticle spoke matches target image size, the radial dimension is much larger, providing little discrimination in that dimension.

Second, a single target can illuminate part of only one spoke at a time while all spokes are illuminated by background.

In preparation for a description of analytic methods appropriate to treatment of realistic reticles, consider the special case illustrated in Figure 14-12. The upper graph is an amplitude plot of a one-dimensional radiance distribution, $o(x)$, which is the object to be scanned. It is a particularly simple distribution being 1 in a very small region around x_o and zero elsewhere. (To be perfectly rigorous, $o(x)$ should be defined as a δ-function.) The center graph is a plot of the transmission $r(u)$ of a simple asymmetric one-dimensional aperture. The aperture-scanning action is effected by translating the orgion of the u coordinate system along the object-space coordinate system x. The lower graph is a plot

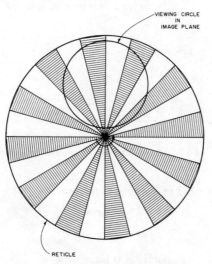

Fig. 14-11. Discrimination reticle.

of the radiant energy $d(x)$ falling on a detector placed behind the aperture and collecting all the object space energy passing through the aperture. The $d(x)$ plot is constructed as follows: assuming unit magnification in this simplified system, the detector's coordinate system will differ from the object's coordinate system only in being located on the other side of the aperture. At any instant the aperture will be considered to be pointing at that position x in object space at which the zero of the u coordinate system is located. At that instant, the amplitude of the integrated energy passing through the aperture will be plotted as a point located at coordinate x in the d coordinate system. As in the previous aperture example, the aperture is considered to be in the object-space plane, so that a single object point will not illuminate the entire aperture.

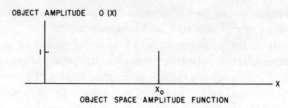

OBJECT SPACE AMPLITUDE FUNCTION

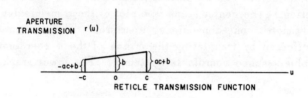

RETICLE TRANSMISSION FUNCTION

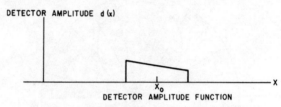

DETECTOR AMPLITUDE FUNCTION

Fig. 14-12. Delta function response of aperture.

The object function $o(x)$ is loosely expressed as

$$o(x) = 0 \text{ for } x < x_o$$
$$o(x) = 1 \text{ for } x = x_o \tag{14-28}$$
$$o(x) = 0 \text{ for } x_o < x$$

therefore

$$o(x) = o(x_o)$$

The aperture function $r(u)$ is

$$r = 0 \text{ for } u < -c$$
$$r = au + b \text{ for } -c \leqslant u \leqslant +c \tag{14-29}$$
$$r = 0 \text{ for } +c < u$$

Then the detector function will be

$$d(x) = [a(x_o - x) + b] o(x_o)$$

or
$$\tag{14-30}$$

$$dx = r(x_o - x) o(x_o)$$

Thus the result of scanning a point source with an aperture is a function similar to the aperture function, differing from it only in being inverted and multiplied by the amplitude of the object function.

If $0(x)$ consists of a number of point functions at different locations $d(x)$ will be given by

$$d(x) = \sum_{j} r(x_j - x) 0(x_j) \tag{14-31}$$

and in the limit of a continuous object function,

$$d(x) = \int_{-\infty}^{\infty} r(x' - x) 0(x') \, dx' \tag{14-32}$$

The output or response of an aperture to a point function input is quite analogous to the response of an electrical filter to an impulse input.

One of the ways of specifying the performance or quality of a lens is to specify its blur circle. A complete specification of blur circle involves a quantitative description of image-plane light distribution resulting from a point source in the object plane. The effect of blur circle is identical to scanning with an aperture having transmission function identical to the blur-circle function. Thus, the effects of optical-system imperfections may be treated by means of the above methods.

Now, consider a two-dimensional reticle of finite dimensions having any configuration $R(u, v)$, where (u, v) is a rectangular Cartesian coordinate system fixed in the reticle. Take the reticle to lie in an image plane (x, y), where x and y are parallel to u and v. For simplicity, assume the reticle to be scanning linearly in the x direction without rotating. Assume an image plane radiation distribution $I(x, y)$ resulting from the focusing of an object-plane's distribution function $O(x, y)$ through a lens with blur function $B(u, v)$. The same nomenclature is used for image- and object-plane coordinate systems since unit magnification is assumed, and the two systems are considered to be parallel to and fixed with respect to each other. The same relationships are assumed to hold between the reticle and lens coordinate systems.

If we generalize the above one-dimensional theory to two dimensions in an obvious way, the following equations describe the performance of the scanning system.

$$I(x, y) = \iint_{-\infty}^{\infty} B[(\xi - x), (n - y)] \, 0(\xi, n) \, d\,\xi dn \tag{14-33}$$

$$D(x, y) = \iint_{-\infty}^{\infty} R[(x' - x), (y', y)] \, I(x', y) \, dx'dy'$$

where D is the detector irradiance as a function of the object-space point (x, y) at which the instrument is pointed.

These equations have the form of the two-dimensional convolution integral. Therefore, we can write those expressions in terms of the two-dimensional Fourier transforms $F_0 (k_1, k_2)$, etc. as

$$F_I(k_1, k_2) = F_B (k_1, k_2) F_0 (k_1, k_2)$$

$$F_D (k_1, k_2) = F_R (k_1, k_2) F_I (k_1, k_2)$$

$$= F_R (k_1, k_2) F_B (k_1, k_2) F_0 (k_1, k_2) \qquad (14\text{-}34)$$

where

$$F_D = \int_{-x_2/2}^{x_2/2} \int_{-y_2/2}^{y_2/2} e^{2\pi i(k_1 x + k_2 y)} D (x, y) \, dx dy$$

$$F_R = \int_{-\infty}^{\infty} \int_{-\infty}^{\infty} e^{2\pi i(k_1 u + k_2 v)} R (u, v) \, du dv$$

$$F_I = \int_{-x_1/2}^{x_1/2} \int_{-y_1/2}^{y_1/2} e^{2\pi i(k_1 x + k_2 y)} I (x, y) \, dx dy \qquad (14\text{-}35)$$

$$F_B = \int_{-\infty}^{\infty} \int_{-\infty}^{\infty} e^{2\pi i(k_1 u + k_2 v)} B (u, v) \, du dv$$

$$F = \int_{-x_0/2}^{x_0/2} \int_{-y_0/2}^{y_0/2} e^{2\pi i(k_1 x + k_2 y)} O (x, y) \, dx dy$$

In those cases with limits other than $\pm\infty$ the transforms do not converge for nonfinite regions.

The variables k_1 and k_2 remain to be elucidated. In electrical circuit theory, where similar methods are employed, the Fourier transform of a function of time t results in a function of frequency f having for its dimensions cycles per unit time. Analogously here, the Fourier transform of a function of x and y having length as its dimension results in a function of variables k_1 and k_2 having for its dimension cycles per unit length. The variables k_1 and k_2 are called wave numbers, and $F_D (k_1, k_2)$ is a wave-number spectrum giving the amplitude per unit wave-number interval; i.e., $F_D (k_1, k_2)$ has the dimensions

$$F_D (k_1, k_2) \sim (\text{amplitude}/k_1, k_2) \qquad (14\text{-}36)$$

The form of Eq. (14-36), in analogy to electrical circuit equations, suggests the terminology "space filtering" for the action of reticles and optical imperfections; i.e., the output signal function F_D equals the input signal function F_0, multiplied by the gain functions F_B and F_R of two filters in series.

For reasons to be clarified shortly it will be found more convenient to work with a quantity $M_D(k_1, k_2)$ rather than with F_D directly. M_D and and M_o are defined as follows:

$$M_D(k_1, k_2) = \lim_{A \to \infty} \frac{1}{A} |F_D(k_1, k_2)|^2$$

$$M_o(k_1, k_2) = \lim_{A \to \infty} \frac{1}{A} |F_0(k_1, k_2)|^2$$

(14-37)

where $A = \Delta x \Delta y$ and Δx and Δy are the finite intervals over which $D(x, y)$ and $O(x, y)$ are integrated in forming the transforms F_D and F_o.

Quantities similar to M_D and M_o occur in electrical circuit theory and represent electrical power spectra. Therefore, M_D and M_o are, effectively, space-frequency or wave-number power spectra. However, rather than employ a special name for them, we will use the term Wiener spectra to designate the general class of power spectra of that form irrespective of the type of frequencies involved. The term Wiener spectra was coined and applied in this fashion by Dr. R. Clark Jones in recognition of the work of Dr. Norbert Wiener in the branch of mathematics involved. In the preparation of this material on reticles, the authors are indebted to Dr. Jones for the opportunity to read his notes for an as yet unpublished book on the use of Wiener spectrum methods.

Applying the definitions of M_D and M_0 to Eq. (14-34) results in the following:

$$M_D(k_1, k_2) = \lim_{A \to \infty} \frac{1}{A} |F_D(k_1, k_2)|^2 = \lim_{A \to \infty} \frac{1}{A} |F_R(k_1, k_2) \, F_I(k_1, k_2) \times$$

$$F_0(k_1, k_2)|^2$$

but the limit process does not affect F_R and F_B since in forming those transforms the region of integration was $\pm\infty$. Therefore

$$M_D(k_1, k_2) = |F_R(k_1, k_2)|^2 \, |F_B(k_1, k_2)|^2 \lim_{A \to \infty} \frac{1}{A} |F_0(k_1, k_2)|^2$$

or

$$M_D(k_1, k_2) = |F_R(k_1, k_2)|^2 \, |F_B(k_1, k_2)|^2 \, M_0(k_1, k_2) \qquad (14\text{-}38)$$

This equation may be used in two ways. Given a specific target or background Wiener spectrum M_0, the equation may be employed to compute an expected device response M_D. In the case of backgrounds it will not usually be possible to specify M_0 analytically in advance. Under those circumstances, a series of measurements may be made producing a measured spectrum M_D. Then Eq. (14-38) may be used to compute the true background spectrum M_0 for use in assessing the performance of other instruments.

Although it will not be discussed here, there is a close relationship between the Wiener spectrum M_0 of an object-space function $0(x,y)$ and the autocorrelation of such a function $0(x,y)$. The Wiener spectrum and the autocorrelation may be computed directly each from the other: they constitute a Fourier pair—each is the transform of the other.

In order to understand the effects of the scanning motion of an infrared instrument, consider for a moment an aperture scanning a simple signal consisting of a single space frequency k_{1a}, i.e., a sine wave of k_{1a} cycles per unit distance along the object-space x axis. If the aperture scans at a rate s linear units per second, the detector illumination will vary at a rate f cycles per second, given by

$$f = sk_{1a} \tag{14-39}$$

If a number of space frequencies are present in a band Δk_1, then a band of frequencies Δf will result in

$$\Delta f = s\Delta k_1 \tag{14-40}$$

The dimensions of $M_D(k_1,k_2)$ are radiant power per unit wavelength interval, i.e.,

$$M_D(k_1,k_2) \sim (\text{radiant power}/k_1 k_2)$$

To express this in terms of frequency for scanning in the x_0 direction, then, it is necessary to write $(1/s) M_D(f/s, k_2)$ which has the dimensions

$$(1/s) M_D(f/s, k_2) \sim (\text{radiant power}/fk_2)$$

Inasmuch as the example under consideration involves no scanning in the y direction there will be no separation of the k_2 wave-number effects in terms of frequency. Therefore, the time variation of the signal falling on the detector, $M_D(f)$ is given by integrating Eq. (14-38) over k_2.

$$M_D(f) = (1/s) \int_{-\infty}^{\infty} M_D(f/s, k_2) dk_2$$

$$M_D(f) = (1/s) \int_{-\infty}^{\infty} |F_R(f/s, k_2)|^2 |F_B(f/s, k_2)|^2 M_0(f/s, k_2) dk_2 \tag{14-41}$$

$M_D(f)$ is the radiant power per unit bandwidth at a frequency f falling on the detector. Then the electrical power output of the detector is given by

$$E(f) = |K|^2 M_D(f) = |k|^2/s \int_{-\infty}^{\infty} |F_R(f/s, k_2)|^2 |F_B(f/s, k_2)|^2 \times$$

$$M_0(f/s, k_2) dk_2 \quad (14\text{-}42)$$

where K is a factor containing the detector responsivity, amplifier gain, function, etc. This is the key result of this section. It is an expression of the detector electrical power output spectrum as a function of detector and electrical system characteristic K, optical system characteristics F_R and F_B, and object-space Wiener spectrum M_0.

The Wiener spectrum is particularly useful as a means of describing backgrounds because it permits averaging over a large number of specific background measurements. Specification of backgrounds in terms of functions $0(x, y)$, or their transforms $F_0(k_1, k_2)$, does not permit simple averaging since both are complex functions. The squaring process involved in the formation of the Wiener spectra M_0 and M_D does, however, involve a loss of phase information. As a result, given its Wiener spectrum, a background cannot be reconstructed in all detail. The Wiener spectrum will provide a correct measure of the mean square signal generated by a background or target and is applicable wherever the mean square signal is the important consideration. The Wiener spectrum will not be useful for highly nonrandom backgrounds where it is possible to capitalize strongly on shape information.

This section has presented a very brief outline of methods for the treatment of discrimination reticles including the Wiener spectrum method of describing targets and backgrounds. The application of these methods will involve many details and subtitles not discussed.

14.5 Information Display

A common method of displaying the information from an air-to-ground scanner is to display it line by line, as it was scanned, on the face of a cathode-ray tube which is then photographed by a continous strip camera. This method brings up two problems: compression of the information at the edges of the strip scanned, and the question of whether the cathode-ray tube presentation should repeat the same information redundancy observed at the edges of the scanned strip due to the increasing instantaneous linear field of view at the edges.

The usual, and simplest, method of recording is to devote the same amount of film width to equal angular increments of information in a line, i.e., to use a linear sawtooth deflection voltage on the cathode-ray tube. Since the linear ground distance corresponding to a given angular interval changes with the angle of viewing the ground, this method introduces some distortion in the final record. The distortion takes the form of a compression in one dimension, at right angles to the flight path, and becomes progressively more pronounced towards the edges of the strip. In scanners covering total scan angles of 60° and 90° this effect is present, but hardly noticeable. In a 180° scanner, the effect is very pronounced, the principal noticeable effect being that all straight lines diagonal to the vehicle flight path appear as S-shaped curves. A corrected print for a 20-mile-wide strip on the ground can be made, but it involves a very wide print. At the center of the picture, the linear resolution is finest. In a scanner with a σ of 3 mrad operated at an altitude of 1000 ft, there will be 3 ft of ground covered by each instantaneous field of view. That sets the scale factor of the print if no information is to be sacrificed. Assume a print paper with a resolution of 40 lines/mm or 1000 lines/in. Three feet of ground information must be devoted to each line; i.e., the print will have a scale of 3000 ft/in. Twenty nautical miles is 120,000 ft, so the print width must be

$$\frac{120,000}{3000} = 40 \text{ in. wide}$$

truly an unwieldy print, but unavoidable if scale-factor correction without information loss is required.

As mentioned and sketched earlier, the scanner's instantaneous field of view covers progressively greater ground areas as it moves towards the edge of the strip being scanned. As a consequence, there will be progressively increasing overlap toward the edges if the scanner is operated for zero overlap directly under the scanner. This brings up the question of whether similar overlap should be incorporated in the display. It can be shown that this is not necessarily desirable, with the result that the simpler method of recording with lines of constant width may be used.

Consider a thin strip of the ground out to the side of the vehicle flight line and running parallel to the flight line. Successive scan lines will overlap by as much as 90 per cent. Designate the true ground signal function along that strip as $P(x)$ where x is a coordinate along the strip. Also ignore all losses and system irregularities, i.e., assume that $P(x)$ is sensed directly by the scanner. On the first line of scan, the device will sense the integrated energy from $x = a$ to $x = a + L$, where L is the linear dimension of the instantaneous field of view along x. The scanner signal will be

$$\int_a^{a+L} P(x)\,dx$$

On the succeeding line, the instantaneous field of view will be advanced along x a distance $1/10\ L$ and the signal from the strip will be

$$\int_{a+1/10L}^{a+11/10\ L} P\left(x\right)dx$$

and so on. Note that $1/10\ L$ is just the width of a line directly below the vehicle.

Now, assume that the scanner output from each line is displayed over a corresponding length L of the final display so that the same type of overlap occurs. There will be a small section of the print which receives energy from lines 1 through 10. Its integrated signal will be

$$\sum_{i=0}^{9}\int_{a+(i/10)L}^{a+[(10+i)/10]L} P\left(x\right)dx \qquad (14\text{-}43)$$

The adjacent spot of similar dimensions in the direction of increasing x will have as its integrated signal

$$\sum_{i=0}^{9}\int_{a+[(i+1)/10]L}^{a+[(11+i)/10]L} P\left(x\right)dx \qquad (14\text{-}44)$$

In both these, an attenuation factor due to the fact that only $1/10$ that energy is actually distributed over the spot in question has been neglected as not significant to the argument. Now, assuming that information is contained principally in the difference in signal from adjacent spots, the resemblance of the displayed contrast to actual contrast over the interval $x = a + 9/10\ L$ to $x = a + L$; i.e.,

$$\int_{x+L}^{x+11/10\ L} P\left(x\right)dx - \int_{x+9/10\ L}^{x+L} P\left(x\right)dx$$

can be obtained by taking the difference between Eqs. (14-43) and (14-44):

$$\int_{a+[(i+1)/10]L}^{a+[(11+i)/10]L} P\left(x\right)dx - \int_{a+(i/10)L}^{a+[(10+i)/10]L} P\left(x\right)dx$$

$$= \int_{a+L}^{a+2L} P\left(x\right)dx - \int_{a}^{a+L} P\left(x\right)dx \qquad (14\text{-}45)$$

Thus, it is apparent that, in the contrast between two adjacent print spots $1/10L$ long, energy from ground positions over a strip $2L$ long are mixed. So the effective resolution would appear to be $2L$ along x in the display.

On the other hand, if as is common practice, the information is displayed in nonoverlapping lines of constant width, which does not correspond to the manner in which the information was observed, adjacent print elements will have the signals

$$\int_{a}^{a+L} P\,(x)\,dx \quad \text{and} \quad \int_{a+1/10\,L}^{a+11/10\,L} P\,(x)\,dx \qquad (14\text{-}46)$$

Taking the difference between these gives

$$\int_{a+1/10\,L}^{a+11/10\,L} P\,(x)\,dx - \int_{a}^{a+L} P\,(x)\,dx = \int_{a+L}^{a+11/10\,L} P\,(x)\,dx -$$

$$\int_{a}^{a+1/10\,L} P\,(x)\,dx \qquad (14\text{-}47)$$

In this case, information is mixed from a segment only $L + 1/10\,L$ long. This looks like an improvement, but is not necessarily so.

To examine the relative merits of the two methods consider $P\,(x)$ to consist of a uniform background with an intense point source in it. In the first method, the point source will be displayed over a section $2L$ long. It will not, however, be of uniform intensity over that interval. The intensity will be greatest in the center segment $1/10\,L$ long and will decrease linearly in both directions to an intensity of $1/10$ maximum at the extremities of the interval $2L$ long. In the second method, the point source will be displayed with uniform intensity over an interval $L + 1/10\,L$ long.

In the first case, the point target has been spread over a segment of the print $2L$ units long. The intensity is not, however, uniform, being greatest at the center and least at the edges, thus giving some indication of the center of the blurred spot. In the second case, the point target has been spread over a segment of the print only $L + 1/10\,L$ units long. In this case, the intensity is uniform, giving no clue as to the center of the blurred image. It would appear that there is little obvious reason to prefer either method other than considerations relative to ease of implementation.

14.6 Signal Processing for Resolution Enhancement

The redundancy in the information in the region where there is great overlap should be of use in improving the resolution. The fact that the above methods have not achieved this merely indicates that the methods were not sufficiently sophisticated. A potentially successful method is described below.

Take a one-dimensional signal $P(x)$ and scan it with an aperture of length L. In the initial or zeroth position of the aperture, let it observe a known, uniform signal of total value A (Figure 14-13). Consider the aperture to advance in steps $(1/M)L$ long and investigate whether pro-

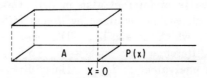

Fig. 14-13. Aperture scanning a one-dimensional signal.

cessing of the data before display can refine the resolution to $(1/M)L$. The signal S_0 in the zeroth aperture position will be

$$S_0 = A \tag{14-48}$$

When the aperture is in position 1, i.e., advanced by an amount $1/ML$, the integrated energy coming through the aperture will be just S_0 less a small amount $(1/M)A$ which passed out of the field of view over the trailing edge and plus a small signal,

$$i_1 = \int_0^{(1/M)L} P(x)\,dx \tag{14-49}$$

which entered the field of view at the leading edge. Thus

$$S_1 = S_0 - (1/M)A + i_1 \tag{14-50}$$

Now S_1 is measured as the detector output, $S_0 = A$ is known by assumption as is $(1/M)A$, so i_1 can be solved for

$$i_1 = S_1 - S_0 + (1/M)A \tag{14-51}$$

But i_1 is just a measure of the signal $P(x)$ over an interval $1/ML$, so, in at least the first step, resolution finer than the instantaneous field is obtainable. It is obvious that for the first M steps, i.e., as long as some part of A is within the field of view, the same method applies, so in general

$$i_n = S_n - S_{n-1} + (1/M)A \tag{14-52}$$

for $0 < n < M$. At the $(M + 1)$st step a new signal i_{M+1} enters the field of view over the leading edge, but the signal leaving the field of view over the trailing edge is no longer $(1/M)A$. The signal leaving is, however, i_1, or just the signal that entered over the leading edge on the Mth previous step. Thus, we can write by induction

$$i_n = S_n - S_{n-1} + i_{n-M} \qquad (14\text{-}53)$$

for $m < n$. So, at least theoretically, the redundancy in the measurements S_n can be used to refine the information.

The last equation is of interest also in that it establishes the limit of improvement which can be obtained by signal differentiation or high-frequency boosting, which is similar. The essence of the derivative process lies in a difference term such as $S_n - S_{n-1}$, and differentiation introduces no term equivalent to i_{n-M}. Thus, differentiation cannot be expected to improve resolution beyond the instantaneous field of view, although it may heighten edge contrast. This is so because the differentiated signal retains the effects of both those signal increments entering and leaving the field of view which are separated by L and contains no term such as i_{n-M} to nullify one of those effects.

In the above method the effects of system noise tend to accumulate so the process cannot be carried on indefinitely. On the other hand, strip map scanners do not scan a single line indefinitely, but periodically start a new line of scan.

1. M. W. Makowski, "A Slide Rule for Radiation Calculations," *Rev. Sci. Instr.* **20**, 14-15 (1949). Another such instrument is a Radiation Calculator compiled by Optics and Color Engineering Component, General Engineering Laboratory, General Electric Company, Schenectady, New York.

INFRARED DESIGN PROBLEMS
ILLUSTRATING THE USE OF RETICLES*

A number of important functions which may be well performed by infrared equipments are discussed in Chapter 13 of this book. Chapter 14 includes a discussion of reticles and reticle properties which often make possible (or more simple) the design of equipment to perform these desired functions. The problems associated with equipment design may be identified and brought into a sharper focus by the calculation of a specific design problem. In this appendix a simple field-of-view manipulation is used to achieve background suppression, after which a two-color chopper is considered as an adjunct to improve the detection ability of the simple system; and then consideration is given to a tracking reticle.

The reticle method has seemed to be so simple and direct that, in the past, many infrared search designs were based upon it. The reticle can be thought to behave much like a matrix of detectors giving rise to sensitive and insensitive areas corresponding to the transparent and opaque areas of a reticle. The practical advantage of the reticle is that through the use of a simple optical system a relatively large field of view can be imaged on a reticle containing a relatively large number of transparent and opaque areas, while an auxiliary optical system, or field lens, uniformly distributes the radiation passing through such a reticle onto a single detector element. (See Section 7.10.) Thus, in practice, the equivalent of a matrix of detectors has been created in a simple device with but a single detector and amplifier. This simplicity is always to be considered whenever the amount of signal from the source is large enough that the optical losses and the increased NEP of the usually necessarily larger detector required for the episcotister do not reduce significantly the output of the detector.

The reticle, together with the field lens and detector, can be considered as a filter-detector package in which the optical losses of the

*Lucien Biberman, University of Chicago, Laboratories for Applied Sciences.

filter (in this case, a reticle) are possibly quite appreciable. The filter, however, can be very effective in improving the signal-to-noise ratio in a simple single-detector assembly by an appreciable amount, and thus is often desirable. It must be remembered, however, that the power loss due to insertion of the filter assembly gives rise to a substantial reduction in target signal at the output of the detector. Thus, even though the ratio of target signal to background noise is materially improved by such a device, the net result may be that the signal itself has been attenuated to a point where detection is no longer feasible.

In an attempt to locate an infrared source at distances where the irradiance from the source approaches the noise equivalent flux density of the detection system, one usually cannot afford the diluting action of the reticle and field lens, as well as the larger noise contribution coming from the relatively large fields of view in a wide-angle reticle system. For this limiting case where the irradiance from the target source approaches the noise equivalent flux density of the available detectors, the most direct system approach is to match approximately the area of the source image with the detector area of the search device.

Implicitly assumed in the preceding discussion is a necessary condition for use of a reticle detection system: relative motion between the source image and the reticle must occur at a fixed and definite rate. The sweeping of the source image over the bars of the reticle, or the bars of the detector matrix, produces a signal frequency which, when fed into the appropriate electrical filter, permits the selection of the target signal characteristics from the background signal characteristics produced by the transfer function inherent in the reticle design. It is this selective action in generating a specific frequency, followed by the action of a specific-frequency electrical filter in the electronic portion of the search device, that makes the reticle or matrix device so effective.

It should be pointed out that, in using the reticle-type search device, a designer should be able to take advantage of the large amount of experience in signal processing reported in the literature; he should be able to achieve quite sophisticated designs based upon past designs and other designers' experiences.

Let us consider a problem in which a small free balloon is to be tracked by triangulation. The balloon is expected to drift over considerable distances so that tracking is required at ranges up to about five miles. Two observation points are located one mile apart on the ground. It is desired that bearings be taken with an accuracy of approximately two minutes of arc. Sightings are to be recorded as a function of time, preferably automatically. Operation is to be under daylight conditions; the local conditions frequently show broken brightly sunlit clouds. The worst background conditions may be considered to involve the sun-illuminated surfaces of clouds, the reflectance of which is taken to be approximately 0.31. The reflected solar radiation is assumed to peak at 0.5 μ. A tungsten lamp has been chosen as the source which will be used as the tracking beacon. This lamp presents to the ground-based instruments the equivalent of a 10-mm^2 2620° C blackbody. No auxiliary optics are used with it.

Let us see how well we might do in designing a simple equipment to locate a balloon which carries this beacon. In Chapter 14 it is stated that the principal task of a search set is the location of a target within some element of space containing background; this is done by recognizing a particular element as distinct and different from all other similar elements of background which do not contain a target. In practice, the problem is often approached by reference to an arbitrary design criterion, in the form of a simple equation.

This equation has been derived by assuming the background to be composed of elements each of which match the projected field of view of the set to be designed. Further, we assume adjacent elements alternate being either a background of maximum radiance or zero radiance. These assumptions are very severe but yield conservative design values. In addition we require that the average radiance from a minimum background element plus a target must differ from that from a maximum background radiance element by an amount greater than the difference between two such elements with no target. In equation form we have:

$$J\tau/R^2 - \omega N_B \geq \omega N_B \quad \text{and thus,} \qquad \text{(A-1)}$$

$$J\tau/R^2 \geq 2\omega N_B. \qquad \text{(A-2)}$$

In this equation, J is the radiant intensity of the source, R is the range in centimeters, τ is the atmospheric transmission, ω is the angular field of view of the radiometer in steradians, and N_B is the maximum value of background radiance.

These criteria can be used to estimate the maximum range at which a set can be used, or, given demands for such a range, can be used to choose limiting values of field of view. Under some conditions this form of solution may place impossible demands on the angular resolution of the system, i.e., the fineness of the field of view. Under other conditions the field of view may be reasonable, but the time needed to search the required field may be excessive. Let us now begin to use some numerical values to get a better grasp of the importance of the quantities mentioned above to our problem.

The lamp filament at 2620° C is a source of approximately 13 watt ster^{-1} peaking at 1.0 μ. These data were calculated from the temperature and area of the filament, assuming for this problem: the emissivity is 1.0; the clouds are illuminated by the sun; the solar constant is 2.0 cal cm^{-2} min^{-1} at the surface of the earth, or approximately 0.13 watt cm^{-2}

The clouds therefore are illuminated by 0.13 watt cm^{-2} and reflect a portion determined by their reflectance (which for this problem is assumed to be 0.31). Let us further assume that the clouds reflect diffusely. Each cloud therefore appears to be a source whose radiance is

$$\frac{0.13 \text{ watt cm}^{-2}}{\pi} \times 0.31$$

or approximately 0.013 watt-cm^{-2} ster^{-1}.

Let us consider a broadband radiometer with a field of view 0.01 $\times$ 0.01 rad, and use Eq. (A-2) to determine how well we might do in finding our targets.

Equation (A-2) shows that

$$J\tau/R^2 \geq 2\,\omega N_B. \tag{A-3}$$

Substituting in this equation, we have

$$13/R^2 \geq 2\,(0.01 \times 0.01) \times 0.013.$$

Solving, we see that the effective range of this instrument in locating the specific source against the cloud background is approximately

$$\sqrt{5} \times 10^3 \text{ cm}$$

or about 75 ft.

Such a range is much less than we hoped for!

If we reduce the field of view, we can improve the performance. Let us consider reducing the field of view to about 0.05° $\times$ 0.05°, about 1 microsteradian. (It should be noted that we ignore atmospheric transmission which, in this broad, rather clear band, is not a very serious consideration.) Then the effective range is extended by a factor of about 10 to a new range of 750 ft. The range is still too small to permit both observation points to see the balloon at any one time. The field of view is so small that we really cannot hope to improve the range by more than a factor of 10 by going to a still smaller field of view. This factor implies a 10^{-8} ster field of view, which is quite close to the Rayleigh limit or the central Airey disc.

Further gains in instrument performance probably must be found by turning to other means. Let us now consider the selection of spectral regions to see what might be accomplished in this manner.

Ordinarily the choice of whether to study first the requirements of spatial filtering, as we have above in a most preliminary manner, or spectral filtering, is designer's choice. The order in which a designer makes the required decisions in a particular problem is sometimes dictated by the problem and sometimes by his personal preference. We shall first select a spectral region and then choose a field of view in keeping with both the spectral radiant intensity of the target and the spectral radiance of the background.

In this problem let us assume that filters with square spectral bandpasses which are multiples of $0.1~\mu$ are available at any wavelength in the region of 0.3 to $3.0~\mu$. We now wish to make a reticle which has alternate bars made of materials with very specific but different optical transmission characteristics. The transmitted power should be the same through each filter for solar radiation. The filters are selected to match within the limits of present producibility the desired center wavelengths and bandpasses. In Figure A-1 the shaded areas correspond to the solar power transmitted through two filters which satisfy this condition. Figure

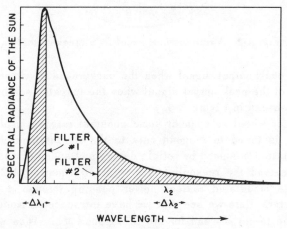

Fig. A-1. Spectral radiance transmitted by filters 1 and 2; λ_1 = center wavelength of filter 1, $\Delta\lambda$, = spectral bandpass for filter 1, subscript 2 indicates filter 2.

A-2 shows a color wheel; A represents one material and B represents the second.

To choose our filters we must compute the following radiant power in various spectral bands from target and background. For a 5530° C source (i.e., for sunlit clouds whose radiation peaks at $0.5~\mu$), computation reveals that the spectral intervals shown in the center column of Table A-1 contain the relative amounts of the total available radiant power shown in per cent in the right-hand column. Thus we find a pair of filters, numbers 5 and 6 in Table A-1, that transmit 22 per cent and 21 per cent, respectively, of the incident solar radiation. A similar calculation for the radiation from the tungsten source shows that the 0.3 to $0.5~\mu$ filter passes 32 per cent of the radiation, while the 1.1 to $3.0~\mu$ filter passes 88 per cent.

If we now place a color wheel, made from these filters, in front of the radiometer, the output of the radiometer will fluctuate by about 5 per

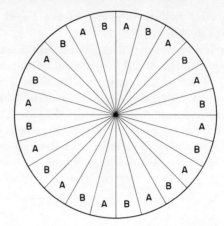

Fig. A-2. A reticle color wheel for a single detector.

cent of the peak output signal when the background is viewed and about 64 per cent of the peak output signal when the tungsten source is viewed. This is illustrated in Figure A-3.

If the color wheel is spun at some constant rate an amplifier can be used which is tuned to respond only to the fluctuations characteristic of the modulation produced by reticle design and speed of rotation.

We now extend the reasoning that leads to equation A-2 in order to consider the modulated radiant power passing through a color wheel to our detector. Here we see that we have introduced a modulation filter factor for the target M_T and for the background M_B. Thus we must consider our modulated irradiance at the detector and write a modified equation

$$M_T \times J/R^2 \geq M_B \times 2\omega N_B.$$

Now if we solve for R^2 we see our form is similar to our previous calculation except for one new term, the ratio of target modulation to background modulation

$$R^2 = (M_T/M_B)\, J/2\omega N_B$$

Table A-1

Fractions of Radiant Solar Power Transmitted

Filter No.	Spectral Intervals (μ)	Fractions of Radiant Power (%)
1	0.0–0.3	3
2	0.0–0.5	25
3	0.0–1.1	77
4	0.0–3.0	98
5	0.3–0.5	22
6	1.1–3.0	21

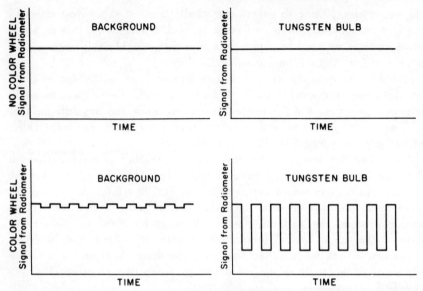

Fig. A-3. Radiometer responses for a tungsten bulb and for background when a color wheel is used and when it is not used.

In our particular problem the filter wheel extends the range by the factor $\sqrt{0.64/0.05}$ or about 3. Even if use is made of high quality optics providing a field of about 10^{-8} steradian we can expect a range of about 7500 ft without the filter wheel discussed above. With it a range of about three times as great (or about 22,500 ft) is possible.

Thus we have done a design study that falls short of our design objectives. To do better we require a better filter wheel, a more powerful lamp or a somewhat more sophisticated approach, i.e., a modulated source rather than a modulated receiver.

It should be noted at this point that nowhere in the above problem have we been limited by the sensitivity of the radiometer. We are still not limited by the sensitivity of the radiometer for, even at a range of 10 miles, the 13-watt-ster^{-1} source presents an irradiance at the aperture of the instrument of approximately 4×10^{-12} watt-cm^{-2}, which is a quite reasonable value of irradiance for detection. The limitations in our design have been imposed entirely by the small contrast between target and background.

If we now attempt to use an instrument as designed above to search for the balloon, difficulties will be experienced in attempts to cover a moderate field of view with an instantaneous field of view of only 10^{-8} ster. For example, suppose we decide to search a $5.7° \times 5.7°$ patch of sky (a field of 10^{-2} ster). This requires 10^6 looks with a 10^{-8}-ster field of view. Assume the response time of the instrument is approximately 10 μsec; then a reasonable value for the dwell time is 30 μsec, and we require 30 sec to search the small patch of sky. Now although this is a reasonable time for a device to track a balloon for this problem, let us assume we need to obtain data at a rate considerably greater than twice a minute, in fact, once a second.

Probably the most direct approach to this problem is the use of a 30-detector array in the focal plane of the radiometer. We can use these 30 detectors to cover a 5.7° vertical field and scan the azimuth field of 5.7° once every second with a return scan once every second. Thus, the scanning rate would be 30 cycles per minute.

If we keep the design within the realm of feasibility, the focal length of the radiometer would now have to be not less than 10 in., so that the detector dimensions would not need to be less than 0.001 in. on a side, a dimension which is close to the lower limit of detector-size feasibility. In this system, the collection optics have to be close to the present state of the art of optical fabrication in order to achieve the 10^{-8}-ster resolution. Thus we may see that we have done about as much as we may do with the tools described above to locate the target against the specified backgrounds.

Perhaps at this time we should consider using a reticle, not to gain an improved signal-to-noise ratio, but to reduce the system to a simpler, one-detector device. Let us construct a reticle, as we did before, of alternate bars of the two filter materials but now arranged in a linear rather than a circular array, as in Fig. A-4.

We choose the dimensions of the filter bar for the 10-in.-focal-length system to be approximately 0.001 in. wide and 0.01-in. long. The 0.001-in. dimension is determined by the resolution required to discriminate against the background, while the 0.01-in. dimension is set by the required bearing accuracy of the instrument. Thus, we have an instrument that is able to locate a target with an uncertainty in elevation angle of about 3′ and in azimuth angle of about 20″.

We introduce into this particular series of alternating filter materials an opaque strip corresponding to something like 10 filter-widths. This is shown as C in Figure A-4. Thus, in the process of location, sweeping a target image across one of the strips in the reticle will cause a signal to be modulated in the manner discussed under the two-color filter wheel, and also to be modulated according to the blanking codes inserted in the reticle. The object of the latter design is to incorporate a means of indicating which row (in the 30-element reticle array) the image was swept over, since all of the energy passing through the reticle would be collected by a simple field-lens system and imaged onto a single detector. Thus, one amplifier and one detector are required to indicate 30 channels of elevation data. The time of signal generation indicates the azimuth position of the target relative to the instrument axis.

This should be called a conceptual solution. It can be used on less

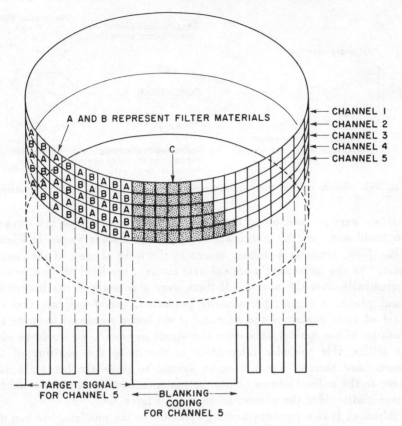

Fig. A-4. A reticle color wheel for a multiple detector.

stringent problems, but in the building of the particular system, the reticle elements must be so small in width and length that there does not appear to be any reasonable method for assembly of the elements into the required two-color reticle. Of course a longer focal-length system (say 100 in.) could be used to permit somewhat larger dimensions for the reticle elements, but such a specification becomes almost meaningless as a result of the mechanical complexities and requirements of such a system.

Another important function of the reticle system is the role of error-signal generation, the heart of the tracking device; it is discussed below.

Error Signal Generators. Let us consider the general characteristics of a few error-signal generators to see how we might go about constructing a tracking system. Let us visualize an instrument employing an optical axis which is inclined at some small angle to and rotating about an instrument reference line, denoted the instrument boresight axis. We have now conceived a simple form of optical tracker (see Figure A-5).

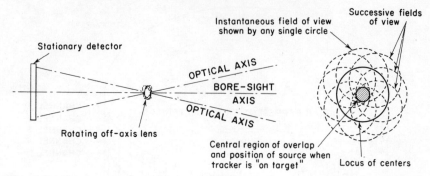

Fig. A-5. Simple optical tracking instrument.   Fig. A-6. Scan pattern.

If we were to look along the boresight axis from behind the tracker, we could see that the instrument scans in the manner shown in Figure A-6. Now, consider a radiant source in the field of view of the instrument. As the instrument's optical axis rotates, the field of view sweeps periodically over the source. If there were a detector at the instrument focal plane, a signal, periodically generated, would indicate that the field of view contained the source. If we had a means of knowing the position of the optical axis when the signal appeared, we would be able to utilize this periodic information to determine the position of the source and thereby direct a servo system to make the boresight axis move to the radiant source (while the instantaneous field of view skirted tangentially about the source, as shown in Figure A-6).

Although it is a poor engineering approach to the problem, one can use a reticle on which is mounted a commutator of five brushes. Four brushes are anchored around the periphery and in the plane of the reticle at points which are denoted up, down, right, and left. The fifth brush is located behind the plane of the four reference brushes and is used to provide a source of voltage to the back portion of the commutator. The commutator is composed of a semicircular wiper arm (see Figure A-7).

In operation, the combination of reticle and commutator works as follows: The commutator is lined up in such a manner that the interface of its conducting and insulating regions is made to coincide with the interface between modulating and nonmodulating portions of the reticle; that is, the region where the reticle has active opaque and transparent spokes corresponds to the conducting region of the commutator. The commutator and reticle are mounted integrally, and, as the reticle and commutator rotate, the boundary between the modulating and nonmodulating portions of the reticle pass by a brush at the same time that the nonconducting-conducting junction of the commutator passes the brush. The effect of this combination is that, as the reticle-commutator combination rotates, the wiper sweeps successively by each of the four successive reference

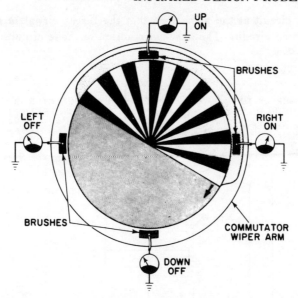

Fig. A-7. Schematic representation of reticle-commutator operation. Meters are shown to indicate a signal can be measured.

signal brushes. See Figure A-8. Thus, each brush receives voltage for a period of 180° of the reticle rotation and then receives no voltage for 180° of reticle rotation. The output of these four brush circuits is connected to four coincidence circuits labeled up, down, right, and left, corresponding to the up, down, right, and left brush positions. The output of the detector is connected to an amplifier, the output of which is in turn connected to the four coincidence circuits. The action of the coincidence circuit is that of a gate which passes the amplified detector output whenever the voltage from the reference brush is applied to the

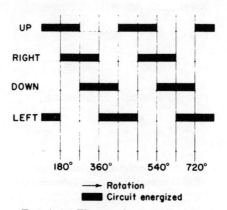

Fig. A-8. Phase reference signals.

coincidence circuit at the same time that the target signal is applied to
the coincidence circuit. The schematic action of these circuits is shown
in Figure A-9.

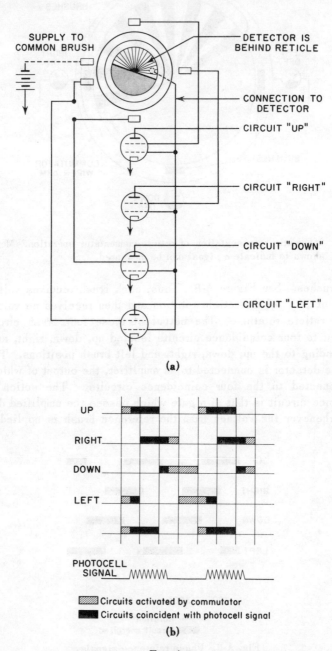

Fig. A-9

The output of the coincidence circuit is connected to electromagnets to pull the optic axis of the seeker in the following manner: the "up" circuit pulls the optic axis up; the "right" circuit pulls the optic axis right, etc. Figure A-10 shows that in this case of target signal position the combined effect of the reference signals and the target signal is such that the optic axis is pulled up for 135°, right for 135°, down for 45°, and left for 45° of rotation. The inertia of the system is sufficient that the system integrates for the opposing effects of the up and down torques and for the right and left torques. The resultant torque, therefore, pulls

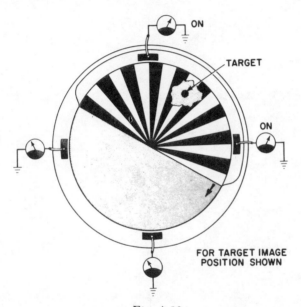

Fig. A-10.

the axis up and to the right equally, i.e., the optic axis is pulled along a 45° line. The optic axis then moves until it rests on the target, at which time the detector puts forth a constant signal with no differential effects caused by the rotation of the reticle, and all differential torque ceases.

Now we have a tracker, a simple source-tracking telescope. This device will work very well whenever there is but one source of radiance to activate the detector. To get more reliable performance in a situation where background radiance cannot be overlooked, the reticle must be given a more sophisticated treatment.

MEASUREMENT OF OCEAN-SURFACE TEMPERATURES*

B.1 Statement of the Problem

It is highly desirable to have a means for rapidly measuring and plotting water-surface temperatures over large areas of ocean. Such information is valuable to hydrographers in charting ocean currents; it has application in long-range weather prediction; and it may be of decided interest to commercial fishing fleets. In addition, since the thermal structure of the ocean is a vital factor in determining the propagation of sonar signals, a large-area plot of surface temperature is valuable for accurate prediction and evaluation of sonar performance.

Previous methods of measuring ocean-surface temperatures have involved highly localized measurements, mainly made from aboard ship. Because of the limitations inherent in these methods, only extremely coarse plots of surface temperature have been available. If suitably accurate surface-temperature measurements could be made from aircraft, daily plots could be made of very large areas of ocean.

The use of infrared radiation provides the only known and practical method for making noncontact, passive, and rapid measurements of the temperature of remote surfaces. If infrared radiation can be used by an instrument in an aircraft to measure ocean surface temperature, important progress can be made in the mentioned applications. The present problem is, then, to investigate the possibilities of using infrared radiation for this purpose, and if determined feasible, to design a system to accomplish this purpose.

B.2 Radiation Characteristics of the Ocean Surface

Over different parts of the world the temperature of the ocean surface ranges from a minimum of $-2\,°C$ (271 °K) to a maximum of 35 °C (308 °K). Only a very thin layer of water is required to absorb infrared radiation

---

*Eric M. Wormser, Barnes Engineering Company, Stamford, Connecticut.

completely.[1] In the infrared region from 4 to 12.5 μ, the emissivity of
the ocean surface is 0.98 for radiation normal to the surface. The reflection for normal radiation is 2 per cent and increases to 4 per cent for
radiation incident at 60° from the normal. Hence, the infrared radiation
characteristics of a water surface closely approach those of a blackbody
at 300°K. Such a body emits maximum radiation at a wavelength of 9.6 μ.
The spectral-radient emittance corresponding to the extremes of ocean-
surface temperature can be represented as emission curves for blackbodies at 35°C (308°K) and -2°C (271°K). See Fig. B-1. Examination of these curves shows that the major portion of energy for the range
of temperatures is included in the region between 6 and 20 μ.

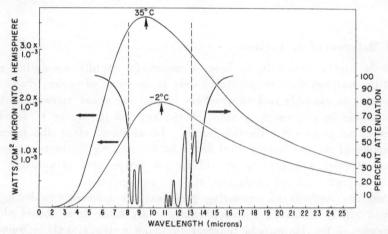

Fig. B-1. Blackbody distribution (Planck law) for -2° C (271° K) and $+35$° C
(308° K), and atmospheric attenuation of 1000 ft. of air path at sea
level (*by permission of Barnes Engineering Co.*)

B.3 Atmospheric Attenuation

One fundamental requirement for remote measurement of temperature by
means of infrared radiation is that the radiation from the object of interest must reach the measuring instrument. The second fundamental
requirement is that the measuring instrument must be able to detect
radiation from the target while discriminating against any other radiation
that may reach the entrance aperture of this instrument.

In this problem there is atmosphere between the measuring instrument
and the ocean's surface. This atmosphere attenuates surface radiation
and emits radiation of its own, thus presenting an interfering condition.

To determine the effects of the atmosphere it is necessary to examine
its attenuation characteristics in the wavelength region between 6 and
20 μ.[2] Figure B-1 also shows a curve of the spectral attenuation through
1000 ft of atmosphere in this wavelength region. (Appendix D gives more
and detailed curves.) Examination of this curve shows that there is a

good transmission window between 7.5 and 12.5 μ. Radiation at the sides of this window will be completely attenuated after traveling through more than 1000 ft of atmosphere.

Thus, the effects of atmospheric attenuation, and of atmospheric emission, can be largely eliminated from the measurement if the instrument includes a 7.5–12.5-μ optical bandpass filter. Use of a radiation slide rule will show that approximately 29 per cent of the radiation emitted by the ocean's surface falls within the wavelength region of this window. To restrict the optical bandpass of the system to the spectral region 7.5–12.5 μ, an optical filter consisting of arsenic trisulfide glass and a thin anti-reflection coated slab of indium antimonide is used. The transmission curve of this filter is shown in Figure B-2.

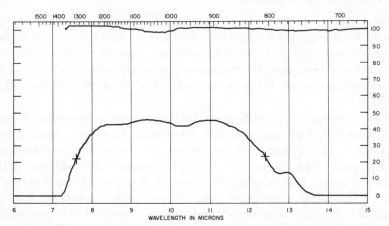

Fig. B-2. Per cent transmission of filter.   Upper trace shows 100 per cent transmission.

B.4 Radiation Differentials to be Detected

Before proceeding to design a system, it is necessary to examine the possibilities of detecting radiation under the most unfavorable conditions. The lowest level of radient power is that emitted by ocean water at $-2\,^{\circ}$ C ($271\,^{\circ}$ K). It is desired to measure radiation differentials corresponding to changes of $1\,^{\circ}$ C or less on the ocean surface for this temperature.

The change in radient emittance (ΔW) for a small change in temperature ($\Delta T = 1\,^{\circ}$ C) can be found from the incremental form of the Stefan-Boltzmann law:

$$\Delta W = 4\,\sigma\,\varepsilon\,T^3\,\Delta T \tag{B-1}$$

where σ = Stefan-Boltzmann constant = 5.6×10^{-12} (watt/cm^2-deg^4)

ε = normal emissivity of water = 0.98

T = average absolute temperature of water = $271\,^{\circ}$ K

$$\Delta W = 4 \times 5.67 \times 10^{-12} \times 0.98 \times (271)^3 \times 1$$
$$= 4.3 \times 10^{-4} \text{ watt/cm}^2 \text{ (total into a hemisphere)}$$

The total incremental radiance ΔN of the water surface in the normal direction is:

$$\Delta N = (\Delta W/\pi) = 1.3 \times 10^{-4} \text{ watt/cm}^2\text{-sterad} \qquad \text{(B-2)}$$

The incremental radiance of the water surface in the 7.5–12.5-μ transmission window is:

$$\Delta N_{7.5-12.5\,\mu} = 0.29 \times 1.3 \times 10^{-4} = 0.4 \times 10^{-4} \text{ watt/cm}^2 \text{ sterad} \qquad \text{(B-3)}$$

B.5 System-Design Parameters

There are two basic types of instruments or systems that can be considered for use in this application. One system scans the ocean surface to the left and right of the aircraft, seeking temperature differentials, and the other provides absolute temperature measurements of a strip of the ocean surface directly below the aircraft. Both types of systems will be analyzed.

Oceanographers have indicated that temperature measurements made 60 ft apart would provide sufficient information for solving most of their problems. This requirement determines the necessary instantaneous field of view. The atmospheric absorption makes it desirable to fly the aircraft at a very low altitude, while aircraft flight performance generally makes it undesirable to fly too low. A reasonable compromise from the point of view of atmospheric transmission, aircraft performance, and ocean-surface coverage would be an operating altitude of 3000 ft.

In order to establish the parameters of the optics and detector system, let us assume an object distance of 3000 ft (1000 m) and an object size of 60×60 ft (20×20 m), which requires a field of view of 0.02×0.02 rad = .0004 sterad. If we select an infrared detector having a sensitive area of 1×1 mm, which is a practical and efficient detector area, we require a mirror or lens of 50 mm (2 in.) focal length to cover the above field of view. For both the scanning and nonscanning instruments it would be practical to use an $f/1.0$ germanium lens, i.e., a lens having both a diameter and focal length of 50 mm (2 in.).

Germanium is selected as the optical material since it has good optical transmission in the region of interest (7.5 to 12.5 μ), it completely attenuates interfering visible radiation and infrared radiation with wavelengths shorter than 1.8 μ, while its high refractive index ($n = 4.0$) permits design of a simple, fast lens of good optical performance.

Let us now apply these system-design parameters to the incremental radiance (ΔN) emitted by the water surface calculated in Eq. (B-3).

Assuming 100 per cent transmission in the 7.5–12.5-μ atmospheric region, the incremental irradiance ΔH (for a $\Delta T = 1°C$) received at the

optical instrument from water surfaces subtending 0.0004 sterad is given
by:

$$\Delta H_{7.5-12.5\,\mu} = N_\lambda \Omega = 0.4 \times 10^{-4} \times 4 \times 10^{-4} = 1.6 \times 10^{-8} \ \text{watt/cm}^2 \qquad \text{(B-4)}$$

where Ω is the solid angle of view.

The entrance aperture of the optical system has a diameter of 5 cm,
resulting in an entrance pupil area of 20 cm^2. As shown below, other
factors reduce this to an effective entrance aperture area of approximately 6 cm^2. We obtain for the increment of radiant power ΔP available for measurement at the infrared detector:

$$\Delta P = A_{\text{eff}} \times \Delta H = 1 \times 10^{-7} \ \text{watt} \qquad \text{(B-5)}$$

B.6 Selection of an Infrared Detector

For the problem outlined, we require a reliable infrared detector having
uniform and sufficient detectivity in the spectral region 7.5–12.5 μ. Two
types of infrared detectors may be considered.

First are the photoconductive detectors, in particular, several types
of impurity-doped germanium photoconductive detectors have recently
become available. The spectral response and relative detectivity of
these detectors, compared with a good-quality thermal detector, is shown
in Figure B-3.[3,4] However, as shown in this figure, the photoconductors
require cooling to liquid air temperatures or lower. The problem of
reliably cooling a photoconductive infrared detector to these low temperatures in an airborne measurement system is formidable.

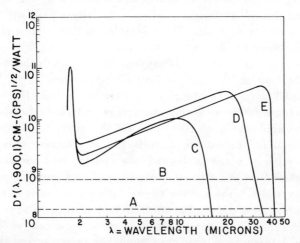

Fig. B-3. Photoconductive and thermal detectors compared. (A) Thermistor,
300° K (1 m sec τ); (B) Equivalent immersed thermistor; (C) Ge-Si
(Zn^{II}), 48° K; (D) Ge(Cu), 20° K; and (E) Ge(Zn^{I}), 4° K.

Thermal detectors operating at ambient temperature represent the other type to be considered. These have uniform response over the wavelength region from ultraviolet through the far infrared; and, consequently, in the 7.5–12.5-μ region of interest. Of these thermal detectors, solid-backed thermistors[5] are the most practical. They are small, rugged, fast, and sensitive, and can be made with sensitive areas having linear dimensions from 0.1 to 10 mm. The NEP (noise equivalent power) of a thermistor is given by:

$$NEP = 1 \times 10^{-8}\sqrt{A}/\tau$$

where A = detector area (mm^2)

   τ = time constant (msec)

the reference bandwidth is taken as $f = 1000/4\tau$ from sampling theory if τ is in milliseconds and f is in cycles per second.

Experience indicates, and the calculations presented below will show, that thermistor-type infrared detectors are adequately fast and sensitive for the problem given, and hence, are preferable, since they do not require cooling.

B.7 Scanning-System-Design Criteria

Now that the basic considerations of both the scanning system and absolute measurement system have been reviewed, it is possible to establish the design criteria for both. The scanning-system design is established first.

In the scanning-system it is desired to sample the ocean surface with a resolution element measuring 20×20 m (60 ft $\times$ 60 ft). The scanning motion along the line of flight will be accomplished by the motion of the aircraft, and scanning at right angles to the flight path will be accomplished by the system itself. The principles of this system are identical to those discussed in Chapters 13 and 14.

In the present case an ideal mapping pattern would be achieved by scanning 20 m strips of ocean surface at right angles to the flight path. These scanned strips would touch each other at their parallel edges.

The procedure for establishing the design criteria is first to consider a typical forward speed of 100 knots for the aircraft. Since one scan must be completed before the aircraft has moved more than 20 m and since no overlap of scans is desired, the elapsed time per scan line can be established from the aircraft ground speed and the left-to-right total angular scan width. The number of resolution elements per scan line is then determined from the total strip width it is desired to scan.

Now the number of resolution elements per second can be established, this in turn determines the required frequency response and the detector time constant. Then there are determined in sequence: the detector

NEP, the optical efficiency, the system's NEPD (noise equivalent power density), and finally the estimated NET (noise equivalent temperature) of the system.

The mathematical derivation of the system's NET follows.

Forward speed of aircraft	100 knots = 55 m/sec
Elapsed time per scan line	20/55 = 0.36 sec
Resolution elements per scan line (for a system with a scan one radian wide and a resolution element 0.02 rad square)	1/0.02 = 50
Resolution elements per second	50/0.36 = 140
Frequency response required	$f = 70$ cps
Detector time constant required	$\tau = 1/2\pi f = 2$ msec
Detector NEP (for $A = 1\,\text{mm}^2$ and $\tau = 2$ msec)	5×10^{-9} watt for $\Delta f = 125$ cps
Area of 50-mm-diameter lens	20 cm^2
Optical transmission	
coated germanium lens	80 per cent
filter	40 per cent
net transmission	32 per cent
"Effective" area of lens	$20 \times 0.32 = 6.4$ cm^2
NEPD of scanning system	

$$\text{NEPD} = \frac{\text{detector NEP} \cdot \text{bridge factor}}{\text{effective lens area}} = \frac{5 \times 10^{-9} \times 2}{6.4} = 1.6 \times 10^{-9} \text{ watts/cm}^2 \quad (\text{B-6})$$

From Eq. (B-4): the flux density at the instrument aperture (irradiance ΔH) from the ocean surface per $\Delta T = 1°\text{C}$ is:

$$\Delta H_{7.5-12.5\mu} = 1.6 \times 10^{-8} \text{ watts/cm}^2$$

Noise equivalent temperature of scanning instrument:

$$\text{NET} = \frac{\text{NEPD}}{\Delta H} = \frac{1.6 \times 10^{-9}}{1.6 \text{ u } 10^{-8}} = 0.1°\text{C}$$

B.8 Description of Possible Scanning System

The design criteria previously established describe the fundamental requirements of the system. Many physical arrangements are possible, and the airborne scanning systems described in Chapters 13 and 14 can be considered as arrangements adequate for the desired purposes.

B.9 Absolute Radiometer System

In order to make absolute measurements of the temperature of the ocean surface, the infrared energy from the surface is continuously compared to the energy from a temperature-controlled blackbody cavity.

It is important to make the absolute temperature measurement as nearly independent of instrumental ambient temperature changes as is possible.

To accomplish this, the critical detector and optical components, including the thermistor infrared detector, the optical filter, the optical chopper, and one-half of the germanium doublet are all enclosed within the temperature-controlled, in-line, blackbody cavity shown in Figure B-4.   The cavity and all the components within are maintained at the precisely controlled temperature of 50°C.   Energy from the target is collected by the fast, two-element germanium lens.   It is transmitted through the lens window, which closes the front end of the cavity, and is focused on the thermistor bolometer, which closes off the rear end of the cavity.   The thermistor bolometer itself is equipped with the filter window described earlier, transmitting radiation only in the 7.5–12.5-μ spectral

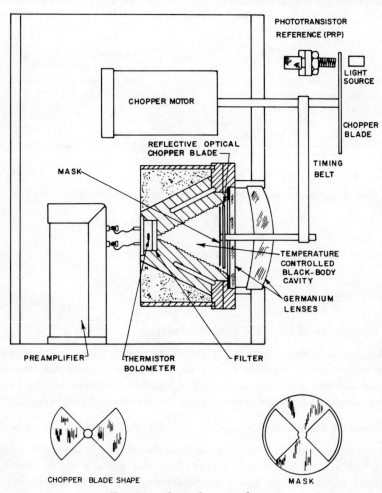

Fig. B-4. Optical system layout.

region. The active and compensating thermistor flakes are connected in series across equal positive and negative bias supply voltages.

The short focal length of the germanium collecting lens permits the required field of view to be matched to a thermistor detector of reasonable size. A lens is employed instead of reflective optical elements; it results in a simpler configuration and is more suitable for airborne use because it seals off the optical head.

A chopper blade and mask are placed at the front end of the cavity. Both mask and chopper blade consist of two opposed 90° sectors. As the blade rotates, it either completely blocks the incoming radiation by closing the 90° sector openings in the mask, or else it allows radiation to be focused by half the lens area onto the detector. (This results in average transmission through one-fourth of the entrance aperture, or a chop factor of 4, as used in the equations below.)

The inner surface of the chopper blade is gold-plated so as to be highly reflective. When the cavity is closed to the incoming radiation, the bolometer receives the blackbody radiation as reflected by the mirror chopper. Thus, as the chopper rotates, the bolometer is alternately irradiated at a 20-cycle rate with energy from the target and from the reference blackbody. The output of the detector which appears at the junction between the active and compensating flake is a 20-cycle signal voltage, the amplitude of which is proportional to the difference between target and reference radiance.

Since the filter, which is the detector window, is positioned behind the optical chopper, the radiation from this filter is not chopped and thus does not contribute to the output signal from the bolometer. Since one germanium collecting lens is in front of the optical chopper, the radiation emitted by this lens will be chopped. However, germanium is quite transparent between 2 and 15 μ and thus emits very little radiation in this wavelength region.

The voltage output from the thermistor bolometer is fed to a high-gain preamplifier stabilized with negative feedback. This preamplifier has sufficient dynamic range to develop a linear output signal for input voltages representing the maximum radiance difference (−2°C target, 50°C reference) which will be encountered. The output of the preamplifier is fed to a synchronous rectifier-amplifier in the electronics and recorder section of the instrument. A schematic diagram of the electronics system is shown in Figure B-5.

B.10 Absolute Radiometer Design Criteria

A chopping rate of 20 cps is selected for this instrument, requiring a detector time constant of 8 msec. The detector size, lens, and optical

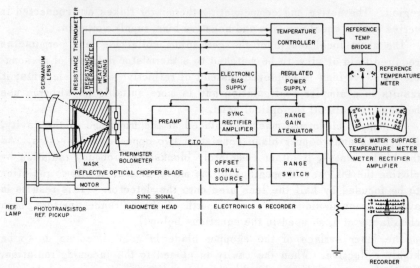

Fig. B-5. Block diagram of the system.

filter are identical to those used in the scanning system considered earlier.

Detector

$$NEP = 1 \times 10^{-8}\sqrt{A}/\tau \text{ watt}$$

For $A = 1 \text{ mm}^2$, $\tau = 8 \text{ m sec}$, $\Delta f = 30 \text{ cps}$,

$$NEP = 1.25 \times 10^{-9} \text{ watt}$$

Radiometer

$$NEPD = \frac{\text{detector NEP} \times \text{bridge factor} \times \text{chop factor}}{\text{effective aperture} \times \sqrt{\text{bandwidth ratio}}}$$

$$= \frac{1.25 \times 10^{-9} \times 2 \times 4}{6.4 \times \sqrt{30/1}} = 2.8 \times 10^{-10} \text{ watt/cm}^2 \quad \begin{array}{c}\text{for 1 cps band pass}\end{array}$$

Noise equivalent temperature of radiometer

$$NET = \frac{2.8 \times 10^{-10}}{1.6 \times 10^{-8}} \sim 0.02 \,^\circ C$$

B.11 Comparison of Absolute Radiometer and Scanning System

We see that the scanning device has a computed noise level equivalent to 0.1 °C in temperature differential, while the absolute radiometer has a computed noise level of 0.02 °C.

B.12 Comparison of Initial System Design and Actual Performance

The system-design problem was originally presented in the summer of 1959 as an exercise at The University of Michigan Engineering Summer Conference course, Fundamentals of Infrared Technology. Since then, the absolute water-surface radiometer has actually been constructed and a prototype unit has undergone flight tests.[6] A photograph of the completed unit is shown in Figure B-6.

It is interesting to compare the design criteria initially established in 1959 with the system characteristics and performance of the unit actually constructed. See Table B-1.

Fig. B-6. Model 14-320: air borne radiation thermometer.

The unit is currently being evaluated in flight operations by the Navy Hydrographic Office; so full operational results are not yet available. From laboratory, environmental test chamber, and limited flight tests the following results have been obtained:

System electronic noise (can be reduced further)	$0.05\,^{\circ}C$
Reference temperature control drift of cavity	$\pm 0.05\,^{\circ}C$
Error due to residual window emission of outer germanium window	$0.04\,^{\circ}C$ per $^{\circ}C$ ambient change referred to $25\,^{\circ}C$

Table B-1

Design Criteria Compared with Performance

	Initial Design Criteria	Actual System Characteristics
Thermistor detector		
Area	$1 \times 1 = 1$ mm^2	$2 \times 2 = 4$ mm^2
Time constant	8 msec	2.5 msec
NEP	1.25×10^{-9}	8×10^{-9}
Optics		
Diameter	2 in. (50 mm)	3 in.
Focal length	2 in.	2 in.
Field of view	$0.02 \times 0.02 = 4 \times 10^{-4}$ sterad	$0.04 \times 0.04 = 16 \times 10^{-4}$ sterad
Chopping rate	20 cps	20 cps
Reference bandwidth	30 cps	100 cps
NEPD for 1-cps system bandwidth		
$\dfrac{\text{detector NEP} \times \text{bridge factor} \times \text{chop factor}}{\text{effective aperture} \times \text{bandwidth ratio}}$	$= \dfrac{1.25 \times 10^{-9} \times 2 \times 4}{6.4 \times \sqrt{30/1}}$	$= \dfrac{8 \times 10^{-9} \times 2 \times 4}{9.6 \times \sqrt{100/1}}$
	$= 2.8 \times 10^{-10}$ watt/cm^2	$= 6.6 \times 10^{-10}$ watt/cm^2
Energy received per ΔT = 1°C at instrument	1.6×10^{-8} watt/cm^2	6.4×10^{-8} watt/cm^2
NET	$= \dfrac{2.8 \times 10^{-10}}{1.6 \times 10^{-8}} \sim 0.02°$C	$= \dfrac{6.6 \times 10^{-10}}{6.4 \times 10^{-8}} \sim 0.01°$C

Comparison of surface-probe measurements using contact thermometers, with the results from the airborne absolute radiation thermometer, shows an average difference of 0.3° C, with the radiation measurement yielding the lower temperature.

1. G. Ewing and E. D. McAlister, "On the Thermal Boundary Layer of the Ocean," *Science* **131**, 1374–76 (1960).
2. H. W. Yates and J. H. Taylor, *Infrared Transmission of the Atmosphere*. N. R. L. Report 5453 (June, 1960).
3. S. F. Jacobs, "Characteristics of Infrared Detectors," *Electronics* **33**, 72–73 (1960).
4. R. C. Jones, "Phenomenological Description of the Response and Detecting Ability of Radiation Detectors," *Proc. IRE* **47**, 1495 (1959).
5. R. DeWaard and E. M. Wormser, "Description and Properties of Various Thermal Detectors," *Proc. IRE* **47**, 1508 (1959).
6. M. Weiss, "Airborne Radiation Thermometer," Vol 6, No 2, *Proc. IRIS*.
7. E. Johnson, "Airborne Radiation Thermometer" (Part II) Vol 6, No 2, *Proc. IRIS*.

SOURCES OF INFORMATION ABOUT INFRARED TECHNOLOGY

The infrared literature contains many unorthodox references—government reports, unclassified articles in classified journals and others which are usually known as "nonarchival." Because there are these unusual means and, therefore, unusual requirements for obtaining information, this appendix has been written to explain the nature of some of the literature sources and agencies which help with the handling of such material. Also included is a bibliography of open literature references. The list, which is extensive but not exhaustive, was originally prepared for the special infrared issue of *Proceedings of the Institute of Radio Engineers*,[1] and it has been revised slightly since then.

C. 1 Information Agencies

Several different agencies have been charged with the responsibility of disseminating information about infrared technology; some also cover other fields. The agencies discussed are ASTIA, the Armed Services Technical Information Agency; IRIS, the Infrared Information Symposia; IRIA, the Infrared Information and Analysis Center; The RAND Corporation; BAMIRAC, the Ballistic Missile Radiation Analysis Center; WGIRB, the Working Group on Infrared Backgrounds.

C. 1. 1 ASTIA*

ASTIA provides a service to military activities of the Department of Defense, their civilian contractors and subcontractors, potential contractors and grantees—educational institutions, industrial concerns and research foundations—as well as other agencies of the executive branch of the Federal Government. ASTIA also is authorized to supply unclassified reports which have no release limitations to NATO and

---

*This section was written by Vietta A. Dowd, Information Officer, ASTIA, and is published with ASTIA's permission.

SEATO nations. ASTIA's services include the furnishing (on request from established requester agencies) the reports themselves, bibliographies, reference tools, and a semimonthly announcement bulletin of new acquisitions. A more complete description of the ASTIA service is given by their descriptive brochure *Operations and Services of the Armed Services Technical Information Agency*. Suffice it to say that work pertinent to the direct support of military research and development is the major concern of ASTIA.

Types of Reports Cataloged by ASTIA

ASTIA catalogs and processes scientific and technical reports which are pertinent to defense-related research and development. The majority of these reports are originated by military organizations and their contractors and may include progress, interim, summary, or final reports on projects or contracts. ASTIA also catalogs reports generated and contributed by non-contractor organizations when such reports are deemed to be of interest to to defense-related research and development.

Report Bibliographies

Report Bibliographies are compiled without charge, upon request from established user agencies. They can be compiled for any given subject, source, author, or even contract number, provided the subject matter falls within the requester's approved fields of interest.

Report Bibliographies are furnished in the form of individual catalog cards or in the form of a booklet containing reproductions of pertinent cards.

Technical Abstract Bulletin (TAB)

A Technical Abstract Bulletin is published twice a month and lists documents recently processed by ASTIA, including abstracts when security permits. The TAB is intended as a rapid announcement medium of documents newly acquired. Documents listed in TAB are announced only once, except when a change in security classification or limitations results in a reannouncement. Cumulative indexes are provided quarterly and annually. The listings are arranged by a subject division according to the distribution guide. The TAB is distributed on an automatic basis to authorized users in accordance with their security clearance and agency category.

C. 1. 2 IRIS*

IRIS, the Infrared Information Symposia, is an organization established by the Office of Naval Research which exists primarily to hold symposia on various topics in infrared. These meetings are generally of a classified nature and therefore can be attended only by those who are working on military problems and have a security clearance and "need to know." The operation of IRIS is of interest, and some of its accomplishments

---

*This description is published with the approval and kind permission of the present Chairman of the Executive Committee of IRIS, T. B. Dowd.

and history are well worth discussing. An excellent description of IRIS
has been written by A. R. Laufer.[2] Part of his paper is reproduced
below.

Since August 11, 1949, the Office of Naval Research Branch Office,
Pasadena, has sponsored a continuing series of joint-service classified
symposia devoted to the military applications of infrared radiation.

In 1951 the Physics Branch of ONR/Washington organized Project
Metcalf to make an objective evaluation of both the military potentialities
of infrared radiation and the Navy's research and development program in
this field. The project supervisor, Mr. Frank B. Isakson of the Physics
Branch, assembled a group of outstanding scientists with broad and
varied backgrounds to conduct this study. His group included, among
others, D. F. Hornig, Associate Dean of the Graduate School of Brown
University; R. Hofstadter, L. I. Schiff, and W. K. H. Panofsky of Stanford
University; L. Goldberg, D. M. Dennison, and G. B. B. M. Sutherland of
The University of Michigan; M. Hamermesh, Head of the Theoretical
Physics Division of Argonne National Laboratory; C. H. Townes of Co-
lumbia University; and J. H. Van Vleck, President of the American Physical Society and Dean of Applied Science at Harvard University.

The final report issued under Project Metcalf, on October 6, 1952, included a strong indictment of the poor state of information exchange in the
infrared field. The report stated that the infrared program was severely
handicapped by the inadequate facilities for the exchange of information,
such exchange being affected at best only with delay and the exercise of
considerable persistence and inquisitiveness. Project Metcalf recommended, in this area of its consideration, that meetings be organized to
bring together personnel engaged in military infrared studies in order to
facilitate the exchange of information. The existence of the West Coast
Symposia was simultaneously acknowledged as an indication of the feasibility of such an effort.

One result of the recommendations of Project Metcalf was the organization in 1955 by ONR of the Infrared Information and Analysis (IRIA) group
initially under Project Michigan at The University of Michigan, with joint-
service sponsorship [now administered by ONR with tri-service sponsorship; see Section C. 1. 3].

Another result of the Project Metcalf recommendations was the decision
late in 1954 by the Executive Committee of the Western IRIS organization
[the meetings mentioned in the first paragraph] to relax somewhat the restrictions on membership in IRIS....

In the spring of 1956 still another step was taken by the IRIS organization in the direction of facilitating the flow of information. With funds
provided by the Physics Branch of ONR/Washington, the publication of the
proceedings of the IRIS meetings was undertaken. The first issue...ap-
peared in June 1956.

During the summer of 1956, the Physics Branch of ONR/Washington...de-
cided that an Eastern version of the IRIS organization would be instituted,
and that the proceedings of both the Eastern and Western groups would be
published....

The IRIS organization is now national in scope; direction is provided by
the Executive Committee which consists of members from many parts of

the country. The members represent industry, the military, and private institutions. The Executive Committee makes the over-all policy decisions of IRIS. Symposia are now held twice a year—one on the East Coast in the fall, and once on the West Coast in the spring. Specialist or Professional Group meetings may be held at any time.

The papers presented at the symposia are published in the journal entitled *Proceedings of the Infrared Information Symposia*. The *Proceedings* are published by the Institute of Science and Technology of The University of Michigan, and printed by the Government Printing Office. Since it is the purpose of IRIS to increase the dissemination of information, papers which have not been presented orally are also accepted for publication. The *Proceedings* also has the usual book review, letters, and news notes sections. This journal has made a vital contribution to information dissemination in classified infrared technology.

C. 1. 3 IRIA

IRIA, The Infrared Information and Analysis Group at IST, the Institute of Science and Technology of The University of Michigan, has a still different purpose: that of providing information in depth about the field of infrared technology. The functions of IRIA are illustrated in Figure C-1. A more comprehensive discussion of the operation of this center has been published in several places.[3,4,5]

IRIA is a tri-service facility for the collection, analysis, and dissemination of information pertinent to infrared research and technology. As one phase of the research activity of IST's Infrared Laboratory, under the direction of G. H. Suits, IRIA employs eight scientists and technicians, who combine their efforts with those of the other personnel at the Infrared Laboratory to form a team for the handling of information.

In 1952, the Metcalf Committee urged the establishment of an infrared information center that would fulfill the ever-increasing need for better exchange of scientific information. In its recommendations, Project Metcalf, stated, "A central information center is an attractive possibility.... [This active center] could be an enormous help in integrating and catalyzing the whole infrared effort."

Three functions are described below so that the service IRIA provides can be better understood.

Collection: Contract work is continually monitored through project cards, contact with military agencies, and direct association with contractors. As a result, most reports are now received by IRIA directly from contractors. Main efforts in the collection of infrared data are directed toward (1) learning new infrared work, (2) arranging for IRIA to be placed on the automatic distribution lists for reports of all infrared contractors, and (3) obtaining all special infrared reports.

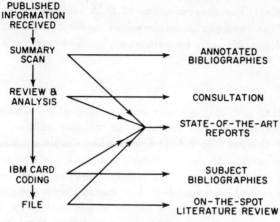

Fig. C-1. IRIA flow chart.

Analysis: The analysis of reports can best be described by referring to Figure C-1, which is a flow diagram of the internal operations of IRIA. As shown in the figure, the reports are received, scanned by the full-time personnel, and reviewed in greater detail by the reviewer-analysts. Then the information is put on library cards and IBM punch cards for retrieval.

The analysis procedure facilitates the provision of a quarterly annotated bibliography, request bibliographies, state-of-the-art reports, and consulting services. The annotated bibliography is a compilation of information from library cards, organized according to the IRIA cataloging system. It is issued quarterly.

Subject bibliographies are prepared on special request. Reports pertinent to a contractor's request are indicated on IBM cards. The request bibliography is prepared from these cards, and is sent only to the requesting contractor. Responsibility for obtaining the reports listed rests with the contractor.

If for some reason a request bibliography is not sufficient—perhaps because of the delay in obtaining reports or because active discussion is desired—the contractor may desire to visit IRIA. IBM techniques are used for locating those reports that are applicable to the particular research and development problem, and the reviewers are available for consultation.

Periodic analyses of various fields of infrared are made by studying the documents on hand, consulting experts, and conferring with the proper contractors. As the occasion arises, consultants from various fields are invited to participate in or conduct, special studies. State-of-the-art-reports are generated from these analyses.

Dissemination: The dissemination of IRIA information is intended to be as broad as security considerations warrant. In all cases requests for information must be authorized by the requester's contracting officer.

C. 1. 4 RAND

ASTIA, IRIA, and IRIS are the main organizations which are instrumental in carrying out the exchange of military infrared information. However, the role of The RAND Corporation should be mentioned. In its unusual relation with the Air Force, it is in a position to be of great use in information exchange. Dr. Sidney Passman there has been particularly active and successful in his undertakings along these lines. Although RAND does not have a formal responsibility for carrying out infrared-information exchange, it is concerned with the broad research, and development program of the U. S. Air Force—particularly concerning infrared techniques associated with ballistic missiles and West Coast infrared activities.

C. 1. 5 BAMIRAC

An organization very similar to IRIA should not be overlooked: BAMIRAC, the Ballistic Missile Radiation Analysis Center, established at The University of Michigan in 1959. It has the responsibility for collection, analysis, and dissemination of information about all radiations from ballistic missiles and their environment. Since BAMIRAC and IRIA work closely together, it is not necessary to request information from both places; the files and retrieval systems are coordinated.

C. 1. 6 WGIRB

For some time now the infrared field has been plagued by problems of nomenclature, test procedures, and calibration techniques. One of the attempts to solve this problem was made by WGIRB, the Working Group on Infrared Backgrounds. The group was established at the request of the three military services; it consisted of the leading scientists engaged in infrared background investigations—primarily radiometry and and spectroradiometry. This group later became affiliated with IRIA, and together they sponsored a symposium on background work at The University of Michigan and published its Proceedings.[6] Subsequently, the group wrote a report entitled Aims, Conclusions, and Recommendations on Background Information.[7] The Group was then requested to consider the problems of target measurements. This work is still in progress. The two major accomplishments of the WGIRB have been to focus attention on the importance of background information and to establish a recommended set of unit symbols and nomenclature. These latter, if not unanimously accepted, are at least widely used.

C. 1. 7 Other

Several outstanding scientists of Great Britain, Canada and the United States have cooperated in an attempt to develop common nomenclature, symbols, and test procedures for the three countries. As an example, Jones, Pullan, and Smith working on detectors would like D^* and NEP values to be the same whether the detector is measured on the east or west side of the Atlantic—and north or south of the Great Lakes.

SUPPLEMENTARY BIBLIOGRAPHY

Textbooks and Books on Infrared in General

G. K. T. Conn and D. G. Avery, *Infrared Methods*. New York: Academic Press, 1960.

J. M. Cork, Heat. New York: Wiley, 1942, Second Edition.

A. J. Dekker, *Solid-State Physics*. Englewood Cliffs, N. J.: Prentice-Hall, 1958.

R. W. Ditchburn, *Light*. New York: Interscience, 1953.

W. C. Dunlap, *An Introduction to Semiconductors*. New York: Wiley, 1957.

H. L. Hackforth, *Infrared Radiation*. New York: McGraw-Hill, 1960.

A. C. Hardy and F. H. Perrin, *The Principles of Optics*. New York: McGraw-Hill, 1932.

G. Herzberg, *Spectra of Diatomic Molecules*. Princeton: D. Van Nostrand, 1950, Second Edition.

G. Herzberg, *Infrared and Raman Spectra of Polyatomic Molecules*. Princeton: D. Van Nostrand, 1954, Second Edition.

F. A. Jenkins and H. E. White, *Fundamentals of Optics*. New York: McGraw-Hill, 1957, Third Edition.

C. Kittel, *Introduction to Solid-State Physics*. New York: Wiley, 1956, Seccond Edition.

F. K. Richtmyer and E. H. Kennard, *Introduction to Modern Physics*. New York: McGraw-Hill, 1955, Fourth Edition.

F. Seitz, *Modern Theory of Solids*, New York: McGraw-Hill, 1940.

R. A. Smith, *Semiconductors*. London: Cambridge Univ. Press, 1959.

R. A. Smith, F. E. Jones, and R. P. Chasmar, *The Detection and Measurement of Infrared Radiation*. London: Oxford Univ. Press, 1957.

J. Strong, *Concepts of Classical Optics*. San Francisco: W. H. Freeman, 1958.

J. Strong, *Procedures in Experimental Physics*. Englewood Cliffs, N. J.: Prentice-Hall, 1938.

H. E. White, *Introduction to Atomic Spectra*. New York: McGraw-Hill, 1934.

R. W. Wood, *Physical Optics*. New York: Macmillian, 1934, Third Edition.

M. W. Zemansky, *Heat and Thermodynamics*. New York: McGraw-Hill, 1957, Fourth Edition.

Bibliographies and General Review Articles

R. B. Barnes, R. C. Gore, U. Liddel, and V. Z. Williams, *Infrared Spectroscopy—Industrial Applications and Bibliography*. New York: Reinhold, 1944.

C. R. Brown, M. W. Ayton, T. C. Goodwin, and T. J. Derby, *Infrared: A Bibliography*. Washington, D. C.: Library of Congress, 1954.

O. S. Duffendack, "Wartime Developments in the Detection and Measurement of Thermal Radiation." *Engrs. Digest* (American), 3, 483, 529-530 (1946).

V. Krizck and V. Vand, "The Development of Infrared Techniques in Germany," *Elec. Eng.* 18, 316-317, 322 (1946).

A. Smakula, "Physical Properties of Optical Crystals with Special Reference to Infrared." Office of Technical Services, U. S. Department of Commerce, Document No. 111053 (October 1952).

G. B. B. M. Sutherland and E. Lee, "Development in the Infrared Region of Spectrum," *Repts. Progr. in Phys.* 11, 144-177 (1947).

V. Z. Williams, "Infrared Instrumentation and Techniques," *Rev. Sci. Instr.* 19, 135-178 (1948).

J. Opt. Soc. Am. 50, 1147 (1960). This entire issue, commemorating the ninetieth birthday of Prof. H. M. Randall, is devoted to infrared topics.

Special Topics in Optics

M. Born and E. Wolf, *Principles of Optics*. New York: Pergamon Press, 1959.

A. Bouwers, *Achievements in Optics*. New York: Elsevier, 1950.

A. C. Candler, *Modern Interferometers*. London: Hilger and Watts, 1951.

Design of Fire Control Optics. The Ordnance Corps, Vols. 1 and 2.

C. Deve, *Optical Workshop Principles*. London: Hilger and Watts, 1954, Second English Edition.

R. W. Ditchburn, *Light*. New York: Interscience, 1953.

S. Flügge, *Encyclopedia of Physics*. Berlin: Springer-Verlag, 1956, Vol. 24.

K. J. Habell, *Engineering Optics, Principles of Optical Methods in Engineering Measurements*. New York: Pitman, 1953.

O. S. Heavens, *Optical Properties of Thin Solid Films*. London: Butterworth's, 1955.

M. Herzberger, *Modern Geometrical Optics*. New York: Interscience, 1958.

A. G. Ingalls, "Amateur Telescope Making." Sci. American, 1-3 (1955).

L. Jacobs, *An Introduction to Electron Optics*. New York: Wiley, 1951.

Z. Kopal (ed.), *Astronomical Optics and Related Subjects*. Amsterdam: North Holland Publishing, 1956.

L. C. Martin, *Technical Optics*. London: Pitman, 1950, Vols. 1 and 2.

G. S. Monk and W. H. McGorkle, *Optical Instrumentation*. New York: McGraw-Hill, 1954.

T. S. Moss, *Optical Properties of Semi-Conductors*. New York: Academic Press, 1959.

The Optical Industry Directory. Huntington, N. Y.: Optical Publishing, 1956-1957.

A. Sommerfeld, "Optics," *Lectures on Theoretical Physics*. New York: Academic Press, 1954, Vol. IV.

J. P. C. Southall, *Mirrors, Prisms and Lenses*. New York: Macmillan, 1918, Third Edition.

S. Tolansky, *Multiple Beam Interferometry of Surfaces and Films*. London: Oxford University Press, 1948.

F. Twyman, *Prism and Lens Making*. London: Hilger and Watts, 1952.

Spectroscopy (Especially Spectroscopic Instruments)

S. S. Ballard, "Spectrophotometry in the United States," in *Proceedings of the London Conference on Optical Instruments, 1950*. New York: Wiley, 1952, pp. 133-150.

E. C. C. Baly, *Spectroscopy*. New York: Longmans Green, 1924, Vols. 1-3.

A. Beer (ed.), *Vistas in Astronomy*. New York: Pergamon Press, 1955-1956, Vols. 1 and 2.

L. J. Bellamy, *Infrared Spectra of Complex Molecules*. New York: Wiley, 1954.

W. R. Brode, *Chemical Spectroscopy*. New York: Wiley, 1943, Second Edition.

W. Brügel, *Einführung in die Ultrarotspektroscopie*. Darmstadt: Dietrich Steinkopf, 1954.

T. A. Cutting, *Manual of Spectroscopy*. New York: Chemical Publishing, 1949.

M. J. E. Golay, "Comparison of Various Infrared Spectrometric Systems," *J. Opt. Soc. Am.*, 46, 422-427 (1956).

C. Haeusler, "Instrumentation in the Far Infrared," *J. Phys. Radium* 16, 882-888 (1955).

G. R. Harrison, R. C. Lord, and J. R. Loofbourow, *Practical Spectroscopy*. Englewood Cliffs, N. J.: Prentice-Hall, 1948.

J. Lecomte, "Infrared Spectrometry and Its Recent Progress." *Cahiers Phys.*, 38, 26-54 (1954).

J. Lecomte, "Spectroscopie dans l'infrarouge," S. Flügge *Encyclopedia of Physics*. Berlin: Springer-Verlag, 1958, Vol. 26, 244-936.

J. Lecomte, P. Le Roux, R. Freyman, H. L. Tardy, and A. Boyle, "La Spectrometrie Infrarouge et ses Applications," *Rev. Opt.* (1934).

E. Lippert, "Apparatus Developments in Infrared Spectroscopy, I-II," *Z. angew. Phys.* 4, 390-397, 434-440 (1952).

R. C. Lord and T. K. McCubbin, Jr., "Infrared Spectroscopy, from 5 to 200 Microns with a Small Grating Spectrometer," *J. Opt. Soc. Am.* 47, 689-697 (1957).

C. Schaeffer and F. Matossi, *Das Ultrarote Spektrum*. Berlin: Julius Springer, 1930.

R. A. Sawyer, *Experimental Spectroscopy*. Englewood Cliffs, N. J.: Prentice-Hall, 1951, Second Edition.

V. Z. Williams, "Infrared Instrumentation and Techniques," *Rev. Sci. Instr.* 19, 135-178 (1948).

Other Instrumentation

American Institute of Physics, *Temperature—Its Measurement and Control in Science and Industry*. New York: Reinhold, 1941, Vol. 1.

W. E. Forsythe, *Measurement of Radiant Energy*. New York: McGraw-Hill, 1937.

W. S. Huxford and J. R. Platt, "Survey of Near Infrared Communication Systems," *J. Opt. Soc. Am.* 38, 253-268 (1948).

"Le Rayonnement Infra-Rouge," *Memorial de l'Artillerie Francaise, 1952*. Paris: Imprimerie Nationale, 1955, Vol. 2.

A. C. Menzies, "Recent Developments in Applied Optics," *J. Sci. Instr.* 30, 441-452 (1953).

J. A. Sanderson, "Emission Transmission and Detection of the Infrared," *Guidance,* Arthur S. Locke (ed.). Princeton: D. Van Nostrand, 1955, Chap. 5.

H. S. Snyder and J. R. Platt, "Principles of Optical Communication Systems," *J. Opt. Soc. Am.* 38, 269-278 (1948).

J. W. Walsh, *Photometry.* London: Constable and Co., 1953.

R. L. Weber, *Heat and Temperature Measurement.* Englewood Cliffs, N. J.: Prentice-Hall, 1950.

H. C. Wolfe (ed.), *Temperature—Its Measurement and Control in Science and Industry.* New York: Reinhold, 1955, Vol. 2.

W. P. Wood and J. M. Cork, *Pyrometry.* New York: McGraw-Hill, 1941, Second Edition.

Optical Materials

S. S. Ballard and K. A. McCarthy, "Optical Materials for Infrared Instrumentation," *Nuovo cimento* 2, Suppl. 3, 648-652 (1955).

Some of the following are not open literature references, but are the best compendia.

S. S. Ballard, L. S. Combes, W. L. Hyde, G. E. Griffith, and K. A. McCarthy, *The Optical and Other Physical Properties of Infra-Red Optical Materials.* Baird Associates (now Baird-Atomic) Inc. (June, 1949).

S. S. Ballard, K. A. McCarthy, and W. L. Wolfe, *IRIA State-of-the-Art Report: Optical Materials for Infrared Instrumentation.* The University of Michigan, Report No. 2389-11-S (January, 1959). Now with a supplement, dated April, 1961.

Engineer Research and Development Laboratories, *Proceedings of the Conference on Optical Materials, Filters, and Films.* (February, 1955).

T. S. Moss, *Photoconductivity in the Elements.* London: Butterworth's, 1952.

T. S. Moss, *Optical Properties of Semiconductors.* London: Butterworth's, 1959.

C. M. Phillippi and N. F. Beardsley, *Infrared Window Studies.* WADC Tech. Note 55-194, Part I (June, 1955); Part II (December, 1956).

A. Smakula, *Physical Properties of Optical Crystals with Special Reference to Infrared.* Office of Technical Services, U. S. Department of Commerce, Document No. 111,052 (October 1952).

R. S. Sosman, *The Properties of Silica.* New York: Chemical Catalog Co., 1927.

Detectors

R. G. Breckenridge, B. R. Russell, and E. E. Hahn (eds.), *Photoconductivity Conference Held at Atlantic City.* New York: Wiley, 1956.

M. Czerny and P. Mollet, "Quasi-Photographic Method of Infrared Detection," *Z. Physik,* 108, 85-100 (1937).

N. Fuson, "The Infrared Sensitivity of Superconducting Bolometers," *J. Opt. Soc. Am.* 38, 845-853 (1948).

M. J. E. Golay, "Theoretical Considerations in Heat and Infrared Detection with Particular Reference to the Pneumatic Detector," *Rev. Sci. Instr.* 18, 347-356 (1947).

M. J. E. Golay, "Pneumatic Infrared Detector," *Rev. Sci. Instr.* 18, 357-362 (1947).

D. F. Hornig and B. J. O'Keefe, "The Design of Fast Thermopiles and the Ultimate Sensitivity of Thermal Detectors," *Rev. Sci. Instr.* 18, 474-482 (1947).

R. C. Jones, "Performance of Detectors for Visible and Infrared Radiation," *Advances in Electronics.* New York: Academic Press, 1953, Vol. 5, Chap. 1.

S. W. Kurnick and R. N. Zitter, "Photoconductive and Photomagnetoelectric Effects in InSb," *J. Appl. Phys.* 27, 278-285 (1956).

M. Lasser, P. Cholet, and E. C. Wurst, Jr., "High-Sensitivity Crystal Infrared Detectors," *J. Opt. Soc. Am.* 48, 468-473 (1958).

T. S. Moss, *Photoconductivity in the Elements.* New York: Academic Press, 1952.

T. S. Moss, "Lead Salt Photoconductors," *Proc. IRE* 43, 1869-1881 (1955).

T. S. Moss, *Optical Properties of Semiconductors.* New York: Academic Press, 1959.

E. M. Wormser, "Properties of Thermistor Detectors," *J. Opt. Soc. Am.* 43, 15-21 (1953).

Properties of the Atmosphere

T. Elder and J. Strong, "Infrared Transmission of Atmospheric Windows," *J. Franklin Inst.* 255, 189-208 (1953).

W. M. Elsasser, "Heat Transfer by Infrared Radiation in the Atmosphere," Harvard Meteorol. Studies, No. 6 (1942).

H. A. Gebbie, W. R. Harding, C. Hilsum, A. W. Price, and V. Roberts, "Atmospheric Transmission in the 1 to 14 μ Region," *Proc. Roy. Soc. (London)* 206A, 87-107 (1950).

R. M. Goody, "Physics of the Stratosphere," London: Cambridge Press, 1954.

Handbook of Geophysics, for Air Force Designers. Geophysics Research Directorate, Air Force Cambridge Research Center, Air Research and Development Command, United States Air Force (1957).

J. N. Howard, D. E. Burch, and D. Williams, "Infrared Transmission of Synthetic Atmospheres. II: Absorption by Carbon Dioxide," *J. Opt. Soc. Am.* 46, 237-241 (1956).

J. N. Howard, D. E. Burch, and D. Williams, "Infrared Transmission of Synthetic Atmospheres. III: Absorption by Water Vapor," *J. Opt. Soc.* 46, 242-245 (1956).

J. N. Howard, D. E. Burch, and D. Williams, "Infrared Transmission of Synthetic Atmospheres. IV: Application of Theoretical Band Models, "*J. Opt. Soc. Am.* 46, 334-338 (1956).

W. E. K. Middleton, *Vision Through the Atmosphere.* Toronto: Univ. of Toronto Press, 1952.

R. Sloan, J. H. Shaw, and D. Williams, "Infrared Emission Spectrum of the Atmosphere," *J. Opt. Soc. Am.* 45, 455-460 (1955).

J. H. Taylor and H. W. Yates, "Atmospheric Transmission in the Infrared," *J. Opt. Soc. Am.* 47, 223-226 (1957).

H. C. Van de Hulst, *Light Scattering by Small Particles.* New York: Wiley, 1957.

C. S. White, *Physics and Medicine of the Upper Atmosphere.* Albuquerque: Univ. of New Mexico Press, 1952.

REFERENCES

1. The bibliography published here is a slight revision of that which appeared as W. L. Wolfe, "A selected Bibliography on Infrared Techniques and Applications," Proc. IRE 47, p. 1647-1649 (1959). It is published with the kind permission of the Institute of Radio Engineers.
2. Laufer, A. R., "Infrared Information Symposia," *Proc. IRIS* 2, No. 1, 56 (1956). (Laufer was the first National Chairman of IRIS.)
3. W. L. Wolfe, "Some Comments on the IRIA Retrieval System," Am. Document. X, No. 1 (1959).
4. W. L. Wolfe, "IRIA, The Infrared Information and Analysis Center," *Proc. IRIS* 2, No. 1 (1957).
5. W. L. Wolfe, "Infrared Information and Analysis," ONR Research Revs. (January, 1959).
6. Proceedings of the Symposium on Infrared Backgrounds. University of Michigan Report Number 2389-2-S (March, 1956). Confidential. Now available only through ASTIA.
7. Report of the Working Group on Infrared Backgrounds. Part I: Aims, Conclusions, and Recommendations on Background Information. University of Michigan Report Number 2389-7-S (July, 1957). Confidential Modified Handling Authorized. Now available only through ASTIA. An up-to-date report has now been published by the group: "Infrared Target and Background Radiometric Measurements; Concepts, Units, and Techniques," University of Michigan Report Number 2389-64-T (January, 1962).

ATMOSPHERIC TRANSMISSION SPECTRA

The measured values of spectral atmospheric transmission obtained by Yates and Taylor,[1-2] and by Gebbie et al,[3] have been replotted as separate curves and are reproduced here for use by the reader. The transmission curves are summarized in Table D-1.

Figure D-1 through D-12 are measurements made over sea-level paths in the Chesapeake Bay area. Figures D-13 and D-14 are measurements made in Hawaii between the mountains Mauna Loa and Mauna Kea with the source at 9300-ft altitude and the receiver at 11,100-ft altitude. Figure D-15 presents measurements made on the east coast of Scotland about 100 ft above sea level with paths for the most part over the sea.

Table D-2 shows the date of the measurements and the associated reference.

Table D-1
Transmission Curves

Worker	Transmission over	Wavelength Region	Precipitable Water Vapor (cm)
Yates and Taylor	1000-ft path	$0.5-15\mu$	$0.11,^{a}$ $0.57,^{b}$
	3.4-mile path		$1.37,^{a}$ 2.2, 4.18, 9.4
	10.1-mile path		$5.2,^{a}$ 5.7, 15.1, 27.7, 30
	17.2-mile path		13, 20
	1000-ft path	$15-25\mu$	$0.22,^{b}$
Gebbie et al.	1 sea mile	$1.0-15\mu$	1.7
		$10-13\mu$	1.95, 2.90

[a]Resolution from 3 to 13 cm^{-1}.
[b]Resolution from 1 to 2.5 cm^{-1}.

407

Table D-2

Data for Figures D-1 through D-15

Figure No.	Date	Reference
D-1	3-20-56	1
D-2	Unknown	2
D-3	Unknown	2
D-4	3-20-56	1
D-5	4-19-56	2
D-6	6-19-56	2
D-7	8-27-56	2
D-8	3-21-56	1
D-9	4-19-56	2
D-10	6-19-56	2
D-11	8-27-56	2
D-12	6-16-57	2
D-13	9-6-57	2
D-14	9-1-57	2
D-15	Unknown	3

1. J. H. Taylor and H. W. Yates, *J. Opt. Soc. Am.* 47, 223–226 (1957).
2. H. W. Yates and J. H. Taylor, *Infrared Transmission of the Atmosphere.* Naval Research Laboratory Report No. 5453 (June 8, 1960).
3. H. A. Gebbie, W. R. Harding, C. Hilsum, A. W. Pryce, and V. Roberts, "Atmospheric Transmission in the 1 to 14 Micron Region, "Proc. Roy. Soc. (*London*) 206, 87 (1951).

Fig. D-1 (*a*), (*b*), (*c*), (*d*), and (*e*). Atmospheric transmission spectrum. 1000-foot (0.3-km) path; temperature $37°$ F; R.H. 62 per cent; 0.11 cm precipitable water vapor; daylight visual range 22 miles (34.6 km); measured transmission at $0.55 \mu = 100$ per cent.

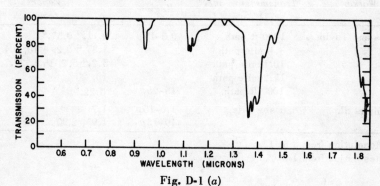

Fig. D-1 (*a*)

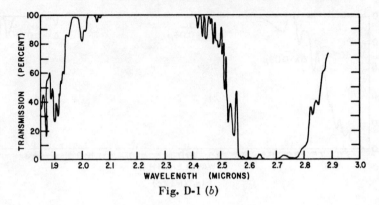

Fig. D-1 (*b*)

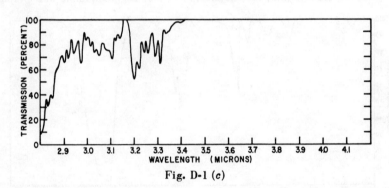

Fig. D-1 (*c*)

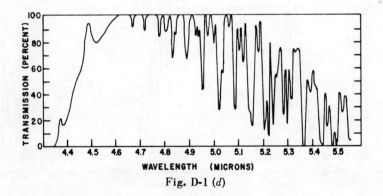

Fig. D-1 (*d*)

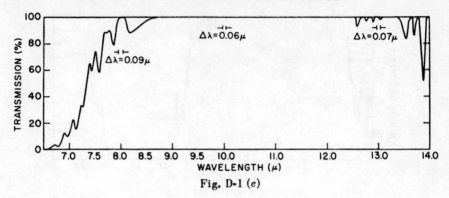

Fig. D-1 (e)

Fig. D-2 (a), (b), (c), (d), and (e).   Atmospheric transmission spectrum.   1000-foot (0.3-km) path; temperature 79° F; 0.57 cm precipitable water vapor.

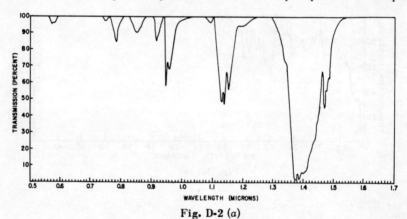

Fig. D-2 (a)

Fig. D-2 (b)

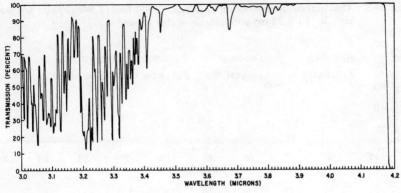

Fig. D-2 (c)

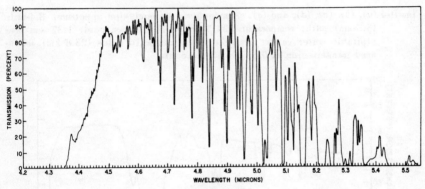

Fig. D-2 (d)

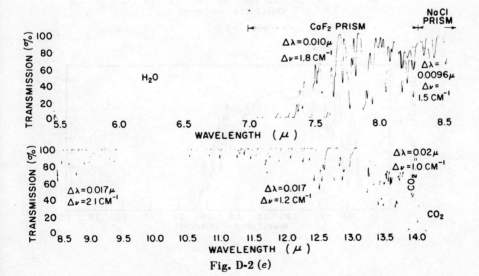

Fig. D-2 (e)

Fig. D-3. Atmospheric transmission spectrum. 1000-foot (0.3-km) path; temperature 56° F; 0.22 cm precipitable water vapor.

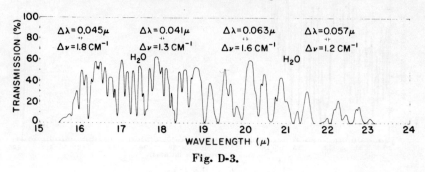

Fig. D-3.

Fig. D-4 (a), (b), (c), (d), and (e). Atmospheric transmission spectrum. 3.4-mile (5.5-km) path; temperature 34.5° F; R.H. 47 per cent; 1.37 cm precipitable water vapor; daylight visual range 16 miles (25.8 km); measured transmission at 0.55 μ = 43 per cent.

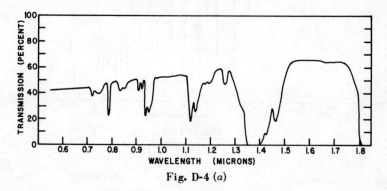

Fig. D-4 (a)

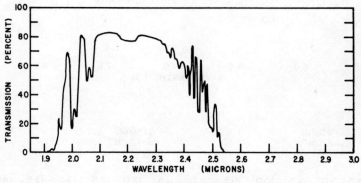

Fig. D-4 (b)

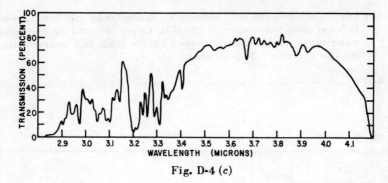

Fig. D-4 (c)

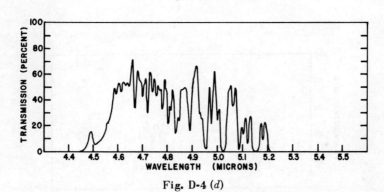

Fig. D-4 (d)

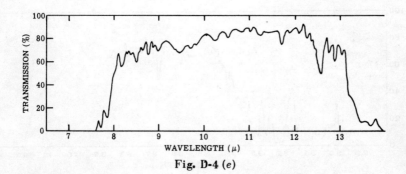

Fig. D-4 (e)

Fig. D-5 (*a*), (*b*), (*c*), (*d*), and (*e*).   Atmospheric transmission spectrum.   3.4-mile (5.5-km) path; temperature 38° F; R.H. 66 per cent; 2.2 cm precipitable water vapor; daylight visual range 15 miles (24.2 km); measured transmission at 0.55 μ = 40.5 per cent.

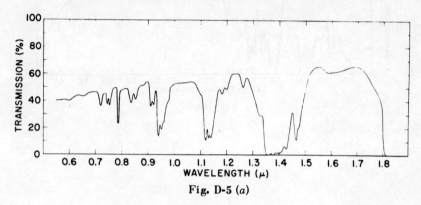

Fig. D-5 (*a*)

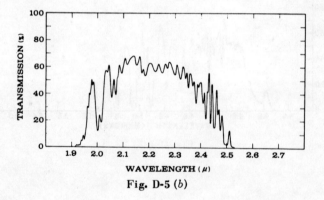

Fig. D-5 (*b*)

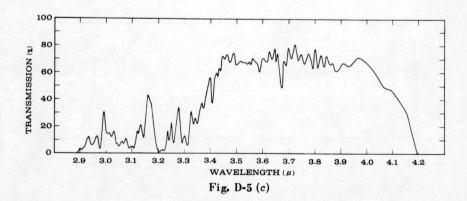

Fig. D-5 (*c*)

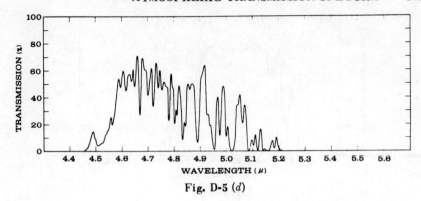

Fig. D-5 (d)

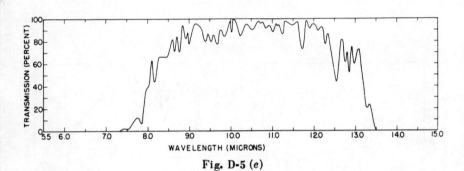

Fig. D-5 (e)

Fig. D-6 (a), (b), (c), (d), and (e). Atmospheric transmission spectrum. 3.4-mile (5.5-km) path; temperature 64° F; R.H. 51 per cent; 4.18 cm precipitable water vapor; daylight visual range 37.3 miles (60 km); measured transmission at 0.55 μ = 70 per cent.

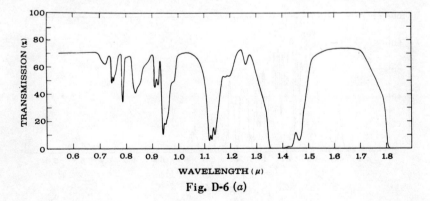

Fig. D-6 (a)

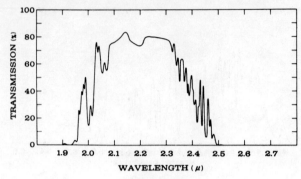

Fig. D-6 (*b*)

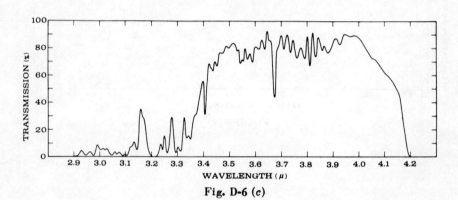

Fig. D-6 (*c*)

Fig. D-6 (*d*)

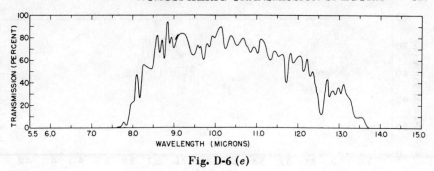

Fig. D-6 (e)

Fig. D-7 (a), (b), (c), (d), and (e). Atmospheric transmission spectrum. 3.4-mile (5.5-km) path; temperature 78° F; R.H. 73 per cent; 9.4 cm precipitable water vapor; daylight visual range 11.8 miles (19 km); measured transmission at 0.55 μ = 30 per cent.

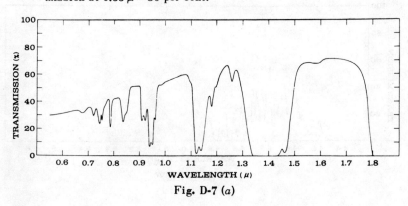

Fig. D-7 (a)

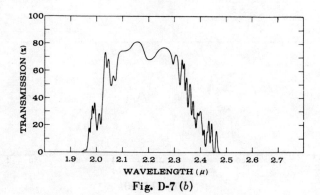

Fig. D-7 (b)

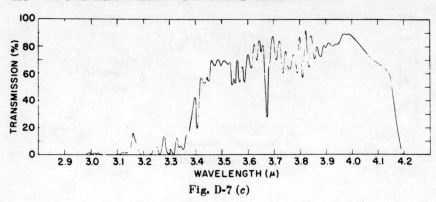

Fig. D-7 (c)

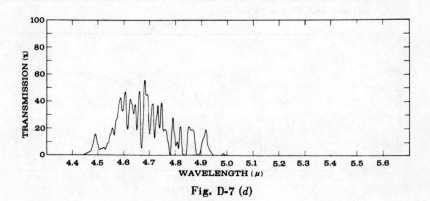

Fig. D-7 (d)

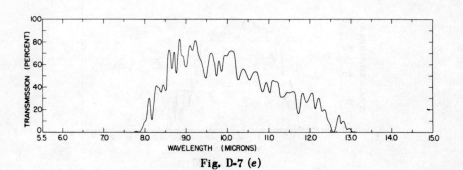

Fig. D-7 (e)

Fig. D-8 (a), (b), (c), (d), and (e). Atmospheric transmission spectrum. 10.1-mile (16.25-km) path; temperature 40.5° F; R.H. 48 per cent; 5.2 cm precipitable water vapor; daylight visual range 24 miles (39 km); measured transmission at 0.55 μ = 20 per cent.

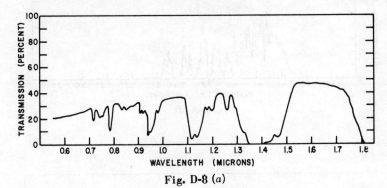

Fig. D-8 (a)

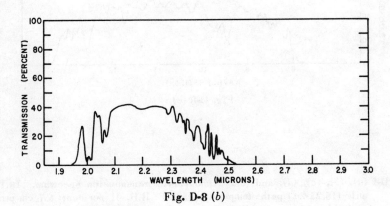

Fig. D-8 (b)

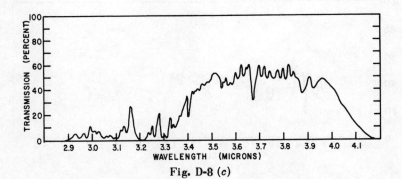

Fig. D-8 (c)

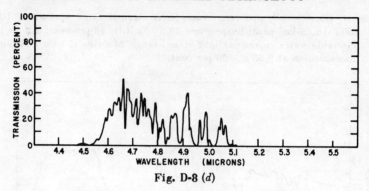

Fig. D-8 (d)

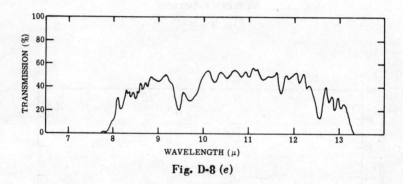

Fig. D-8 (e)

Fig. D-9 (a), (b), (c), (d), and (e).   Atmospheric transmission spectrum.   10.1-mile (16.25-km) path; temperature 53° F; R.H. 41 per cent; 6.7 cm precipitable water vapor; daylight visual range 33.5 miles (54 km); measured transmission at 0.55 μ = 30 per cent.

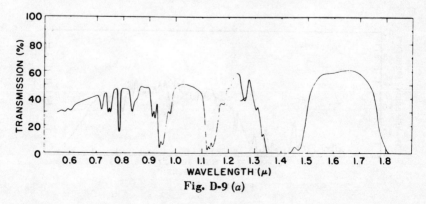

Fig. D-9 (a)

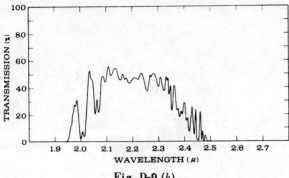

Fig. D-9 (b)

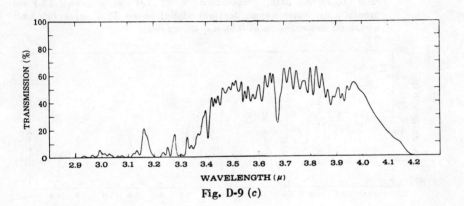

Fig. D-9 (c)

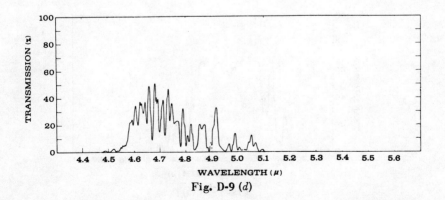

Fig. D-9 (d)

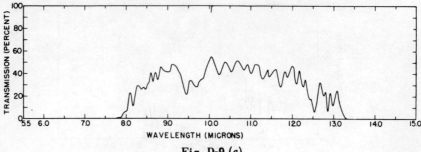

Fig. D-9 (e)

Fig. D-10 (a), (b), (c), (d), and (e). Atmospheric transmission spectrum. 10.1-mile (16.25-km) path; temperature 69° F; R.H. 53 per cent; 15.1 cm precipitable water vapor; daylight visual range 37.3 miles (60 km); measured transmission at 0.55 μ = 43 per cent.

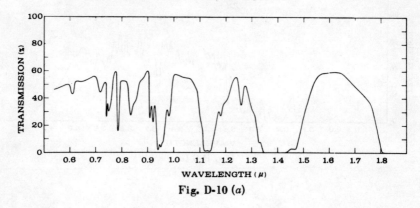

Fig. D-10 (a)

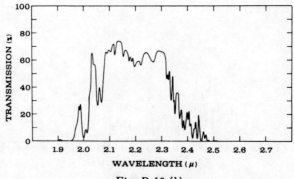

Fig. D-10 (b)

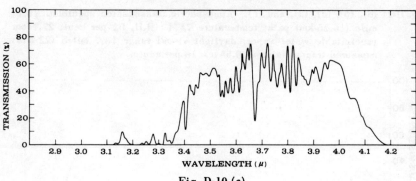

Fig. D-10 (c)

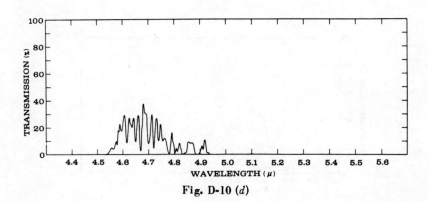

Fig. D-10 (d)

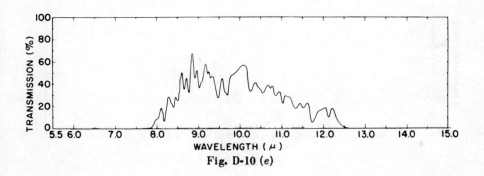

Fig. D-10 (e)

Fig. D-11 (*a*), (*b*), (*c*), (*d*), and (*e*).   Atmospheric transmission spectrum. 10.1-mile (16.25-km) path; temperature 74°F; R.H. 82 per cent; 27.7 cm precipitable water vapor; daylight visual range 13.7 miles (22 km); measured transmission at 0.55 μ = 10 per cent.

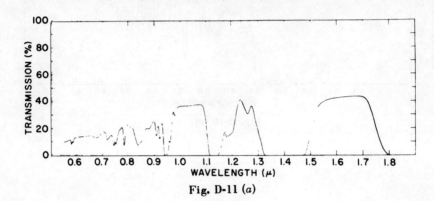

Fig. D-11 (*a*)

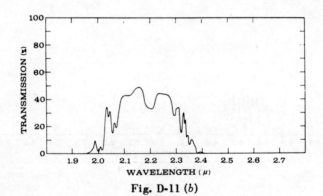

Fig. D-11 (*b*)

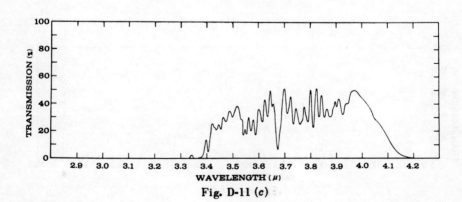

Fig. D-11 (*c*)

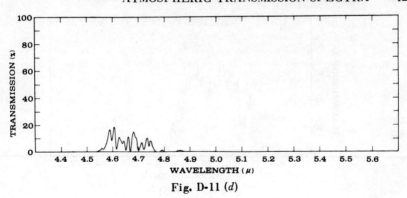

Fig. D-11 (*d*)

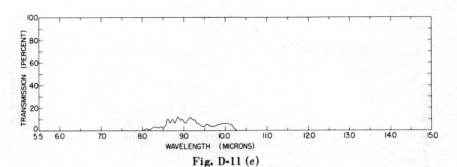

Fig. D-11 (*e*)

Fig. D-12 (*a*), (*b*), (*c*), and (*d*). Atmospheric transmission spectrum.   10.1-mile (16.25-km) path; temperature 87.5° F; R.H. 59 per cent; 37 cm precipitable water vapor; daylight visual range 11.8 miles (19 km); measured transmission at 0.55 μ = 2 per cent.

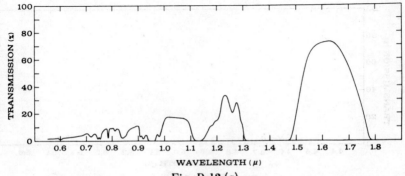

Fig. D-12 (*a*)

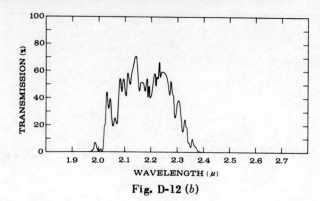

Fig. D-12 (*b*)

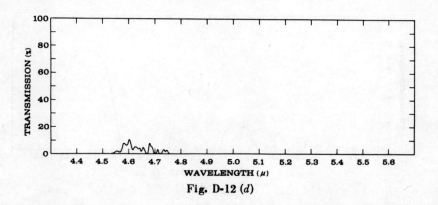

Fig. D-12 (*c*)

Fig. D-12 (*d*)

Fig. D-13 (a), (b), (c), (d), and (e). Atmospheric transmission spectrum. 17.2-mile (27.7-km) path; at 10,500-foot elevation; 13 cm precipitable water vapor; daylight visual range 77.6 miles (124.9 km); measured transmission at 0.55 μ = 42 per cent.

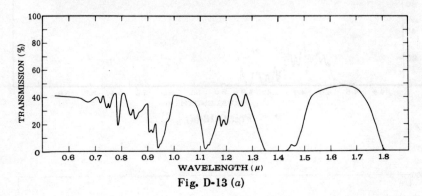

Fig. D-13 (a)

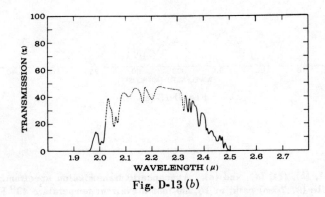

Fig. D-13 (b)

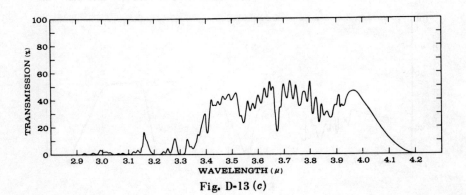

Fig. D-13 (c)

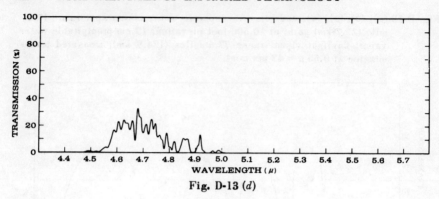

Fig. D-13 (d)

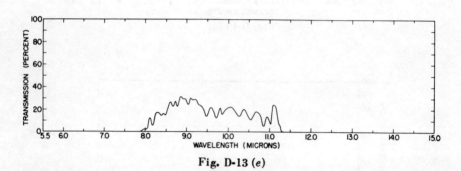

Fig. D-13 (e)

Fig. D-14 (a), (b), (c), (d), and (e). Atmospheric transmission spectrum. 17.2-mile (27.7-km) path; at 10,500-foot elevation; temperature 43° F; R.H. 100 per cent; 20 cm precipitable water vapor; daylight visual range 51.9 miles (83.4 km); measured transmission at 0.55 μ = 26.5 per cent.

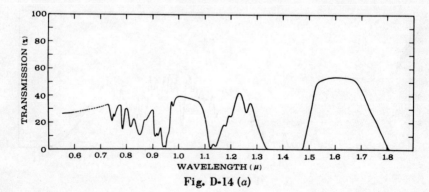

Fig. D-14 (a)

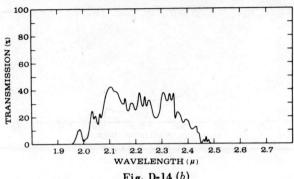

Fig. D-14 (b)

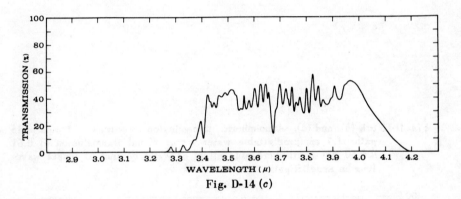

Fig. D-14 (c)

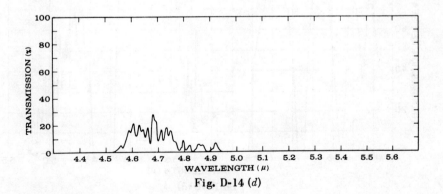

Fig. D-14 (d)

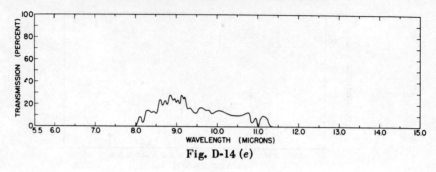

Fig. D-14 (e)

Fig. D-15 (a), (b), and (c). Atmospheric transmission spectrum. 1 sea mile path; 1.7 cm precipitable water vapor; visual transmission at 0.61 μ = 60 per cent; increasing effect of water content at longer wavelengths seacliff path.

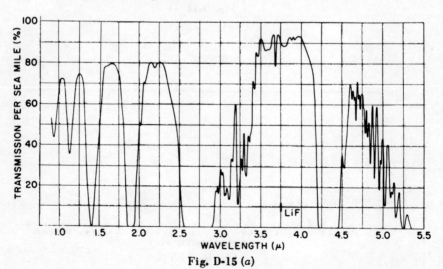

Fig. D-15 (a)

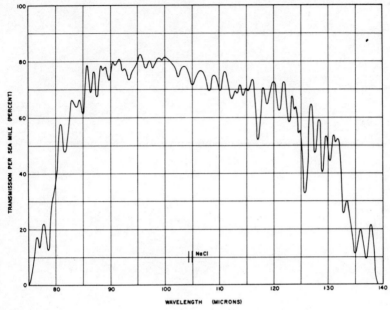

Fig. D-15 (*b*)

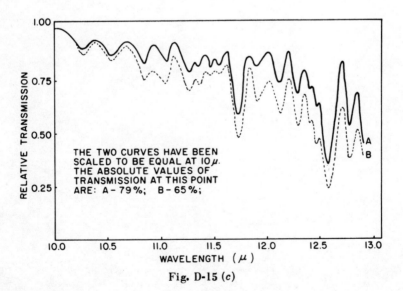

Fig. D-15 (*c*)

INDEX

Absolute humidity
  ρ_w, 71
Absorptance
  α, definition of, 3, 6
Absorption, 126
  by free electrons, 132
  by optically thick gas, 74
  by optically thin gas, 74
Absorption coefficient
  a, 72, 122, 125
Absorption features of the atmosphere,
  71
Absorption filters, 183
Absorption law, 72
Absorption of radiation, 1
Absorption
  selective, of emitted bands, 79, 81
Acceptor level, 201
Airglow, 29
Ammonia in the atmosphere, 70
Angular momentum quantized, 20
Anharmonic oscillator, 24
Aperture effects
  elementary analytic treatment, 347–9
Aperture effects
  general analytic treatment, 355–61
Aperture effects
  qualitative treatment, 346–7
Aperture response to δ function, 355–7
Aperture stop, 113
Aplanatism, 116
Apparent radiant intensity, J', 7
Apparent radiance
  N', 7
Apparent radiometric quantities, 7
Applications
  civil and military, 315–6

Argon in the atmosphere, 70
Aspect dependency, 40, 43
ASTIA
  Armed Services Technical Informa-
    tion Agency, 395
Astigmatism, 117
Atmosphere
  constituents, 70
Atmospheric absorption, 71
Atmospheric effects, 69
Atmospheric emission in device de-
    sign, 333
Atmospheric phenomena, 69
Atmospheric transmission, 75
Atmospheric transmission
  procedures for corrections for, 79, 80
Atmospheric transmission spectra
  measured, 407–31
Attenuating media, 7
Attenuation, 322–4
Attenuation
  atmospheric, 382
Attenuation coefficient, 95, 124
Aurora, 30

Backgrounds
  data, derived and primary, 60
  definition of, 29
  description of, 31
  ground, 31
  measurement of, 31
  obscuration by, corrections for target
    measurements, 64, 65
  radiation from, 248
    contribution to G-R noise, 249
    thermal noise, 250
  sea, 31

433

FLIR   FORWARD LOOKING
        INFRARED